WE CELEBRATE
WORSHIP RESOURCE

Hymnal

D1517918

World Library Publications
a division of J. S. Paluch Company, Inc.
Schiller Park, Illinois

Project Manager
Thomas Strickland

Editors
Laura Dankler
Nicholas T. Freund
Alan J. Hommerding
Steven R. Janco
Peter M. Kolar
Peter Mazar
Ron Rendek
Thomas Strickland

Introductions
David Philippart

Copyright Acquisitions
Jeanne M. Grzelak

Copyright Permissions
Rita Larkin Cavallaro

Typesetting and Layout
Tammi Nolde
John S. Paluch
Maggie Redmond

Music Engraving
Thomas Schaller

Proofreading and Support Staff
Paul M. French
Richard Siegel
Kathy Wilczynski
Welborn E. Young

Art Coordinator
Elizabeth Rizo

Art and Cover
Michael O'Neill McGrath

Managing Editor
Laura Dankler

Marketing Director
Dan McGuire

Production Manager
John Ficarra

President
William Rafferty

Publishers
Margaret A. Paluch
Mary L. Rafferty

Table of Contents

The Liturgy of the Church

The poet Gerard Manley Hopkins wrote: "The world is charged with the grandeur of God." Those who celebrate the liturgy know this to be true. While we have many ways of praying—of listening to God's voice and whispering in God's ear—our most important ways make use of the things of creation.

Some of these things are created directly and solely by God (such as fire and water); most are created by divine-human cooperation, things "that earth has given and human hands have made."

A bonfire on a chilly spring night, a pillar of the finest beeswax, a pool of fresh water, a jar of expensive perfumed oil, a robe of the finest linen, wedding rings, bread and wine—these are the "stuff" of our worship. It's what we do with these things that makes ordinary objects extraordinary icons of God's presence and love. It's what we do with them that allows us to perceive the presence of God at hand.

So what do we do with these things that are "charged with the grandeur of God"? What we do is called "liturgy": a liturgy of baptism or confirmation or eucharist; a liturgy of penance or anointing the sick; a liturgy of morning prayer or evening prayer; a liturgy of blessing; a liturgy of marriage, of ordination, of burial.

The Greek root of the word "liturgy" means "the work of the people." The liturgy is the work of the Church, the body of Christ. Christ is the head of the body, and we who are baptized into Christ are members of the body. Members have different roles—all for the common good.

The body of Christ is made up of those chosen to insure "holy order" in the church: the bishop, the priests, the deacons, all of the baptized, and even those preparing for baptism, the catechumens.

When the Church celebrates liturgy, not everyone does everything. Various roles ensure good order: There is the one who presides. There are those who welcome and seat us, those who proclaim the scriptures, those who lead the singing and play instruments, those who help with communion, those who serve at the table.

The original meaning of words can offer insights into the Church's understanding about its "holy order." For instance, the word "bishop," which comes from the Greek word *episkopos*, means "overseer." "Priest" comes from *presbyteros* and means "elder." "Deacon" means "servant," and "catechumen" means "someone who learns by hearing," that is, by hearing the word of God. The word "laity" comes from the Greek *laios* and simply means "people." All of us are members of the household of faith, members of the body of Christ.

Remember the story of Jacob wrestling with the angel? Jacob sought God heartily, and the angel came to him at night to deliver a message. Jacob grabbed hold of the angel and would not let go until the angel blessed him. But the angel did more than bless Jacob; the angel changed Jacob's name to "Israel," meaning "one who wrestles with God."

The Church is like Jacob, and the liturgy is how we wrestle with God. We don't let go until we are changed by the liturgy that we celebrate.

Liturgy is more like a wrestling match than a stage play. It requires skill and strength and perseverance on our part. We can't just sit back and let somebody else do it. Each of us has an active role to take. All of us must be mindful of what it is that we are doing. We must pay attention. We must sing the prayers, listen to the scriptures, make the gestures, or assume the postures deliberately and gracefully. The whole self must participate in the liturgy: body, mind, and soul.

"Lift up your hearts," the presider bids us, using that ancient and beautiful metaphor *"heart,"* meaning *"all of me."* "We lift them up to the Lord," we sing back, meaning what we say, doing what we mean.

But why these particular actions? Why the water bath of baptism, why the rubbing of olive oil on the sick, why the profession of marriage vows and the exchange of rings, why the offering of bread and wine?

First, because Jesus told us so: "Do this in memory of me." Also, we do the liturgy a certain way because it is simply the right thing to do. "Let us give thanks to the Lord our God," the presider says. And what is our answer? Our wise response is, "It is right to give God thanks and praise." It is right and we "do well" always and everywhere to give God thanks.

Or look at it this way: You may ask, "Why do we baptize the way we do?" And here begins an answer: Because God created the heavens and the earth, and separated the waters above from the waters below. Because God carried Noah and his family and the pairs of all living things to safety in an ark. Because God saved the Israelites by allowing them to pass dry-footed through the sea while the mighty armies of Pharaoh were drowned. Because God made water flow from the rock in the desert. Because God let the Israelites cross the River Jordan into the promised land. Because God hallowed the waters of that same river when Jesus went down into it to be baptized. Because God raised Jesus from the dead after blood and water flowed from his pierced side.

The answer unfolds even further: Because God continues to raise up those who are put down. Because God stirs the hearts of people and leads them to our parishes to inquire about the Church's faith, and then leads them into the catechumenate—because God did these things and does these things, we "do well" to huddle around the font on a chilly spring night, the holy night we keep vigil for Easter.

We make the amazing claim that the font is the tomb in which each of us is buried and the womb from which each of us is born. Here are the waters of chaos, the waters of the flood and of the exodus and of the River Jordan, here in our own parish! We "do well" to take hold of those who have struggled so hard and so long to stand here with us. We "do well" to lead them into this water and then pull them out— gasping and sputtering for breath—as God's beloved newborn children.

What else could we do?

And when we do these things with love and care in the house of the Church, something happens. We begin to see how the world of worship is really a glimpse of God's plan for the entire world. "Go in peace to love and serve the Lord." We know that we are sent to make the world more and more a place where everyone is invited by God, called by name, and welcomed in.

Throughout the year, the liturgy invites us to enter into the mystery of Christ. The seasons of the church's year, year after year, inscribe on our bodies, minds, and hearts ever more deeply the image of Christ, the firstborn from the dead.

The liturgy hurries the time when Christ will return and harvest us into eternity, the time beyond time when we will be made whole, when love will be the judgment pronounced. In God's good time, crowned with a wreath of victory, robed in light, and anointed with gladness, we'll sit together under the tree of life. "Holy," we'll cry together, in one loud and beautiful voice, "Worthy is the Lamb!"

Until that day comes, we have the work of the liturgy and the work of the gospel to do. Are you ready? Lift up your hearts. Give thanks and praise. Go in peace to love and serve the Lord.

The Liturgy of the Hours

Most days we are unaware of sunset—the lengthening of shadows, the sinking of the sun, the dying of the day. Most mornings we are too rushed to notice the dawn—the boundless horizon becoming a pink line that slowly widens into bright blue sky.

But every so often we are stopped by the beauty of a spectacular sunset or arrested by the brightness of a full moon. In late autumn we mourn the short hours of daylight; in June we marvel at (or gripe about) how the sun rises before we do.

Throughout the year people of faith are thankful for the daily cycle of light and darkness; the arc of morning, noon and evening; the rhythm of day and night. Morning, evening, and bedtime are natural times to pray. It has always been so—ever since people first noticed the invariable pattern and sensed something of the Creator's marvelous design.

But Christians have a particular reason to mark the holiness of the daily cycle. We see in the rising sun an image of Jesus, the firstborn of the dead. Our hearts are moved to praise as we prepare to work anew for the coming reign of God. And we see in the setting sun an image of human destiny, of our eventual giving way, of our dying. But this is not an image without hope: Even in the night sky the moon and stars shine. At evening we light candles and turn on lamps, and we sing: "Christ our Light. Thanks be to God." Our hearts are moved to give thanks for the blessings of the day, to seek forgiveness for failures, and to ask God's help through the night.

We pray at morning, evening, and bedtime as individuals, perhaps as households, and also as the Church. Our morning prayer, evening prayer, and night prayer at home can take many forms. We can pray spontaneously, perhaps, or use well-worn words we know by heart. We simply can sign ourselves or each other with the cross as we hurry out the door in the morning, return home in the evening, and pull the covers up around ourselves at night. Or, like the early Christians, we can make sure to pray the Lord's Prayer every morning, noon, and night.

When we pray at morning or evening (and sometimes at night time) in church as the Church, we use a liturgical pattern of prayer that includes singing the psalms and canticles of the Bible, listening to a brief scripture reading and also perhaps to a homily, burning incense, praying for the needs of the world and the Church, and perhaps sharing a sign of peace.

Together, the rites of morning, evening, and night prayer are called "the liturgy of the hours."

Before Christians developed the practice of daily Mass, morning and evening prayer were the only weekday rituals by which the Church gathered to give God thanks and praise. This tradition was continued in many cathedral parishes. Monks and nuns in monasteries still chant the liturgies of morning and evening prayer and sometimes shorter rites at other hours of the day.

Today, parishes are taking up again the ancient practice of turning to God in ritual, song, and prayer at the turning points of the day. The daily liturgy of the hours prepares Christians for the solemn celebration of the eucharist on Sunday, the Lord's Day. In turn, our participation in Sunday Mass leads us to continue always and everywhere to give God thanks and praise by celebrating the liturgy of the hours throughout the days of the week.

And so we fulfill the hope of the psalmist: "From the rising of the sun to its setting, praised be the name of the Lord."

MORNING PRAYER

The transition from night into day is an image for us of the day of resurrection, for which we wait in hope. Every morning the Church gathers to give praise to God. We remember our baptism into the paschal mystery of the Lord, who is the resurrection and the life.

Invitatory

All stand.

1

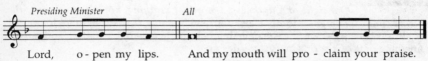

Lord, o - pen my lips. And my mouth will pro - claim your praise.

Howard L. Hughes
Text and music © 1970, 1976, 1978, ICEL

Morning Hymn

A song of praise appropriate to the morning or to the liturgical season is sung.

2 Sing Gently, O Earth

1. Sing gent - ly, O earth, A hymn of
2. The sun sheds its light In gold - en
3. To Fa - ther and Son And Spir - it

1. spring, A song of new birth,
2. ray, Dis - pel - ling the night,
3. true, Great God, Three - in - One,

1. — An ode to your Lord and King.
2. — An-nounc-ing the dawn - ing day.
3. — All glo - ry and praise is due.

Becket G. Senchur
Text and music © 1994, WLP

Psalmody

All sit. Psalm 63 or another psalm appropriate to the morning is sung.

3 Psalm 63/My Soul Is Thirsting for You

REFRAIN

My soul is thirst-ing for you, O Lord my God._____

VERSES

1. O God, you are my God whom I seek;
   for you my flesh pines and my soul thirsts
   like the earth, parched, lifeless and without water.

2. Thus have I gazed toward you in the sanctuary
   to see your power and your glory,
   For your kindness is a greater good than life;
   my lips shall glorify you.

3. Thus will I bless you while I live;
   lifting up my hands, I will call upon your name.
   As with the riches of a banquet shall my soul be satisfied,
   and with exultant lips my mouth shall praise you.

4. I will remember you upon my couch,
   and through the nightwatches I will meditate on you:
   You are my help,
   and in the shadow of your wings I shout for joy.

Text (ref.) © 1969, ICEL
Text (vss.) © 1970, CCD

Dolores M. Hruby
Music © 1985, 1994, WLP

A second psalm may follow. Each psalm is followed by a period of silence and a prayer.

Reading

Silence

Gospel Canticle

As the canticle begins, all stand and make the sign of the cross.

4 Canticle of Zechariah

MUNDELEIN   CMD

1. Blest be the God of Is - ra - el Who sets all peo - ple
2. God's prom - ised mer - cy will be— shown And cov - e - nant re -
3. My child, as proph - et of the— Lord, You will pre - pare his

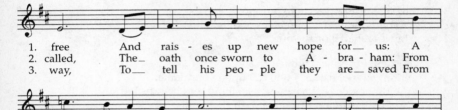

1. free And rais - es up new hope for— us: A
2. called, The— oath once sworn to A - bra - ham: From
3. way, To— tell his peo - ple they are— saved From

1. Branch from Da - vid's tree. So have the proph - ets
2. foes to free us all, That we might serve God
3. sin's e - ter - nal sway. Then shall God's mer - cy

1. long de - clared That with a might - y arm God
2. with - out fear And ev - er sing God's praise In—
3. from on high Shine forth and nev - er cease To—

1. would turn back our en - e - mies And all who wish us harm.
2. ho - li - ness and right - eous - ness Be - fore God all our days.
3. drive a - way the gloom of— death And lead us in - to peace.

Carl P. Daw Jr.
Text © 1989, Hope Publishing Co.

Steven R. Janco
Music © 1994, WLP

Intercessions

By custom, the intercessions in the morning may be a litany of praise and thanksgiving.

5

Byzantine chant

Lord's Prayer

Concluding Prayer

Blessing and Dismissal

Priest or deacon: The Lord be with you.

All: **And also with you.**

Priest or deacon: May almighty God bless you, the Father, and the Son, and the Holy Spirit.

All: **Amen.**

In the absence of a priest or deacon:

Presiding minister: May the Lord bless us, protect us from all evil and bring us to everlasting life.

All: **Amen.**

EVENING PRAYER

The transition from day into night is an image for us of the hour of our death and the arrival of the day of judgment. Every evening the Church gathers to pray for forgiveness, healing, and peace. We call upon Christ our Light to guide us homeward through the darkness.

Light Service

During the Easter season the paschal candle is already burning brightly as the people assemble. At other times, while all stand, the presiding minister lights a candle and sings:

6 Lucernarium

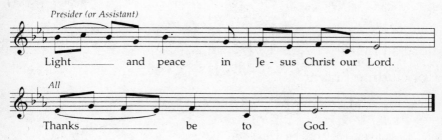

Presider (or Assistant)

Light_____ and peace in Je - sus Christ our Lord.

All

Thanks_____ be to God.

J. Michael Joncas
Music © 1995, WLP

Evening Hymn

A song appropriate to the evening or to the liturgical season is sung.

7 Evening Hymn

1. When dark - ness bids our la - bor cease and
2. For gifts un - earned and yet re - ceived, for
*3. In you the sea - sons come and go, the
4. Let ev - 'ry voice in har - mo - ny ac -

1. na - ture's eyes have closed in peace, may we, cre - a - tion's
2. things un - seen and yet be - lieved, for trust in your un -
3. o - ceans find their ebb and flow. In you the plan - ets
4. claim the Ho - ly Trin - i - ty. Let earth, in splen - did

1. priest - ly crown, pro - claim in hope the com - ing dawn:
2. fail - ing word, for joy in Je - sus Christ the Lord:
3. spin their course, in you all be - ing finds its source.
4. sym - pho - ny, pro - claim your gen - tle ma - jes - ty:

1. God of Light, be praised, be___ for-ev - er praised!___
2. God of Grace, be praised, be___ for-ev - er praised!___
3. God of Time, be praised, be___ for-ev - er praised!___
4. God of All, be praised, be___ for-ev - er praised!___

Seasonal options for Verse 3:

Advent/Nativity

3. The night is dark, the winter long, but God incarnate makes us strong,
   who chooses here with us to dwell, the Holy One, Emmanuel.
   God in Flesh, be praised, be forever praised.

Lent:

3. Oppressed by evil, crushed by sin, we hear a still, small voice within:
   "Arise, return, and bare your soul, for Christ would touch and make you whole."
   God in Christ, be praised, be forever praised.

Eastertide:

3. This is the day the Lord has made: rejoice, no longer be afraid,
   for like the crocus in full bloom has Christ arisen from the tomb.
   God of Life, be praised, be forever praised.

Delores Dufner
Text © 1995, Sisters of St. Benedict

J. Michael Joncas
Music © 1995, WLP

Psalmody

All sit. During the singing of Psalm 141 (or another psalm appropriate to the evening) we offer to God our evening sacrifice.

8 Psalm 141/Like Incense before You

REFRAIN

O Lord, to you I call. Has-ten to hear my voice. My prayer comes like in - cense be - fore your throne, O God.

VERSES

1. With a loud voice I cry to the Lord. My prayer, like incense,
   comes before you. Watch me, O Lord, direct what I say.
   Form ev'ry word in my mouth as I pray.

2. Let not my eyes be drawn from your gaze. Lord,
   let me see your goodness always. Kindness and truth will follow
   my ways. Though sinners strike me, your name I will praise.

3. Let my head never be blest by the foe; Lord, watch my footsteps
   wherever I go. For to you, Lord, shall my eyes ever turn.
   Guide me, O Lord, so your ways I may learn.

Paul E. Page
Text and music © 1995, WLP

A second psalm may follow. Each psalm is followed by a period of silence and a prayer.

Reading

Silence

Gospel Canticle

As the canticle begins, all stand and make the sign of the cross.

9 You, O God, My Soul Does Magnify

1. You,— O— God, my soul does mag - ni - fy, And
2. Haugh - ty— hearts you scat - ter to and fro, And
3. Is - ra - el you have with love re- deemed, Ful -

1. all my be - ing finds its joy in you,— Most High! For
2. those who sub - ju - gate the weak you o - ver - throw. But
3. fill - ing what our proph-ets long a - go— had dreamed. Our

1. you have worked most awe - some deeds in me, And
2. those in need, the hun - gry, meek, and poor, You
3. chil - dren shall a - bun - dant bless - ings reap Be -

1. hon - ored by all peo - ples shall I ev - er be!
2. shall em - brace and crown with light at heav - en's door!
3. cause your cov - e - nant with us you deigned to keep!

Becket G. Senchur
Text and music © 1990, WLP

RESPONSE

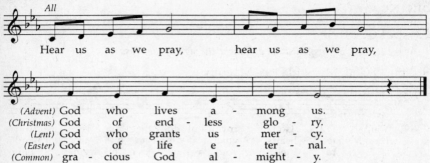

(Advent)	God	who	lives	a -	mong	us.
(Christmas)	God	of	end -	less	glo -	ry.
(Lent)	God	who	grants	us	mer -	cy.
(Easter)	God	of	life	e -	ter -	nal.
(Common)	gra -	cious	God	al -	might -	y.

Alan J. Hommerding

J. Michael Joncas

Lord's Prayer

Concluding Prayer

Blessing and Dismissal

> Priest or
> deacon: The Lord be with you.
> All: **And also with you.**

> Priest or
> deacon: May almighty God bless you,
> the Father, and the Son, and the Holy Spirit.
> All: **Amen.**

In the absence of a priest or deacon:

> Presiding
> minister: May the Lord bless us,
> protect us from all evil
> and bring us to everlasting life.
> All: **Amen.**

The Order of Mass

"Lift up your hearts!" How do we come to this holy moment, this moment when we join with the whole of creation to sing to God what can be sung to God alone: "Holy, holy, holy"?

First, Christ gathers us together. We come from our homes and assemble in this holy place. We greet one another as we would greet Christ, bless ourselves with holy water, and take our places. A procession forms. We sing, our many voices raised as the one, mighty voice of the body of Christ. We sign ourselves with the cross. Depending on the season of the year, we may sing the song of the angels ("Glory to God"), bless water and be sprinkled with it, or cry out "Lord, have mercy." The priest calls us to pray, and after a moment of silence, says words that gather all our praise and petitions into one prayer.

In all of this, we know that Christ is present in the assembled church. Now we are ready to hear God's word and ponder it in our hearts.

So we listen. We listen hard. We listen hard together. The readers proclaim two readings from scripture. At the conclusion of each, the reader looks at us and says "The word of the Lord." To what or to whom does the lector refer? To the scripture in the book, of course—but also to us. Christ is the word-made-flesh, and we have been baptized in Christ. We too are word-made-flesh: living proclamations of the wonders of God. We sit in silence and awe at such mystery, allowing the word to sink in and saturate us.

In between the readings we sing a psalm, one of the songs of Israel that also have become the songs of the Church. The psalm is how the whole assembly proclaims God's word. We jump to our feet to welcome the gospel, the good news. Lord Jesus comes to us in his words and deeds. Then, in the homily, the priest or deacon breaks open the scriptures like a loaf of fresh bread, so that all may be nourished.

As baptized Christians, we profess our faith. We offer petitions to God for the world and for the church, and we stand ready to be part of God's answer to those petitions. Through all of this, God invites us to come to Christ's table, the breakfast-banquet of eternal life, the wedding feast of heaven and earth. So we gather gifts for the poor and for the Church; we prepare the altar with candles, linens, a book of prayer, a cup of wine, and bread. Now we are ready to respond to God's invitation, to Christ's command: Do this in remembrance of me.

Hearts lifted high, we give thanks and praise to God for life and for love, for our past, for our destiny, and most of all, for Jesus. We call to mind what Jesus did for us by sitting at the table, by accepting the cross, by dying, by rising from the tomb and breathing the Holy Spirit on us. We give to God our lives under the sign of bread and wine. And God gives us back the bread of life and the cup of eternal salvation. In this holy exchange, in these holy gifts, Christ is present.

We then make some last minute preparations: praying the words that the Savior gave us, sharing a sign of peace, breaking the bread that is Christ's body, pouring out into cups the wine that is Christ's blood. In walking and singing during the communion procession, in sharing in the body and in the blood, we become what we eat and drink, we become who we are: the body of Christ raised up for the life of the world, the blood of Christ poured out in love for the world.

Now we are ready to be sent out. After silence and a common prayer, after announcements and the sending out of communion ministers to the sick, we too are sent out: sent out to live according to God's word, sent out to be food and drink for a world starving for peace and thirsting for justice, sent out to lift up our hearts as living sacrifices of praise until we can assemble once again.

ORDER OF MASS

Introductory Rites

Entrance Song

All stand. A suitable psalm or hymn is sung.

Greeting

> *Priest:* In the name of the Father, and of the Son,
> and of the Holy Spirit.
>
> *All:* **Amen.**

A *Priest:* The grace of our Lord Jesus Christ and the love of God
and the fellowship of the Holy Spirit be with you all.
> *All:* **And also with you.**

B *Priest:* The grace and peace of God our Father and the
Lord Jesus Christ be with you.
> *All:* **And also with you.**

C *Priest:* The Lord be with you.
> *All:* **And also with you.**

The Mass of the day may be briefly introduced.

Rite of Blessing and Sprinkling Holy Water

On Sundays and Saturday evenings this rite may take the place of the penitential rite. The priest blesses water. The priest then sprinkles the people while an appropriate antiphon or hymn is sung.

11 Cleanse Us, Lord

REFRAIN

Cleanse us, Lord, from all our sins; wash us and we shall be clean as new snow. Cleanse us, Lord, from all our sins; wash us and we shall be clean as new snow.

VERSES

1. Springs of water, bless the Lord; give God glory, glory and praise!
   Seas and rivers, bless the Lord; give God glory and praise!

2. I will pour clean water over you; I will wash you from all your sin.
   I will place a new heart within you: You are my people and I am your God!

3. You are a people God calls to be born, calls to be born as an off'ring of
   praise, praise that God called you from darkness to light,
   praise that God called you from death into life!

4. I saw water, I saw water flowing from the temple; it brought God's life,
   it brought God's life, it brought God's life and salvation.

Sing Praise and Thanksgiving!
Text (ref.) © 1973, ICEL
J. Michael Joncas
Text (vss.)and music © 1989, WLP

Penitential Rite

The priest invites the people to recall their sins. Then one of the following forms is used:

A *All:* **I confess to almighty God,**
and to you, my brothers and sisters,
that I have sinned through my own fault

All strike their breast.

in my thoughts and in my words,
in what I have done,
and in what I have failed to do;
and I ask blessed Mary, ever virgin,
all the angels and saints,
and you, my brothers and sisters,
to pray for me to the Lord our God.

Priest: May almighty God have mercy on us,
forgive us our sins,
and bring us to everlasting life.
All: **Amen.**

12 Lord, Have Mercy

Cantor _____ All _____
Lord, _____ have mer - cy. Lord, _____ have
Ky - ri - e, e - le - i - son. Ky - ri - e, e -

Cantor
mer - cy. Christ, _____ have mer - cy.
le - i - son. Chri - ste, e - le - i - son.

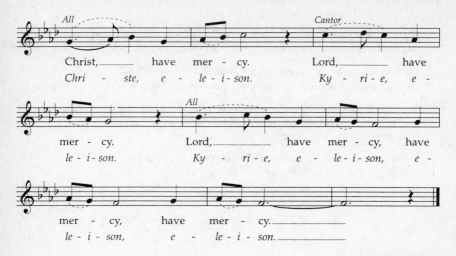

Christ,_____ have mer - cy. Lord,_____ have
Chri - ste, e - le - i - son. Ky - ri - e, e -

mer - cy. Lord,_____ have mer - cy, have
le - i - son. Ky - ri - e, e - le - i - son, e -

mer - cy, have mer - cy._____
le - i - son, e - le - i - son._____

Sing Praise and Thanksgiving!
J. Michael Joncas
Music © 1989, WLP

Priest: Lord, have mercy.   *or*   Kyrie, eleison.
All: **Lord, have mercy.**   **Kyrie, eleison.**

Priest: Christ, have mercy.   Christe, eleison.
All: **Christ, have mercy.**   **Christe, eleison.**

Priest: Lord, have mercy.   Kyrie, eleison.
All: **Lord, have mercy.**   **Kyrie, eleison.**

B *Priest:* Lord, we have sinned against you:
Lord, have mercy.
All: **Lord, have mercy.**

Priest: Lord, show us your mercy and love.
All: **And grant us your salvation.**

Priest: May almighty God have mercy on us,
forgive us our sins,
and bring us to everlasting life.
All: **Amen.**

C *The priest or another minister addresses Christ in a series of invocations,
and all respond.*

13 Lord, Have Mercy

Cantor

You were sent to heal the con-trite: Lord, _____ have
Ky - ri - e, e -

All

mer - cy. Lord, _____ have mer - cy.
le - i - son. Ky - ri - e, e - le - i - son.

Cantor

You came to call _____ sin - ners: Christ, _____ have
Chri - ste, e -

All

mer - cy. Christ, _____ have mer - cy.
le - i - son. Chri - ste, e - le - i - son.

Cantor

You plead for us at the right hand of the Fa - ther:

All

Lord, _____ have mer - cy. Lord, _____ have
Ky - ri - e, e - le - i - son. Ky - ri - e, e -

mer - cy, have mer - cy, have mer - cy. _____
le - i - son, e - le - i - son, e - le - i - son. _____

Sing Praise and Thanksgiving!
J. Michael Joncas
Music © 1989, WLP

Priest
(or other minister): …Lord, have mercy.
All: **Lord, have mercy.**

Priest: …Christ, have mercy.
All: **Christ, have mercy.**

Priest: …Lord, have mercy.
All: **Lord, have mercy.**

Priest: May almighty God have mercy on us,
forgive us our sins,
and bring us to everlasting life.
All: **Amen.**

Gloria

*This hymn is part of Mass on Sundays (outside Advent and Lent), on solemnities,
and on feasts.*

14 Glory to God

REFRAIN

Glo-ry to God, glo-ry to God, glo-ry to God in the
high - est; glo-ry to God, glo-ry to God, and
peace to his peo-ple, his peo-ple on___ earth!

Cantor: Lord God, heavenly King, almighty God and Father, we worship you,
we give you thanks, we praise you for your glory. *(To Refrain)*

Cantor: Lord Jesus Christ, only Son of the Father, Lord God, Lamb of God,
Lord Jesus Christ, you take away the sin of the world: have mercy on us;
you are seated at the right hand of the Father: receive our prayer.
(To Refrain)

Cantor: For you alone are the Holy One, you alone are the Lord,
you alone are the Most High, Jesus Christ,

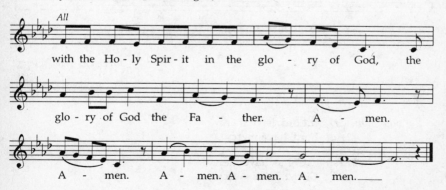

with the Ho - ly Spir - it in the glo - ry of God, the
glo - ry of God the Fa - ther. A - men.
A - men. A - men. A - men. A - men.___

Sing Praise and Thanksgiving!
J. Michael Joncas
Music © 1989, WLP

Glory to God in the highest,
  and peace to his people on earth.

Lord God, heavenly King,
almighty God and Father,
  we worship you, we give you thanks,
  we praise you for your glory.

Lord Jesus Christ, only Son of the Father,
Lord God, Lamb of God,
you take away the sin of the world:
  have mercy on us;
you are seated at the right hand of the Father:
  receive our prayer.

For you alone are the Holy One,
you alone are the Lord,
you alone are the Most High,
  Jesus Christ,
  with the Holy Spirit,
  in the glory of God the Father. Amen.

Opening Prayer

Liturgy of the Word

First Reading
All sit.

> *At the end of the reading:*
> > *Reader:* The word of the Lord.
> > *All:* **Thanks be to God.**

Responsorial Psalm

Second Reading
> *At the end of the reading:*
> > *Reader:* The word of the Lord.
> > *All:* **Thanks be to God.**

Gospel Acclamation
All stand.

15 Alleluia

REFRAIN

Cantor/All

Al - le-lu - ia, al - le-lu - ia,

al - le-lu - ia, al - le-lu - ia, al - le - lu - ia.

Sing Praise and Thanksgiving!
J. Michael Joncas
Music © 1989, WLP

During Lent, one of the following acclamations is used:

16 Praise to You, Lord Jesus Christ

REFRAIN

Cantor/All

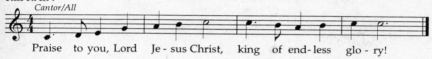

Praise to you, Lord Je - sus Christ, king of end-less glo - ry!

Sing Praise and Thanksgiving!
J. Michael Joncas
Music © 1989, WLP

Text © 1969, ICEL

A Praise to you, Lord Jesus Christ, king of endless glory!

B Praise and honor to you, Lord Jesus Christ!

C Glory and praise to you, Lord Jesus Christ!

D Glory to you, Word of God, Lord Jesus Christ!

Gospel

Deacon or
priest: The Lord be with you.
All: **And also with you.**

Deacon or
priest: A reading from the holy gospel according to N.
All: **Glory to you, Lord.**

At the end of the gospel:
Deacon or
priest: The gospel of the Lord.
All: **Praise to you, Lord Jesus Christ.**

Homily
All sit.

Profession of Faith
All stand.

Nicene Creed

We believe in one God,
   the Father, the Almighty,
   maker of heaven and earth,
   of all that is seen and unseen.

We believe in one Lord, Jesus Christ,
   the only Son of God,
   eternally begotten of the Father,
   God from God, Light from Light,
   true God from true God,
   begotten, not made, one in Being with the Father.
   Through him all things were made.

For us men and for our salvation
   he came down from heaven:
All bow during these two lines.
by the power of the Holy Spirit
   he was born of the Virgin Mary, and became man.
For our sake he was crucified under Pontius Pilate;
   he suffered, died, and was buried.
   On the third day he rose again
      in fulfillment of the Scriptures;
   he ascended into heaven
      and is seated at the right hand of the Father.
He will come again in glory to judge the living and the dead,
   and his kingdom will have no end.

We believe in the Holy Spirit, the Lord, the giver of life,
   who proceeds from the Father and the Son.
   With the Father and the Son he is worshiped and glorified.
   He has spoken through the Prophets.
   We believe in one holy catholic and apostolic Church.
   We acknowledge one baptism for the forgiveness of sins.
   We look for the resurrection of the dead,
      and the life of the world to come. Amen.

The Apostles' Creed may be used at Masses with children.

Apostles' Creed

I believe in God, the Father almighty,
    creator of heaven and earth.

I believe in Jesus Christ, his only Son, our Lord.
    He was conceived by the power of the Holy Spirit
        and born of the Virgin Mary.
    He suffered under Pontius Pilate,
        was crucified, died, and was buried.
    He descended to the dead.
    On the third day he rose again.
    He ascended into heaven,
        and is seated at the right hand of the Father.
    He will come again to judge the living and the dead.

I believe in the Holy Spirit,
    the holy catholic Church,
    the communion of saints,
    the forgiveness of sins,
    the resurrection of the body,
    and the life everlasting. Amen.

General Intercessions

After the priest invites all to pray, the deacon or other minister sings or says the petitions. The following or another response may be used:

17 General Intercessions

Lord,_____ in your mer - cy, hear our prayer.

Sing Praise and Thanksgiving!
J. Michael Joncas
Music © 1989, WLP

After the final petition, the priest says a concluding prayer.

Liturgy of the Eucharist

Preparation of the Altar and Gifts

All sit. While the altar is prepared and the gifts are brought forward, a song may be sung or instrumental music played while the priest quietly prays.

If there is no singing, the priest may pray aloud and the people respond:
Blessed be God forever.

Prayer over the Gifts

Priest: Pray, ... that our sacrifice may
be acceptable to God, the almighty Father.

All: **May the Lord accept the sacrifice at your hands**
for the praise and glory of his name,
for our good, and the good of all his Church.

All stand during the prayer over the gifts.

Eucharistic Prayer

18 Eucharistic Acclamations

Introductory Dialogue

Sing Praise and Thanksgiving!

Text © 1973, ICEL

J. Michael Joncas
Music © 1989, WLP

Priest: The Lord be with you.
All: **And also with you.**

Priest: Lift up your hearts.
All: **We lift them up to the Lord.**

Priest: Let us give thanks to the Lord our God.
All: **It is right to give him thanks and praise.**

The priest then sings or says the preface.

Holy, Holy, Holy

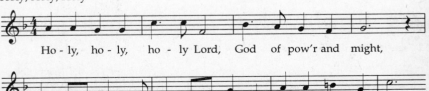

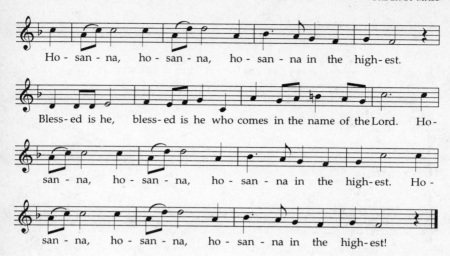

Ho - san - na, ho - san - na, ho - san - na in the high- est.

Bless- ed is he, bless- ed is he who comes in the name of the Lord. Ho -

san - na, ho - san - na, ho - san - na in the high- est. Ho -

san - na, ho - san - na, ho - san - na in the high- est!

Sing Praise and Thanksgiving!
J. Michael Joncas
Music © 1989, WLP

All: **Holy, holy, holy Lord, God of power and might,
heaven and earth are full of your glory.
Hosanna in the highest.
Blessed is he who comes in the name of the Lord.
Hosanna in the highest.**

Memorial Acclamation

After the words of institution, when the priest has replaced the cup on the altar and genuflected:

Priest

Let us pro - claim the mys - ter - y of faith:

All

Christ has died, Christ is ris - en, Christ will come a - gain.

Christ has died, Christ is ris - en, Christ will come a - gain.

Sing Praise and Thanksgiving!
J. Michael Joncas
Music © 1989, WLP

Priest: Let us proclaim the mystery of faith:

A   *All:* **Christ has died,**
                Christ is risen,
                Christ will come again.

B   *All:* **Dying you destroyed our death,**
                rising you restored our life.
                Lord Jesus, come in glory.

C   *All:* **When we eat this bread and drink this cup,**
                we proclaim your death, Lord Jesus,
                until you come in glory.

D   *All:* **Lord, by your cross and resurrection**
                you have set us free.
                You are the Savior of the world.

Doxology and Great Amen

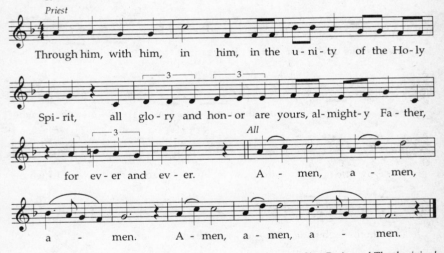

Through him, with him, in him, in the u-ni-ty of the Ho-ly Spi-rit, all glo-ry and hon-or are yours, al-might-y Fa-ther, for ev-er and ev-er. A-men, a-men, a-men. A-men, a-men, a-men.

Sing Praise and Thanksgiving!
J. Michael Joncas
Music © 1989, WLP

Text © 1973, ICEL

Priest: Through him,
        with him,
        in him,
        in the unity of the Holy Spirit,
        all glory and honor is yours,
        almighty Father,
        for ever and ever.

All: **Amen.**

Communion Rite

Lord's Prayer

All stand. The priest invites all to pray the Lord's Prayer.

19 Lord's Prayer

Priest
Let us pray for the com-ing of the king-dom   as Je-sus taught us:

All
Our Fa - ther,   who art in heav - en,   hal-low-ed be thy name;   thy

king-dom come, thy   will be done   on   earth as it is   in   heav-en.

Give us this day   our dai - ly bread;   give   us this day our dai-ly

bread;   and for- give us   our tres-pass-es as   we for-give those who

tres - pass a - gainst us.   And   lead us not   in - to temp-

ta - tion,   but de - liv - er   us from   e -   vil.

Priest
De-liv-er us, Lord,   from   ev - 'ry   e - vil, and grant us peace in our

day.   In   your mer - cy   keep us free from sin   and pro-

tect us from all anx - i - e-ty   as we wait in joy-ful hope for the

com-ing of our Sav - ior, Je - sus Christ.

All

For the king - dom, the pow - er, and the glo - ry are

yours, now and for ev - er.

Sing Praise and Thanksgiving!
J. Michael Joncas
Music © 1989, WLP

Sign of Peace

Priest: Lord Jesus Christ…for ever and ever.
All: **Amen.**

Priest: The peace of the Lord be with you always.
All: **And also with you.**

Deacon or priest: Let us offer each other the sign of peace.

Breaking of the Bread
20 Lamb of God

Cantor

Lamb of God, you take a-way the sins of the world:

All

have mer-cy on us, have mer-cy on us.

Cantor

Lamb of God, you take a-way the sins of the world:

All

grant us peace, grant us peace.

Sing Praise and Thanksgiving!
J. Michael Joncas
Music © 1989, WLP

Text © 1973, ICEL

The litany may be repeated until the breaking of the bread is finished; the litany always concludes with: **Grant us peace.**

All: **Lamb of God, you take away the sins of the world:**
have mercy on us.
Lamb of God, you take away the sins of the world:
have mercy on us.
Lamb of God, you take away the sins of the world:
grant us peace.

Communion

Priest: This is the Lamb of God
who takes away the sins of the world.
Happy are those who are called to his supper.

All: **Lord, I am not worthy to receive you,**
but only say the word and I shall be healed.

Communion minister: The body of Christ.
Communicant: **Amen.**

Communion minister: The blood of Christ.
Communicant: **Amen.**

The communion song is begun while the priest receives the body and blood of Christ.

Period of Silence or Song of Praise

All sit. After communion there may be a period of silence, or a song of praise may be sung.

Prayer after Communion

All stand.

Concluding Rite

The blessing and dismissal follow any brief announcements.

Greeting and Blessing

Priest: The Lord be with you.
All: **And also with you.**

Priest: May almighty God bless you,
the Father, and the Son, and the Holy Spirit.
All: **Amen.**

Dismissal

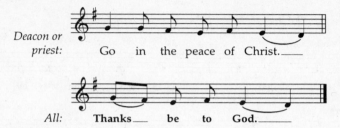

Deacon or priest: Go in the peace of Christ.___

All: Thanks___ be to God.___

Deacon or
priest: **A** Go in the peace of Christ.

B The Mass is ended, go in peace.

C Go in peace to love and serve the Lord.

All: **Thanks be to God.**

From the Easter Vigil through the Second Sunday of Easter, and on Pentecost and its Vigil, **alleluia, alleluia** *is added to the dismissal and the response.*

Deacon or
priest: Go in the peace of Christ, al - le - lu - ia,
al - le - lu - ia.___

All: **Thanks be to God,** al - le - lu - ia,
al - le - lu - ia.___

Mass may conclude with song, with instrumental music, or with silence.

People's Mass
Jan Vermulst

21 Lord, Have Mercy

Priest/Deacon/Cantor   All

Lord, have mer - cy. Lord, have mer - cy.

Priest/Deacon/Cantor   All

Christ, have__ mer - cy. Christ, have__ mer - cy.

Priest/Deacon/Cantor   All

Lord,__ have mer - cy. Lord,__ have mer - cy.

People's Mass
Jan M. Vermulst, 1925–1994
Music © 1970, WLP

22 Glory to God

Glo-ry to God in the high-est, and peace to his peo-ple on earth. Lord

God, heav-en-ly King, al-might-y God and Fa-ther, we wor-ship you, we

give you thanks, we praise you for__ your glo-ry. Lord Je-sus__

Christ, on - ly Son of the Fa-ther, Lord God, Lamb of__ God,

you take a-way the sin of the world: have mer-cy on us; you are

seat-ed at the right hand of the Fa-ther: re - ceive____ our prayer.

For you a - lone are the Ho - ly One, you a - lone are the Lord,

you a - lone are the Most____ High, Je - sus Christ, with the

Ho - ly Spir-it, in the glo - ry of God the Fa-ther. A - men.

People's Mass
Jan M. Vermulst, 1925–1994
Music © 1970, WLP

Gospel Acclamation 23

REFRAIN

Al - le-lu - ia, al - le-lu - ia, al - le-lu - ia.

People's Mass
Jan M. Vermulst, 1925–1994
Music © 1984, WLP

Lenten Gospel Acclamation 24

Praise to you, Lord Je - sus Christ, king of end-less glo - ry!
Praise and hon - or to you, Lord____ Je - sus Christ!____
Glo - ry and praise to you, Lord____ Je - sus Christ!____
Glo - ry to you, Word of God, Lord____ Je - sus Christ!____

Text © 1969, ICEL

People's Mass
Jan M. Vermulst, 1925–1994
Music © 1984, WLP

25 Eucharistic Acclamations

HOLY, HOLY, HOLY

Ho-ly, ho-ly, ho-ly Lord,___ God of pow-er and might, heav-en and earth are__ full of your glo - ry Ho-san-na in the high - est. Bless-ed is he who comes in the name of the Lord. Ho - san - na in the high - est.___

MEMORIAL ACCLAMATION

A

Christ has died, Christ is ris - en, Christ will come a - gain.

B

Dy - ing you de - stroyed our death, ris - ing you re - stored our life. Lord Je - sus, come in glo - ry.

C

When we eat this bread and drink this cup, we pro - claim your death, Lord Je-sus, un - til you come in glo - ry.

D

Lord, by your cross and re - sur - rec - tion you have set us

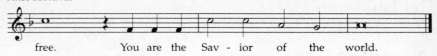

free. You are the Sav - ior of the world.

GREAT AMEN

A - men. A - men. A - men.

People's Mass

Text (Mcm. Accl.) © 1973, ICEL

Jan M. Vermulst, 1925–1994
Music © 1970, 1984, WLP

Lamb of God 26

*1. Lamb of God, you take a - way the sins of the
3. Lamb of God, true bread of life, the food of our

1. world: have mer - cy on us.
3. souls: have mer - cy on us.

2. Lamb of God, you take a - way the sins of the
4. Lamb of God, our nour - ish - ment, our man - na from

2. world: have mer - cy on us.
4. heav'n: have mer - cy on us.

5. Lamb of God, you take a - way the sins___ of the

5. world: grant us___ peace.

People's Mass

Text (vss. 1, 2, 5) © 1973, ICEL
Text (vss. 3–4) © 1984, WLP

Jan M. Vermulst, 1925–1994
Music © 1970, WLP

*Vss. 1, 2, and 5 must be sung. The additional invocations in vss. 3–4 are only suggestions and may be used, altered,
expanded or omitted according to the period of time needed for the breaking of the bread and pouring of the wine.*

Danish Amen Mass
David Kraehenbuehl

27 Lord, Have Mercy

Priest/Deacon/Cantor   All   Priest/Deacon/Cantor

Lord, have mer - cy. Lord, have mer - cy. Christ, have mer - cy.

All   Priest/Deacon/Cantor   All

Christ, have mer - cy. Lord, have mer - cy. Lord, have mer - cy.

Danish Amen Mass
David Kraehenbuehl, 1923–1997
Music © 1973, WLP

28 Glory to God

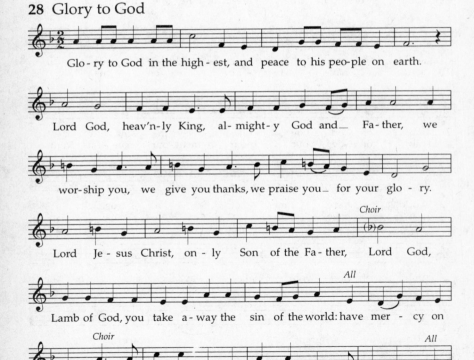

Glo - ry to God in the high - est, and peace to his peo-ple on earth.

Lord God, heav'n-ly King, al - might-y God and— Fa - ther, we

wor-ship you, we give you thanks, we praise you— for your glo - ry.

Lord Je - sus Christ, on - ly Son of the Fa - ther, Lord God,

Lamb of God, you take a - way the sin of the world: have mer - cy on

us; you are seat-ed at the right hand of the Fa-ther: re -

ceive— our— prayer. For you a-lone are the Ho-ly One, you a-

lone are the Lord, you a-lone are the Most High, Je-sus Christ, with the

Ho-ly Spir-it, in the glo-ry of God the Fa-ther. A - men.

Danish Amen Mass
David Kraehenbuehl, 1923–1997
Music © 1973, WLP

Gospel Acclamation 29

Al - le - lu - ia, al - le - lu - ia.

Danish Amen Mass
David Kraehenbuehl, 1923–1997

Eucharistic Acclamations 30

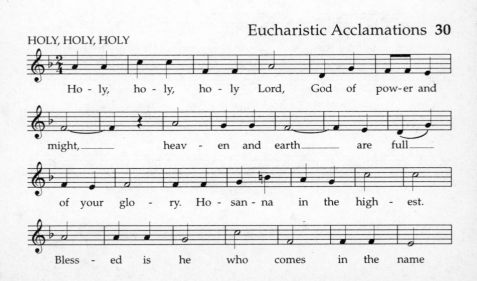

HOLY, HOLY, HOLY

Ho - ly, ho - ly, ho - ly Lord, God of pow-er and

might,_____ heav - en and earth_____ are full_____

of your glo - ry. Ho - san - na in the high - est.

Bless - ed is he who comes in the name

of the Lord. Ho - san - na in the high - est.

MEMORIAL ACCLAMATION

A

Christ has died, Christ is ris - en, Christ will come a - gain.

B

Dy - ing you de - stroyed our death, ris - ing you re -

stored our life. Lord Je - sus, come in glo - ry.

C

When we eat this bread and drink this cup, we pro - claim your

death, Lord Je - sus, un - til you come in glo - ry.

D

Lord, by your cross and re - sur - rec - tion, you have set us

free. You are the Sav - ior of the world.

GREAT AMEN

A - men. A - men. A - men.

Danish Amen Mass
David Kraehenbuehl, 1923–1997
Acc. by Charles G. Frischmann
Music © 1970, 1973, WLP

Lamb of God 31

Lamb of God, you take a-way the sins of the world: have mer-cy on us. Lamb of God, you take a-way the sins of the world: have mer-cy on us. Lamb of God, you take a-way the sins of the world: grant___ us peace.

Danish Amen Mass
David Kraehenbuehl, 1923–1997
Acc. by Charles G. Frischmann
Music © 1971, 1973, WLP

Mass in Honor of Pope Paul VI
Edward E. Connor

Lord, Have Mercy 32

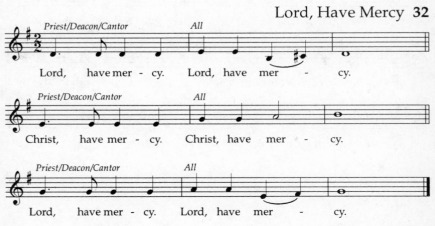

Priest/Deacon/Cantor   *All*

Lord, have mer-cy. Lord, have mer - cy.

Priest/Deacon/Cantor   *All*

Christ, have mer - cy. Christ, have mer - cy.

Priest/Deacon/Cantor   *All*

Lord, have mer-cy. Lord, have mer - cy.

Mass in Honor of Pope Paul VI
Edward E. Connor
Music © 1976, WLP

33 Glory to God

Glo - ry to God in the high - est, and peace to his peo - ple on earth.

Lord God, heav-en-ly King, al- might-y God and Fa - ther, we

wor-ship you, we give you thanks, we praise you for your glo - ry.

Lord Je-sus Christ, on-ly Son of the Fa - ther, Lord God, Lamb of

God, you take a-way the sin of the world: have mer - cy on us;

you are seat-ed at the right hand of the Fa - ther: re - ceive___ our

prayer. For you a-lone are the Ho-ly One, you a-lone are the Lord,

you a-lone are the Most High, Je - sus Christ, with the Ho-ly

Spir - it, in the glo-ry of God the Fa - ther. A - men.

Mass in Honor of Pope Paul VI

Edward E. Connor
Music © 1970, WLP

HOLY, HOLY, HOLY

Ho - ly, ho - ly, ho - ly Lord, God of pow-er and might,_____ heav - en and earth are full of your glo - ry. Ho-san - na in the high - est. Bless - ed is he who comes in the name of the Lord. Ho - san - na in the high - est.

MEMORIAL ACCLAMATION

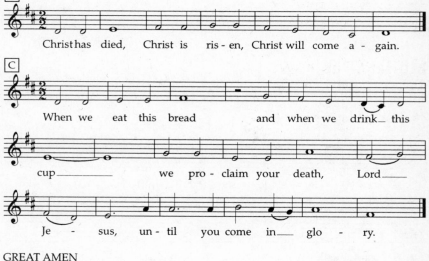

A

Christ has died, Christ is ris-en, Christ will come a - gain.

C

When we eat this bread and when we drink_ this cup_____ we pro - claim your death, Lord_ Je - sus, un - til you come in_ glo - ry.

GREAT AMEN

A - men. A - men._ A - men.

Mass in Honor of Pope Paul VI
Edward E. Connor
Music © 1970, 1994, WLP

35 Lamb of God

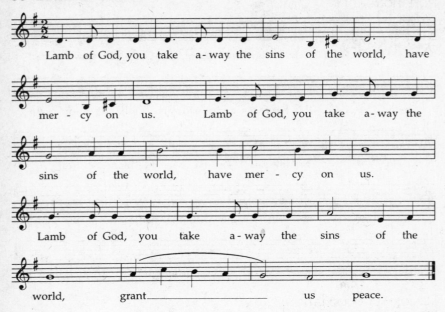

Lamb of God, you take a-way the sins of the world, have mer-cy on us. Lamb of God, you take a-way the sins of the world, have mer-cy on us. Lamb of God, you take a-way the sins of the world, grant us peace.

Mass in Honor of Pope Paul VI
Edward E. Connor
Music © 1970, WLP

Jubilate Deo
Gregorian Chant

36 Lord, Have Mercy

Priest/Deacon/Cantor Ky-ri - e, e - lé - i - son. *All* Ky-ri - e, e - lé - i - son.

Priest/Deacon/Cantor Chri - ste, e - lé - i - son. *All* Chri - ste, e - lé - i - son.

Priest/Deacon/Cantor Ky - ri - e, e - lé-i-son. *All* Ky-ri - e, e - lé - i - son.

Jubilate Deo
Chant, Mass XVI, Mode III

Gló-ri-a in ex-cél-sis De - o.   Et in ter-ra pax ho-mí-ni-bus

bo-nae vo-lun-tá - tis.   Lau-dá - mus te.

Be-ne-dí-ci-mus__ te.__   Ad-o-rá - mus__ te.

Glo-ri - fi - cá-mus te.   Grá-ti-as á-gi-mus__ ti - bi

pro-pter ma-gnam gló-ri-am tu-am.   Dó-mi-ne De-us, Rex cae-lé-stis.

De-us__ Pa-ter__ o - mní - po - tens.   Dó-mi-ne Fi-li u-ni-gé-ni-te,

Je - su__ Chri - ste.   Dó-mi-ne De-us,__ A-gnus De - i,

Fí-li-us__ Pa - tris.   Qui tol-lis pec-cá-ta mun - di,__

mi-se-ré - re__ no - bis.   Qui tol-lis pec-cá-ta mun - di,

sú-sci-pe de-pre-ca-ti-ó-nem__ no - stram.__

Qui se-des ad déx-te-ram Pa - tris,   mi-se-ré-re no - bis.

Quó-ni-am tu so-lus San-ctus. Tu so-lus__ Dó - mi - nus.

Tu so-lus Al - tís - si-mus,__ Je - su__ Chri - ste.

Cum San-cto__ Spí - ri-tu, in gló-ri - a De - i

Pa - tris.__ A - men.

Jubilate Deo
Mass VIII, Mode V, 16th cent.

38 Eucharistic Acclamations

PREFACE DIALOGUE

Priest
Dó - mi - nus vo - bís - cum. *All* Et cum spí - ri - tu tu - o.

Priest
Sur - sum cor - da.__ *All* Ha - bé - mus ad

Dó - mi - num.__ *Priest* Grá - ti - as__ a - gá - mus

Dó-mi - no__ De - o no-stro. *All* Di - gnum et ju - stum est.__

Chant, Mode II

HOLY, HOLY, HOLY

San-ctus,__ San-ctus,__ San-ctus Dó-mi-nus De-us Sá-ba-oth.

Ple - ni sunt cae - li et ter - ra gló - ri - a tu - a.

Ho-sán-na in ex-cél-sis. Be-ne-dí-ctus qui ve-nit in

nó-mi-ne Dó-mi-ni. Ho-sán - na in ex-cél - sis.___

Jubilate Deo
Mass XVIII, Chant, Mode VIII

MEMORIAL ACCLAMATION

Mor-tem tu - am an-nun-ti-á-mus, Dó - mi-ne, et tu - am

re-sur-rec-ti-ó-nem con-fi-té - mur, do - nec vé-ni - as.

Jubilate Deo
Chant, Mode III

2

Quo-ti-es-cúm - que man-du-cá-mus pa-nem hunc et

cá-li-cem bí - bi-mus, mor-tem tu - am

an-nun-ti-á-mus, Dó - mi-ne, do - nec vé-ni - as.

Chant, Mode III

3

Sal-vá-tor mun-di, sal - va nos, qui per cru - cem et

re-sur-rec-ti-ó-nem tu - am li-be-rá-sti___ nos.

Chant, Mode III

39 Lamb of God

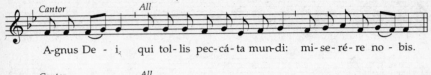

A-gnus De - i, qui tol- lis pec-cá- ta mun-di: mi- se- ré- re no - bis.

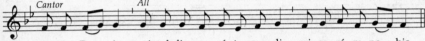

A-gnus De - i, qui tol- lis pec-cá- ta mun-di: mi- se- ré- re no - bis.

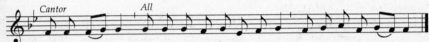

A-gnus De - i, qui tol- lis pec-cá- ta mun-di: do- na no-bis pa - cem.

Jubilate Deo
Mass XVIII, Chant, Mode VIII

Mass for Christian Unity
Jan Vermulst

40 Lord, Have Mercy

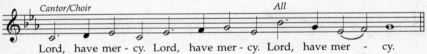

Lord, have mer - cy. Lord, have mer - cy. Lord, have mer - cy.

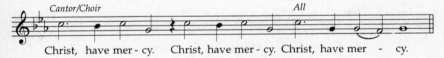

Christ, have mer - cy. Christ, have mer - cy. Christ, have mer - cy.

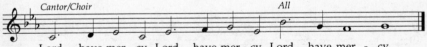

Lord, have mer - cy. Lord, have mer - cy. Lord, have mer - cy.

Mass for Christian Unity
Jan M. Vermulst, 1925–1994
Music © 1964, WLP

HOLY, HOLY, HOLY

Ho - ly, ho - ly, ho - ly Lord, God of pow'r and might, heav - en and earth are full___ of your glo - ry. Ho - san - na___ in the high - est. Bless - ed is he who comes in the name of the Lord. Ho - san - na___ in the high - est.

MEMORIAL ACCLAMATION

A

Christ has died, Christ is ris - en, Christ will come a - gain.

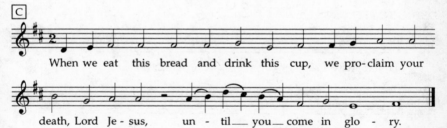

C

When we eat this bread and drink this cup, we pro-claim your death, Lord Je - sus, un - til___ you___ come in glo - ry.

GREAT AMEN

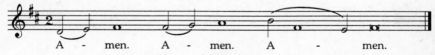

A - men. A - men. A - men.

Mass for Christian Unity

Jan M. Vermulst, 1925–1994

Text (Mem. Accl.) © 1973, ICEL
Music (Holy, Holy, Holy) © 1964, WLP
Music (Mem. Accl. and Great Amen) © 1987, WLP

42 Lamb of God

Lamb of God, you take a - way the sins of the world:
have mer - cy on us. Lamb of God, you take a - way the
sins of the world: have mer - cy on us. Lamb of God,
you take a - way the sins of the world: grant us peace.

Mass for Christian Unity
Jan M. Vermulst, 1925–1994
Music © 1964, WLP

Mass of Creation
Marty Haugen

43 Lord, Have Mercy

OSTINATO REFRAIN

Lord, have mer - cy, Christ, have mer - cy.
Lord, have mer - cy.

Mass of Creation
Marty Haugen
Music © 1984, GIA

Glory to God 44

REFRAIN

Glo - ry to God in the high - est,_____ and peace_____ _____ to his peo - ple on earth._____

VERSE 1

1. Lord God, heav - en - ly King, al - might - y
1. God and Fa - ther,_____ we wor - ship you, we
To Refrain
1. give you thanks, we praise you for your glo - ry._____

VERSE 2

2. Lord Je - sus Christ, on - ly Son of the Fa - ther,_____ Lord
2. God, Lamb of God, you take a - way the sin of the world: have
2. mer - cy on us;_____ you are seat - ed at the right hand
To Refrain
2. of the Fa - ther: re - ceive our prayer._____

VERSE 3

3. For you a - lone are the Ho - ly One, you a - lone are the Lord,__

3. ___ you a - lone are the Most___ High, Je - sus

3. Christ, ___ with the Ho - ly Spir - it, in the glo - ry of

To Refrain

3. God the Fa - ther.___ A - men.___ A - men.___

REFRAIN

Glo - ry to God in the high - est, ___ and peace

to his peo - ple on earth.___

Mass of Creation
Marty Haugen
Music © 1984, GIA

45 Gospel Acclamation

REFRAIN

Al - le - lu - ia, al - le - lu - ia. Praise the Word of truth and life.

Mass of Creation
Marty Haugen
Text and music © 1984, GIA

46 Eucharistic Acclamations

PREFACE DIALOGUE

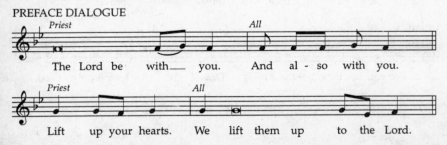

Priest   *All*

The Lord be with___ you. And al - so with you.

Priest   *All*

Lift up your hearts. We lift them up to the Lord.

Priest

Let us give thanks to the Lord our God.

All

It is right to give him thanks and praise.

HOLY, HOLY, HOLY

All

Ho-ly, ho-ly, ho - ly Lord, God of pow-er, God of might, heav-en and earth are full of your glo-ry._____ Ho-san- na in the high-est._____ Bless-ed is he who comes in the name of the Lord._____ Ho- san - na in the high-est._____ Ho- san - na in the high - est.

MEMORIAL ACCLAMATION

Priest (Deacon)

Let us pro-claim the mys-ter-y of faith:

All

Christ has died, Christ is ris-en, Christ will come a - gain.

Christ has died, Christ is ris-en, Christ will come a - gain.

DOXOLOGY AND GREAT AMEN

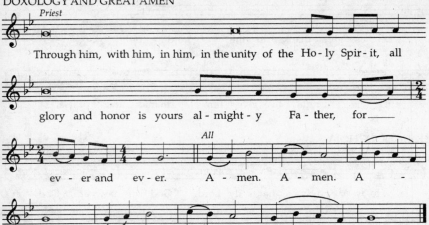

Through him, with him, in him, in the unity of the Ho-ly Spir-it, all glory and honor is yours al-might-y Fa-ther, for____ ev-er and ev-er. A-men. A-men. A-men. A-men. A-men. A-men. A-men.

Mass of Creation
Marty Haugen
Music © 1984, GIA

Text (Mem. Accl.) © 1973, ICEL

47 Lamb of God

Cantor/Choir   All
*1. Je-sus, Lamb of God,____ you take a-way the sins of the
2. Je-sus, bread of life,____

world:____ have mer-cy on__ us.

Final Invocation
Cantor/Choir   All
Je-sus, Lamb of God,____ you take a-way the

sins of the world: grant us your__ peace.

Mass of Creation
Marty Haugen
Music © 1984, GIA

*Sing "Jesus, Lamb of God" for first and last invocations, adding additional invocations as needed.

Cleanse Us, O Lord 48

REFRAIN

Cleanse us, O Lord, from all our sins; wash us and we shall be____ clean - er than snow.

Music for the Banquet
William Ferris
Music © 1993, WLP

Text © 1973, ICEL

Wash Me With Fresh Water 49

REFRAIN

Wash____ me with fresh wa - ter, make me__ bright as__ snow.____

Ps 51 (adapt.)

Ron Rendek
Text and music © 1994, WLP

Springs of Water 50

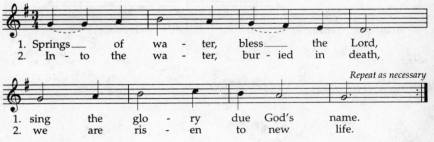

1. Springs__ of wa - ter, bless__ the Lord,
2. In - to the wa - ter, bur - ied in death,

Repeat as necessary

1. sing the glo - ry due God's name.
2. we are ris - en to new life.

Mike Hay
Text (vs. 1) © 1973, ICEL
Text (vs. 2) and music © 1994, WLP

51 Waters of Life

REFRAIN

1. Wa - ters of life, Wa - ters of life,
2. Wa - ters of life, Wa - ters of life,

1. Cre - at - ing life, Cre - at - ing life,
2. Spir - it of God, Spir - it of God,

1. Bap - tized in faith, Bap - tized in faith,
2. Called as your own, Called as your own,

1. Sealed with your love, Sealed with your love.
2. Light for our lives, Light for our lives.

Laura Kutscher
Text and music © 1992, Laura Kutscher

52 You Will Draw Water Joyfully

REFRAIN

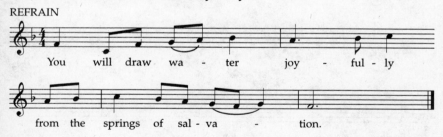

You will draw wa - ter joy - ful - ly

from the springs of sal - va - tion.

Is 12:3
Text © 1969, ICEL

Donald J. Reagan
Music © 1984, WLP

I Saw Water Flowing 53

lu - ia!___ Al - le - lu - ia!___ Al - le -

lu - ia!___ Al - le - lu - ia!___

Ez 47:1, 9
The Roman Missal
Text © 1973, ICEL

Michael Ward
Music © 1991, WLP

54 Send Us Flowing Water

REFRAIN

Send us flow-ing wa - ter, Lord,___ we shall all re - ceive.

___ Send us flow-ing wa - ter, Lord,___

we shall all be- lieve! lieve! Send us flow-ing

wa - ter, Lord!___ We shall all be - lieve.

Joe Mattingly
Text and music © 1988, WLP

Lord, Have Mercy 55

Music for the Banquet
William Ferris
Music © 1993, WLP

Penitential Rite 56

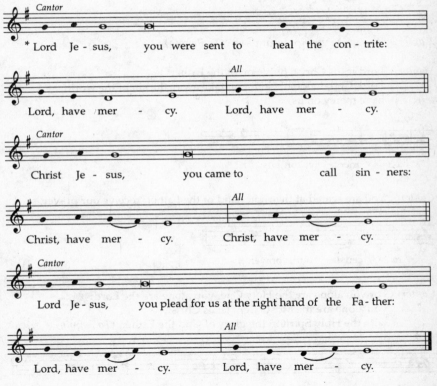

Text © 1973, ICEL

Arr. by Steven R. Janco
Arr. © 1997, WLP

Other invocations may be substituted.

57 Glory to God

REFRAIN

Last time to Amen

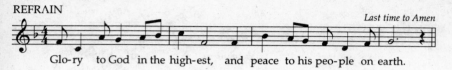

Glo-ry to God in the high-est, and peace to his peo-ple on earth.

Cantor: Lord God, heavenly King, almighty God and Father, we worship you,

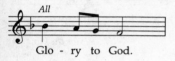

Glo - ry to God.

Cantor: We give you thanks,

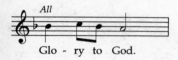

Glo - ry to God.

Cantor: We praise you for your glory. *(To Refrain)*

Cantor: Lord Jesus Christ, only Son of the Father,
Lord, God, Lamb of God, you take away the sin of the world:
have mercy on us,

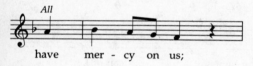

have mer - cy on us;

Cantor: You are seated at the right hand of the Father: receive our prayer,

re - ceive— our prayer.

Cantor: For you alone are the Holy One, you alone are the Lord;
you alone are the Most High, Jesus Christ,
with the Holy Spirit in the glory of God the Father. *(To Refrain)*

A - men! A - men!

Steven R. Janco
Music © 1992, WLP

Glory to God 58

REFRAIN

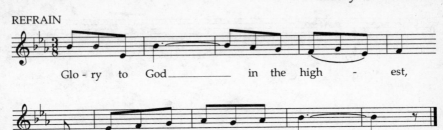

Glo - ry to God_____ in the high - est, and peace to his peo - ple on earth._____

Mass of Hope
Becket G. Senchur
Music © 1970, GIA

Chant Style Gloria 59

REFRAIN 1

Glo - ry to God in the high - est,_____ and peace to his peo - ple on earth._____

REFRAIN 2*

Gló - ri - a in ex - cél - sis De - o. Gló - ri - a in ex - cél - sis De - o.

Howard L. Hughes
Music (except melody of Ref. 2) © 1990, WLP

Optional refrain for Christmas season.

60 Gospel Acclamation

Al - le-lu - ia, al - le-lu - ia.

Norah Duncan IV
Music © 1987, WLP

61 Gospel Acclamation

Al - le - lu - ia, al - le - lu - ia, al - le - lu - ia.

Robert F. Twynham
Music © 1958, 1964, WLP

62 Gospel Acclamation

Al - le - lu - ia,___ al - le - lu - ia, al - le - lu - ia.

Robert F. Twynham
Music © 1958, 1964, WLP

63 Gospel Acclamation

REFRAIN

Al - le - lu - ia, al - le - lu - ia.

Lucien Deiss
Music © 1970, 1973, WLP

Gospel Acclamation **64**

Al - le - lu - ia, al - le - lu - ia.

Al - le - lu - ia, al - le - lu - ia.

Al - le - lu - ia, al - le - lu - ia.

James V. Marchionda
Music © 1981, 1982, 1984, WLP

Gospel Acclamation **65**

Al - le - lu - ia, al - le - lu - ia,_____

al - le - lu - ia, al - le - lu - ia.

Wolfgang A. Mozart, 1756–1791

Gospel Acclamation **66**

Al - le - lu - ia, al - le - lu - ia, al - le - lu - ia.

James Gerrish
Music © 1971, WLP

67 Festive Alleluia

REFRAIN

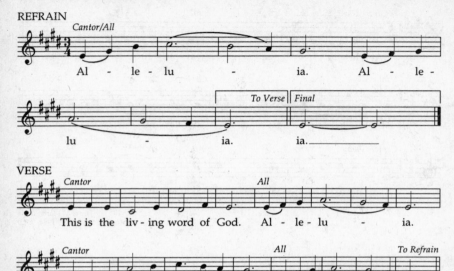

Al - le - lu - ia. Al - le -
lu - ia. ia.

VERSE

This is the liv - ing word of God. Al - le - lu - ia.

Tell-ing of all God's won-der-ful deeds. Al - le - lu - ia.

James V. Marchionda
Text and music © 1994, WLP

68 Fanfare and Alleluia

ALLELUIA

Al - le - lu - ia. Al - le - lu - ia. Al - le -
lu - ia. Al - le - lu - ia. Al - le - lu - ia,
al - le - lu - ia, al - le - lu - ia.

Donald J. Reagan
Music © 1982, WLP

Gospel Acclamation **69**

Al - le - lu - ia,   al - le - lu - ia,___   al - le - lu - ia.

Chant, Mode VI

Gospel Acclamation **70**

Al - le - lu - ia,   al - le - lu - ia.

William Ferris
Music © 1996, WLP

Gospel Acclamation **71**

Al - le - lu - ia,   al - le - lu - ia,

al - le - lu - ia,   al - le - lu - ia.

Noël Goemanne
Music © 1992, WLP

Lenten Gospel Acclamation **72**

Praise and hon - or to you,   Lord Je - sus Christ!

Praise and hon - or to you,   Lord Je - sus Christ!___

Paul M. French
Music © 1994, WLP

73 Lenten Gospel Acclamation

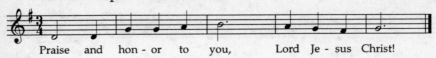

Praise and hon - or to you, Lord Je - sus Christ!

James E. Wilbur
Music © 1973, WLP

Text © 1969, ICEL

74 Lenten Gospel Acclamation

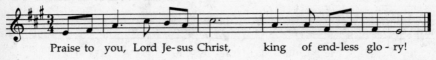

Praise to you, Lord Je-sus Christ, king of end-less glo - ry!

James E. Wilbur
Music © 1973, WLP

Text © 1969, ICEL

75 Lenten Gospel Acclamation

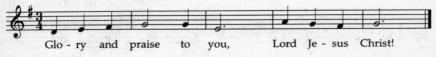

Glo - ry and praise to you, Lord Je - sus Christ!

James E. Wilbur
Music © 1973, WLP

Text © 1969, ICEL

76 Lenten Gospel Acclamation

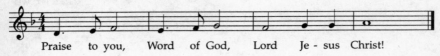

Praise to you, Word of God, Lord Je - sus Christ!

Charles Gardner
Music © 1992, 1993, WLP

Text © 1969, ICEL

General Intercessions 77

Gra - cious Lord, hear us, we pray.

Ronald F. Krisman
Music © 1977, Ronald F. Krisman

General Intercessions 78

Cantor/Choir ... *All*

...let us pray to the Lord. Lord, hear our prayer.
or Lord, have mer - cy.

Byzantine chant

General Intercessions 79

Lord,— hear our prayer.

The Roman Missal
Music © 1973, ICEL

General Intercessions 80

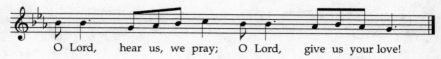

O Lord, hear us, we pray; O Lord, give us your love!

Lucien Deiss
Text and music © 1970, WLP

General Intercessions 81

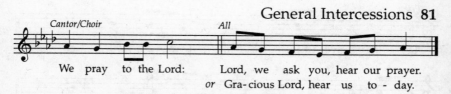

Cantor/Choir *All*

We pray to the Lord: Lord, we ask you, hear our prayer.
or Gra - cious Lord, hear us to - day.

Adapt. from *Litany of the Saints*

82 Trilingual Intercessions

REFRAIN

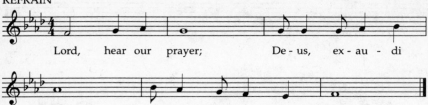

Lord, hear our prayer; De - us, ex - au - di nos; Se - ñor, es - cú - cha - nos.

Mike Hay
Music © 1994, WLP

Measures 3 and 4 may be omitted or alternate languages may be substituted.

83 Oyenos, Señor / O God, Hear Us

ESTRIBILLO/REFRAIN

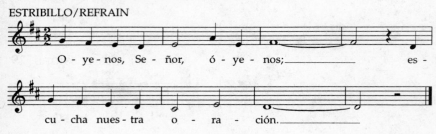

O - ye - nos, Se - ñor, ó - ye - nos;_____ es - cu - cha nues - tra o - ra - ción._____

Pedro Rubalcava
Text and music © 1995, WLP

84 Introductory Dialogue

Priest The Lord____ be with you. *All* And al - so with you.

Priest Lift____ up____ your hearts.____ *All* We lift____ them up to the Lord.____

Priest Let us give thanks to the Lord____ our God.

All It is right to give him thanks____ and praise.____

SANTO, SANTO, SANTO

San - to, San - to, San - to es el Se - ñor, Dios del Un - i -

ver - so.___ Lle - nos es - tán el cie - lo y la tie - rra

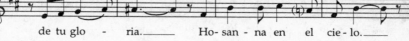

de tu glo - ria.___ Ho - san - na en el cie - lo.___

Ho - san - na en el cie - lo.___ Ben - di - to el que

vie - ne en nom - bre___ del Se - ñor.___ Ho -

san - na en el cie - lo.___ Ho - san - na en el cie - lo.___

ACLAMACION MEMORIAL

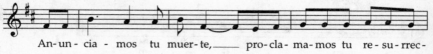

An - un - cia - mos tu muer - te,___ pro - cla - ma - mos tu re - su - rrec -

ción.___ ¡Ven, Se - ñor Je - sús! ¡Ven, Se - ñor Je - sús!

AMEN

A - mén. A - mén.

Misa de Sta. Maria del Lago

Steven R. Janco
Music © 1995, WLP

86 Christ Has Died, Alleluia

Christ has died,— al-le-lu - ia.— Christ is ris - en,
al-le-lu - ia.— Christ will come a - gain,—
al-le-lu - ia, al-e-lu - ia.—

Text © 1968, ICEL

Joseph E. Wise
Music © 1971, 1972, GIA

87 Great Amen

A - men.— A - men.

Chant

88 Great Amen

A - men. A - men.

Dresden

89 Lord's Prayer

Priest: Let us pray...Savior gave us:

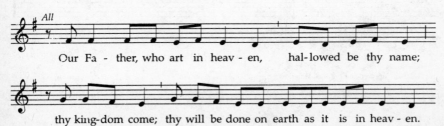

Our Fa - ther, who art in heav - en, hal-lowed be thy name;

thy king-dom come; thy will be done on earth as it is in heav - en.

Give us this day our dai-ly bread; and for-give us our tres-pass-es

as we for-give those who tres-pass a-gainst___ us;

and lead us not in-to temp-ta - tion,

but de-liv-er us from e-vil.

Priest: Deliver us, Lord, … Savior, Jesus Christ.

All

For the king-dom, the pow'r, and the

glo-ry are yours, now and for ev - er.

Chant
Adapt. by Robert J. Snow

Lamb of God 90

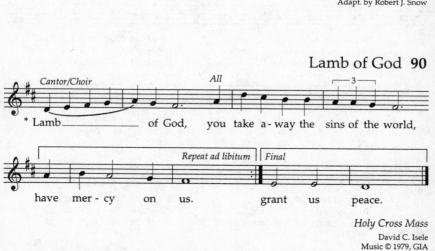

Cantor/Choir   *All*   ⎡— 3 —⎤

* Lamb_____ of God, you take a-way the sins of the world,

Repeat ad libitum | *Final*

have mer-cy on us. grant us peace.

Holy Cross Mass
David C. Isele
Music © 1979, GIA

*Sing "Lamb of God" for first and last invocations, adding additional invocations as needed.

91 Lamb of God

1. Lamb_ of God,_____ Re-deem - er__ of__ all,
Christmas 2. Lamb_ of God,_____ true Day-spring from on__ high,
Easter 3. Lamb_ of God,_____ our ris - en__ Lord,

1. you take a - way the sins of the world:
2. you take a - way the sins of the world:
3. you take a - way the sins of the world:

1. have mer - cy on us, have mer - cy on us.
2. have mer - cy on us, have mer - cy on us.
3. have mer - cy on us, have mer - cy on us.

1. Lamb of God, our priest and judge, you take a - way the
2. Lamb of God, our prom-ised Lord, you take a - way the
3. Lamb of God, our Pas - chal feast, you take a - way the

1. sins of the world: have mer - cy on us,
2. sins of the world: have mer - cy on us,
3. sins of the world: have mer - cy on us,

1. have mer - cy on us. Lamb of God, our Lord of
2. have mer - cy on us. Lamb of God, true Morn-ing
3. have mer - cy on us. Lamb of God, re - deem-ing

1. life, you take a - way the sins of the world:
2. Star, you take a - way the sins of the world:
3. Light, you take a - way the sins of the world:

1. grant us peace,___ grant us peace.___
2. grant us peace,___ grant us peace.___
3. grant us peace,___ grant us peace.___

Music for the Banquet
William Ferris
Text (tropes) and music © 1993, WLP

*Assembly may join once they have become familiar with piece.

The Psalms

Think of a time when you felt that all was right with the world. Remember a time when pain was so deep that you forgot what joy was. Call to mind a time when you needed something so much that all you could do was to ask again and again for it. Recall a time when you were so happy that you thought you would burst.

These human experiences are given voice in the songs of Israel, the Bible's hymns, the psalms.

Some of the psalms, such as Psalm 1, are songs of stable faith and peaceful life: God is in heaven, the good life is in reach, we have only to follow God's law and all will be well. Some of the psalms are songs of lamentation, deep stirring songs of sorrow, such as Psalm 51 ("Have mercy on me, God, in your goodness"), or songs of inconsolable suffering, such as Psalm 88 ("My only friend is darkness").

Some psalms are prayers of petition, such as Psalm 86: "Incline your ear, O Lord; answer me, for I am afflicted and poor." Some of the psalms, such as Psalm 148, are the poetry of sheer, exulting praise: "Fire and hail, snow and mist, storm winds,…you mountains and all you hills, you fruit trees and all you cedars, you wild beasts and all tame animals, you creeping things and you winged fowl,…praise the name of the Lord."

Taken together, the psalms give voice to our joys and pains, fears and hopes. They address our hearts' concerns to the God who listens and cares. And something happens when we take these sacred words and make them our own. Baptized into Christ, we sing these songs as Christ's own songs to God! Throughout the year, by singing the psalms, we take on the very compassion of Christ. We enlarge our capacity to experience emotions that make us human, that lead us to God in wonder. And we stand with those who must lament and with those who can laugh.

At Mass, a psalm has a privileged place in the liturgy of the word. The psalm is the scripture "reading" that the whole assembly proclaims. Coming between the first two readings, the psalm is usually sung "responsorially"—the cantor first sings the response and then everyone repeats it, repeating it again after the cantor sings each verse. By singing the psalm response over and over we inscribe it in our hearts; at prayer we can sing it throughout the week.

Psalms also may be sung at the beginning of Mass, during the presentation of the gifts, and during the communion procession. Many of the hymns that we sing are paraphrases or adaptations of the psalms, or at least are inspired by their poetic images. After all, the psalms and other scriptural songs make up the first and best hymnal of the Church.

The Church's daily prayer consists mostly of psalms, and certain psalms are traditional for certain times of day. Psalm 63 ("My lips shall glorify you") has, since ancient times, been associated with morning prayer. These words of Psalm 141 have become the Church's sunset song: "Let my prayer come like incense before you; the lifting up of my hands, like the evening sacrifice." We can go to bed with these words from Psalm 4 on our lips: "As soon as I lie down, I fall peacefully asleep, for you alone, O Lord, bring security to my dwelling."

The psalms teach us how to see all things—the good and the bad, the beautiful and the ugly, the wide range of human emotions—as points of conversation with God. Watch for the psalms in the liturgy, and get to know them at home, too. Invite the psalms into your prayer. Ask yourself who in the world today—individuals or groups of people— might be experiencing the pain or the promise evoked by a psalm. Then, in spirit, sing with them these songs of Zion, the songs in which God is with us in sorrow and joy, in pain and pleasure, and in infinite promise.

201 Psalm 16/Harbor of My Heart

REFRAIN

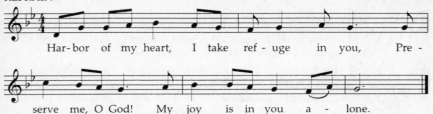

Har-bor of my heart, I take ref-uge in you, Pre-
serve me, O God! My joy is in you a-lone.

VERSES

1. Preserve me, O God, my Savior; I take refuge within your embrace.
I say to the Lord "You are my God. My joy alone is found in you." **R/.**

2. He has put into my heart a wondrous love for the faithful who dwell
in your land.
It is you, O Lord, who are my cup, you alone, my portion and my prize. **R/.**

3. My destiny, O Lord, is my delight; how I welcome your will for me!
I will bless the Lord who gives me counsel, who at night is the compass
of my heart. **R/.**

4. The pathway of my life will be shown to me, the fullness of joy
in your presence.
At your side, my soul will sing forever, to the One who brought life
unto my spirit. **R/.**

Steven C. Warner
Text and music © 1995, WLP

202 Psalm 17/Lord, Bend Your Ear

REFRAIN

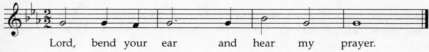

Lord, bend your ear and hear my prayer.

VERSES

1. I am innocent, O Lord! I pray and beg for help!
Won't you listen? For I have followed you. **R/.**

2. O God, I pray to you, because you are my help.
Listen and answer my prayer! **R/.**

3. O keep me as the apple of your eye;
hide me in the shadow of your wings. **R/.**

Text (ref.) © 1969, ICEL

Jeffrey Honoré
Text (vss.) and music © 1994, WLP

Lord, You Have the Words/Psalm 19

REFRAIN

Lord, you have the words of ev-er-last-ing life,

the words of ev - er - last - ing life._____

ALTERNATE REFRAIN

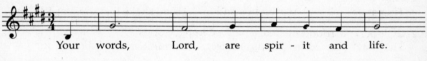

Your words, Lord, are spir - it and life.

Your words,_ Lord, are spir - it and life._____

VERSES

1. The law of the Lord is perfect,
   refreshing the soul;
   The decree of the Lord is trustworthy,
   giving wisdom to the simple. **R/.**

2. The precepts of the Lord are right,
   rejoicing the heart;
   The command of the Lord is clear,
   enlightening the eye. **R/.**

3. The fear of the Lord is pure,
   enduring forever;
   The ord'nances of the Lord are true,
   all of them just. **R/.**

4. They are more precious than gold,
   than a heap of purest gold;
   Sweeter also than syrup
   or honey from the comb. **R/.**

Text (ref.) © 1969, ICEL
Text (vss.) © 1970, CCD

Marty Haugen
Music © 1987, WLP

204 Psalm 22/My God, My God

REFRAIN

My God, my God, look up - on me;

Why have you a - ban - doned me?

VERSES

1. All who see me laugh and jeer at me;
   They mock me with parted lips and in derision shake their heads. **R/.**

2. Evildoers surround me like a pack of hungry dogs;
   They have pierced my hands and feet, I can number all my bones. **R/.**

3. They divide my garments among them, they gamble for my clothes;
   O Lord, my strength and helper, hasten to my side. **R/.**

4. I will proclaim your name to all my people;
   In the midst of the assembly I will give you praise and glory. **R/.**

Donald J. Reagan
Text and music © 1982, WLP

205 Psalm 23/The Lord Is My Shepherd

REFRAIN 1

Cantor/All

The Lord is my shep - herd; noth-ing shall I want;

in ver - dant pas - tures I find my re - pose.

REFRAIN 2

Cantor/All

The Lord spreads a ban - quet be -

fore me and re - fresh - es my soul.

REFRAIN 3

Cantor/All

God leads me a-long safe paths; noth-ing_ shall I fear.

VERSES

Cantor

1. To waters of peace God leads me;
2. Though I should walk in the valley of darkness,
3. You spread a banquet be - fore me
4. Surely goodness and kindness shall follow me
5. Give glory to the Father al - mighty,

1. and there re - freshes my soul.
2. no evil shall I fear;
3. with - in the sight of my foes;
4. __ all the days of my life;
5. to Christ, be - loved Son;

1. My shepherd leads me a - long safe paths
2. With rod and staff you are near me,
3. You a - noint my head with oil,
4. I will dwell in the house of the Lord
5. To the Spirit who guides the Church

To Refrain

1. for - ever faith - ful and true.
2. with these you give me____ comfort.
3. my cup is o - ver - flowing.
4. for - ever and ev - er - more.
5. both now and for - ever. A - men.

Omer Westendorf

Jan M. Vermulst, 1925–1994
Text and music © 1963, WLP

206 Psalm 23/My Shepherd Is the Lord

REFRAIN

My shep-herd is the Lord; noth-ing in-deed shall I want.

VERSES

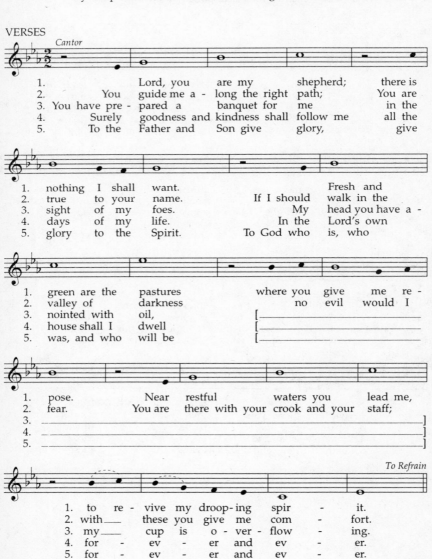

1.   Lord, you   are my   shepherd;   there is
2.   You   guide me a - long the right   path;   You are
3. You have pre - pared a   banquet for   me   in the
4.   Surely   goodness and kindness shall follow me   all the
5.   To the   Father and   Son give   glory,   give

1. nothing   I   shall   want.   Fresh and
2. true   to   your   name.   If I should   walk in the
3. sight   of   my   foes.   My   head you have a -
4. days   of   my   life.   In the   Lord's own
5. glory   to   the   Spirit.   To God who   is, who

1. green are the   pastures   where you   give   me   re -
2. valley of   darkness   no   evil   would   I
3. nointed with   oil,   [_____
4. house shall I   dwell   [_____
5. was, and who   will be   [_____

1. pose.   Near   restful   waters you   lead me,
2. fear.   You are   there with your crook and your   staff;
3. _____]
4. _____]
5. _____]

To Refrain

1. to   re - vive my droop-ing   spir   -   it.
2. with___   these you give   me   com   -   fort.
3. my___   cup   is   o - ver - flow   -   ing.
4. for   -   ev   -   er   and   ev   -   er.
5. for   -   ev   -   er   and   ev   -   er.

Shepherd Me, O God / Psalm 23 **207**

REFRAIN

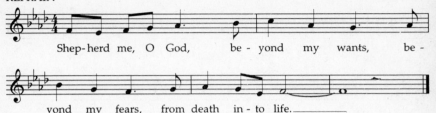

Shep-herd me, O God, be - yond my wants, be -
yond my fears, from death in - to life. _____

VERSES

1. God is my shepherd, so nothing shall I want;
   I rest in the meadows of faithfulness and love;
   I walk by the quiet waters of peace. **R/.**

2. Gently you raise me and heal my weary soul;
   you lead me by pathways of righteousness and truth;
   my spirit shall sing the music of your name. **R/.**

3. Though I should wander the valley of death, I fear no evil,
   for you are at my side; your rod and your staff, my comfort and
   my hope. **R/.**

4. You have set me a banquet of love in the face of hatred,
   crowning me with love beyond my pow'r to hold. **R/.**

5. Surely your kindness and mercy follow me all the days of my life;
   I will dwell in the house of my God forevermore. **R/.**

Marty Haugen
Text and music © 1986, GIA

208 Psalm 25/You Are My Guide

REFRAIN

Cantor/All

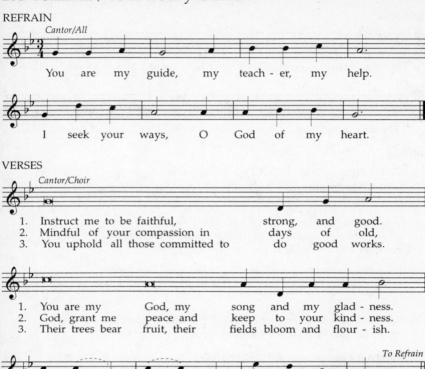

You are my guide, my teach-er, my help.

I seek your ways, O God of my heart.

VERSES

Cantor/Choir

1. Instruct me to be faithful, strong, and good.
2. Mindful of your compassion in days of old,
3. You uphold all those committed to do good works.

1. You are my God, my song and my glad-ness.
2. God, grant me peace and keep to your kind-ness.
3. Their trees bear fruit, their fields bloom and flour-ish.

To Refrain

1. I call your name___ by night and by day.
2. Do not re-call___ my wrongs or my shame.
3. You watch___ o-ver the gen-tle and just.

Paul A. Lisicky
Text and music © 1995, WLP

The Lord Is My Light/Psalm 27 **209**

REFRAIN

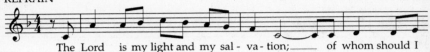

The Lord is my light and my sal - va - tion;____ of whom should I

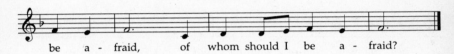

be a - fraid, of whom should I be a - fraid?

VERSES

1. The Lord is my light and my help; whom should I fear?
   The Lord is the stronghold of my life; before whom should I shrink? **R/.**

2. There is one thing I ask of the Lord; for this I long;
   To live in the house of the Lord all the days of my life. **R/.**

3. I believe I shall see the goodness of the Lord in the land of the living;
   Hope in God, and take heart. Hope in the Lord! **R/.**

David Haas
Text and music © 1983, GIA

God Is My Light/Psalm 27 **210**

REFRAIN

God is my light and my sal - va - tion:

God is the ref - uge of my life.

VERSES

1. The Lord is my saving light;
   whom should I fear?
   God is my fortress;
   what should I dread? **R/.**

2. One thing I ask the Lord,
   one thing I seek:
   to live in the house of God
   ev'ry day of my life,
     caught up in God's beauty,
     at prayer in his temple. **R/.**

3. I know I will see
   how good God is
   while I am still alive.
   Trust in the Lord. Be strong.
   Be brave. Trust in the Lord. **R/.**

Text (vss.) from *The Liturgical Psalter: Text for Study and Comment,* © 1994, ICEL

David Clark Isele
Text (ref.) and music © 1995, WLP

211 Psalm 29/Lord, Bless Your People

REFRAIN *Cantor/Choir/All*

Lord, bless your peo-ple; Lord bless your

peo-ple with peace, with the gift___ of your peace.

VERSES *Cantor*

1. O give the Lord, you chil-dren of our God,___
2. The voice of God, re-sound-ing on the wa-ters,
3. The voice of God breaks Le-ba-non's great ce-dars,
4. God's glo-ry breaks like thun-der in the moun-tains;

1. O give the Lord___ great glo-ry and pow-er,
2. The voice of God,___ im-mense on the seas!___
3. God's voice re-sounds,___ and shat-ters the trees!___
4. With-in the tem-ple are cries of great glo-ry!

1. O give the Lord___ a name filled with glo-ry,
2. The voice of God,___ re-splen-dent with pow-er,
3. God's voice will flash,___ like fire new-ly kin-dled,
4. Our God pre-sides o'er the depths of the wa-ters,

To Refrain

1. A-dore the Lord in a sa-cred__ place.
2. The song of God, full of splen-dor and might.
3. The song of God fills the wil-der-ness.
4. The Lord pre-sides for-ev-er-more.

Steven C. Warner
Text and music © 1995, WLP

Lord, Let Your Mercy/Psalm 33   **212**

REFRAIN

Cantor/All

Lord, let your mer-cy be up-on us,

as we place our trust in you.

VERSES

Cantor

1. For the word of the Lord___ is faith - ful,___
2. For the Lord___ loves jus - tice and right-eous - ness;___
3. By God's word___ the heav - ens span o - ver us,___
4. Let us sing to the Lord a new mel - o - dy;

To Refrain

and the works___ of God are___ true.___
___ God fills___ the earth with___ love.___
by the breath of God's mouth all the stars.___
let us sing with our hearts and our minds.___

Steven C. Warner

REFRAIN

Cantor/All

I will give thanks___ to you, my Lord; I will

praise___ your name for - ev - er.___ My

heart o - ver - flows with thanks.___

VERSES

Cantor

1. I seek the Lord who___ an - swers me and
2. Glo - ri - fy the___ Lord with me; to -
3. Our Lord is close to the bro - ken hearts; and

1. takes all my fears___ a - way.___ When I
2. geth - er give praise to God's name.___ O___
3. those crushed in spir - it are saved.___ I will

1. look to God I am filled___ with joy, and
2. taste and see that the Lord___ is good; how
3. bless the Lord ev - 'ry night___ and day; with

To Refrain

1. from my dis - tress___ I'm saved.___
2. hap - py are all___ who trust God.
3. song I will praise God for - ev - er.

Eugene E. Englert
Text and music © 1982, WLP

Taste and See/Psalm 34

REFRAIN 1

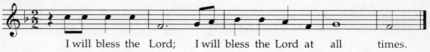

I will bless the Lord; I will bless the Lord at all times.

REFRAIN 2

Taste and see; taste and see the good-ness of the Lord.

VERSES

1. I will bless the Lord at all times;
   his praise shall be ever in my mouth.
   Let my soul glory in the Lord;
   the lowly will hear me and be glad. **R/.**

2. Glorify the Lord with me,
   let us together extol his name.
   I sought the Lord, and he answered me
   and delivered me from all my fears. **R/.**

3. Look to him that you may be radiant with joy,
   and your faces may not blush with shame.
   When the afflicted man called out, the Lord heard,
   and from all his distress he saved him. **R/.**

4. The angel of the Lord encamps
   around those who fear him, and delivers them.
   Taste and see how good the Lord is;
   happy the man who takes refuge in him. **R/.**

215 Psalm 40/Here I Am, God

REFRAIN

Cantor/Choir/All

Here I am, O God, I come to do your will, I come to do your will.

VERSES

Cantor

1. ____ I____ wait-ed for the Lord, and my
2. A____ new song was put in-to my mouth, a____
3. How____ man-y, O Lord,____ my____ God, are your
4. It is writ-ten with-in the Ho-ly Word, that____

1. Mak-er bent down to hear me. My____ cry and my
2. hymn of my Cre-a-tor; for the man-y shall
3. won-ders and your de-signs!____ The____ mar-vels you
4. I should do your will.____ In the depths of my

To Refrain

1. prayer were heard in the heart of God.
2. see and trust in the Lord, our God.
3. work are great be-yond all praise.
4. heart I sing be-fore your Word.

Steven C. Warner
Text and music © 1993, WLP

216 Psalm 42/When Shall We Meet

REFRAIN

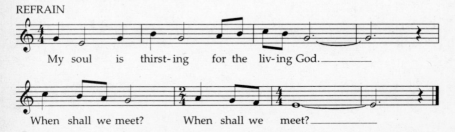

My soul is thirst-ing for the liv-ing God.____

When shall we meet? When shall we meet?____

VERSES

1. As the deer longs for running streams, so my soul rests in you.
Thirsty is my soul for the living God. When shall I see your face? **R/.**

2. Send your light and your faithfulness. They shall lead me on.
Bring me, by your truth, to your holy mountain, your holy dwelling place. **R/.**

3. I shall go to your altar, O God of gladness and joy.
There I give you thanks playing on the harp, O my loving God. **R/.**

4. I went with the crowd and I led them to your home,
there amid our cries of laughter and thanksgiving, we sang with great joy. **R/.**

Matthew S. Nagi
Text and music © 1994, WLP

As the Deer Longs for Running Water/Psalm 42   **217**

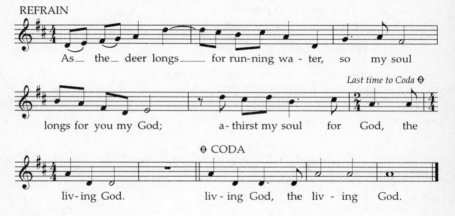

VERSES

1. Then I shall go and behold the face of God.
My tears are my food day and night as they say to me day after day:
"Where is your God?" **R/.**

2. Those days I recall, as I pour out my soul, when I went, singing in
procession with the crowd.
I went with them to the house of God with songs of thanksgiving,
keeping the festival. **R/.**

3. Why are you downcast, my soul, why mourn with me?
Wait for God, whom I shall praise; my Savior and my God. **R/.**

Richard J. Siegel
Text and music © 1995, WLP

218 Psalm 51/Be Merciful, O Lord

REFRAIN

Be mer - ci - ful, O Lord, for we have sinned.

VERSES

1. Have mercy on me, O God, in your goodness;
   in the greatness of your compassion wipe out my offense.
   Thoroughly wash me from my guilt
   and of my sin cleanse me. **R/.**

2. For I acknowledge my offense,
   and my sin is before me always:
   "Against you only have I sinned,
   and done what is evil in your sight." **R/.**

3. A clean heart create for me, O God,
   and a steadfast spirit renew within me.
   Cast me not out from your presence,
   and your holy spirit take not from me. **R/.**

4. Give me back the joy of your salvation,
   and a willing spirit sustain in me.
   O Lord, open my lips, and my mouth shall proclaim,
   my mouth shall proclaim your praise. **R/.**

Text (ref.) © 1969, ICEL
Text (vss.) © 1970, CCD

Michael Ward
Music © 1987, WLP

219 Psalm 51/Be Merciful, O Lord

REFRAIN

Cantor/All

Be mer - ci - ful, O Lord,___ for we___ have___ sinned.___
or: Re- mem - ber, O Lord,___ your faith - ful - ness and love.___

Be mer - ci - ful, O Lord,___ for we___ have___ sinned.___
Re- mem - ber, O Lord,___ your faith - ful - ness and love.___

VERSES

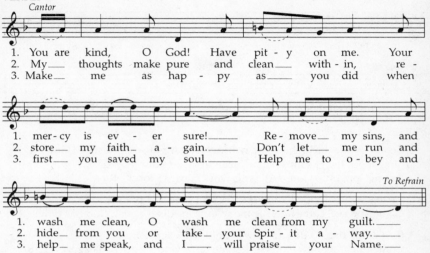

1. You are kind, O God! Have pit-y on me. Your
2. My thoughts make pure and clean with-in, re-
3. Make me as hap-py as you did when

1. mer-cy is ev-er sure! Re-move my sins, and
2. store my faith a-gain. Don't let me run and
3. first you saved my soul. Help me to o-bey and

To Refrain

1. wash me clean, O wash me clean from my guilt.
2. hide from you or take your Spir-it a-way.
3. help me speak, and I will praise your Name.

Text (ref.) © 1969, 1981, ICEL

Michael Bedford
Text (vss.) and music © 1994, WLP

Your Love Is Finer Than Life/Psalm 63   220

REFRAIN

O God, I seek you, my soul thirsts for you;

your love is fin-er than life.

VERSES

1. As a dry and weary desert land, so my soul is thirsting for my God,
and my flesh is faint for the God I seek, for your love is more to me
than iife. **R/.**

2. I think of you when at night I rest, I reflect upon your steadfast love,
I will cling to you, O Lord my God, in the shadow of your wings I sing. **R/.**

3. I will bless your name all the days I live, I will raise my hands and call on
you, my joyful lips shall sing your praise, you alone have filled my
hungry soul. **R/.**

Marty Haugen
Text and music © 1982, GIA

221 Psalm 66/Let All the Earth Cry Out to God

REFRAIN

VERSES

1. Tell ev'ryone throughout the world to shout praises, praises to God!
   Sing about the glorious Name, bringing God your praises.
   Say to God, unto God, "All your work speaks glory!" **R/.**

2. "You are worshipped on the earth, sing praises," praises to God.
   Come and see, come and see the wondrous deed which God has done! **R/.**

3. God made the sea dry up so we could walk across.
   Come celebrate now; come celebrate now. God's pow'r rules forever. **R/.**

Text (ref.) © 1969, 1981, ICEL

Michael Jothen
Text (vss.) and music © 1994, WLP

222 Psalm 67/O God, Let All the Nations Praise You

REFRAIN

VERSES

1. May God have pity on us and bless us;
   may he let his face shine upon us.
   So may your way be known upon earth;
   among all nations, your salvation. **R/.**

2. May the nations be glad and exult
   because you rule the peoples in equity;
   the nations on the earth you guide.
   O God, let all the nations praise you. **R/.**

3. May the peoples praise you, O God;
   may all the peoples praise you!
   May God bless us,
   and may all the ends of the earth fear him! **R/.**

Text (ref.) © 1969, 1981, ICEL
Text (vss.) © 1970, CCD

Richard T. Proulx
Music © 1997, WLP

Justice Will Flourish in His Time/Psalm 72 223

REFRAIN

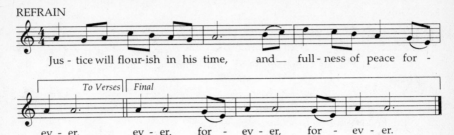

Jus - tice will flour-ish in his time, and__ full - ness of peace for -

To Verses | Final

ev - er.   ev - er,   for - ev - er,   for - ev - er.

VERSES

1. God, give the king your good judgment that all will know your honesty and fairness, especially the poor, especially the poor. **R/.**

2. Let ev'ryone be treated fairly. Let there be peace until the moon is no more. Let peace and justice stretch from sea to sea, to the ends of the earth, the ends of the earth. **R/.**

3. The homeless, the homeless will find shelter. The poor, the poor will be saved. The weak and the lowly will be protected in the day of the Lord, the day of the Lord. **R/.**

Text (ref.) © 1969, 1981, ICEL

Ann Celeen Dohms
Text (vss.) and music © 1994, WLP

This Is the Cause of My Grief/Psalm 77 224

REFRAIN

This   is   the   cause   of   my   grief,___   that the

ways   of   the   Most High   have changed.___

VERSES

1. I cry aloud to my God. Cry aloud that God might hear me. In the day of my distress I sought the Lord. My hands were raised without ceasing. My soul refused to be consoled. **R/.**

2. I remember my God and groan. Ponder my God and faint. You withheld sleep from my tired eyes. I was troubled and I could not speak and I thought of days long ago. **R/.**

3. At night I muse within my heart. Ponder and my spirit questions: will the Lord reject us evermore? Show favor to us nevermore? Has God's mercy and compassion come to an end? **R/.**

Mike Hay
Text and music © 1993, WLP

225 Psalm 85/Lord, Let Us See Your Kindness

REFRAIN

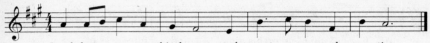

Lord, let us see your kind-ness, and grant us your sal - va - tion.

VERSES

1. I will hear what God proclaims:
   the Lord — for he proclaims peace, peace.
   Near indeed is his salvation to those who fear him,
   glory dwelling in our land. **R/.**

2. Kindness and truth shall meet;
   justice and peace shall kiss.
   Truth shall spring out of the earth,
   and justice shall look down from heaven. **R/.**

3. The Lord himself will give his benefits;
   our land shall yield its increase,
   And justice shall walk before him,
   along the way of his steps. **R/.**

Text (ref.) © 1969, ICEL
Text (vss.) © 1970, CCD

Paul M. French
Music © 1997, WLP

226 Psalm 89/For Ever I Will Sing

REFRAIN

For ev - er I will sing the good-ness of the Lord._____

VERSES

1. I have found David, my servant;
   with my holy oil I have anointed him,
   That my hand may be always with him,
   and that my arm may make him strong. **R/.**

2. My faithfulness and my kindness shall be with him,
   and through my name shall his horn be exalted.
   He shall say of me, "You are my father,
   you are my God, the rock, my savior." **R/.**

Text (ref.) © 1969, 1981 ICEL
Text (vss.) © 1970, CCD

Robert E. Kreutz, 1922–1996
Music © 1984, 1985, WLP

Be with Me, Lord/Psalm 91   227

REFRAIN

Be with me, Lord, when I am in trou-ble;__

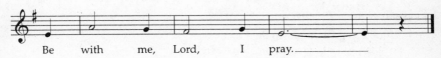

Be with me, Lord, I pray._____

VERSES

1. You who dwell in the shelter of the Lord, Most High,
   who abide in the shadow of our God, Say to the Lord:
   "My refuge and fortress, the God in whom I trust." **R/.**

2. No evil shall befall you, no pain come near, for the angels stand close
   by your side, Guarding you always and bearing you gently,
   watching over your life. **R/.**

3. Those who cling to the Lord live secure in God's love, lifted high, those
   who trust in God's name, Call on the Lord, who will never forsake you;
   God will bring you salvation and joy. **R/.**

Marty Haugen
Text and music © 1980, GIA

Be with Me, Lord/Psalm 91   228

REFRAIN

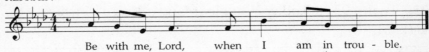

Be with me, Lord, when I am in trou - ble.

VERSES

1. You who dwell in the shelter of the Most High,
   who abide in the shadow of the Almighty,
   Say to the Lord: "My refuge and my fortress,
   my God, in whom I trust." **R/.**

2. No evil shall befall you,
   nor shall affliction come near your tent,
   For to his angels he has given command about you,
   that they guard you in all your ways. **R/.**

3. Upon their hands they shall bear you up,
   lest you dash your foot against a stone.
   You shall tread upon the asp and viper;
   you shall trample down the lion and dragon. **R/.**

4. Because he clings to me, I will deliver him;
   I will set him on high because he acknowledges my name.
   He shall call upon me, and I will answer him;
   I will be with him in distress;
   I will deliver him and glorify him. **R/.**

Text (ref.) © 1969, 1981, ICEL.
Text (vss.) © 1970, CCD

William Ferris
Music © 1996, WLP

229 Psalm 92/Lord, It Is Good to Give Thanks

REFRAIN

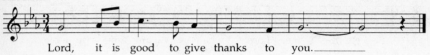

Lord, it is good to give thanks to you._____

VERSES

1. It is good to give thanks to the Lord,
     to sing praise to your name, Most High,
   To proclaim your kindness at dawn
     and your faithfulness throughout the night. **R/.**

2. The just shall flourish like the palm tree,
     like a cedar of Lebanon shall he grow.
   They that are planted in the house of the Lord
     shall flourish in the courts of our God. **R/.**

3. They shall bear fruit even in old age;
     vigorous and sturdy shall they be,
   Declaring how just is the Lord,
     my Rock, in whom there is no wrong. **R/.**

230 Psalm 95/If Today You Hear God's Voice

REFRAIN

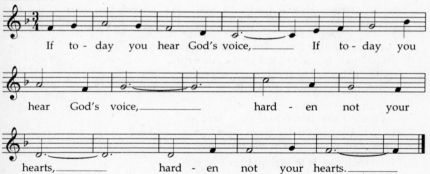

If to-day you hear God's voice,_____ If to-day you

hear God's voice,_____ hard - en not your

hearts,_____ hard - en not your hearts._____

VERSES

1. Sing joyful songs to the Lord! Praise the rock of our salvation.
   Come, worship God with thanks in your heart, with joyful songs
   of praise. **R/.**

2. How great, how great is our God. Greatest God, the king o'er all others.
   Earths deepest part and mountain peaks are held in God's own hand.
   The oceans and dry lands were formed by the one Creator of them all. **R/.**

3. Come, bow down and worship the Lord! Our God and our Creator!
We are the flock; the sheep in God's care who hear and listen today! **R/.**

Text (ref.) © 1969, ICEL

Jeffrey Honoré
Text (vss.) and music © 1994, WLP

Let Us Sing to the Lord/Psalm 95   **231**

REFRAIN

Let us sing with joy___ to the Lord! And ac-
claim the God of our sal - va - tion. Let us greet God with thanks-
giv - ing, and___ praise the name of the Lord.

VERSES

1. Come, let us join in worship, let us bow before the Lord who made us.
For this is God, and we are the people that God shepherds,
the flock God guides. **R/.**

2. We love you, Lord, our strength, our Rock, our Fortress, our Savior.
O Lord, send out your Spirit, and renew the face of the earth. **R/.**

3. In your hands are the depths of the earth, and the mountains were
raised by you.
Yours is the sea, for you have made it, and the dry lands your hands
have formed. **R/.**

4. Sing to the Lord, to the Lord a new song, sing to the Lord,
and bless the Name.
Tell God's glory among the nations; among all peoples,
God's wondrous deeds. **R/.**

Eugene E. Englert
Text and music © 1993, WLP

232 Psalm 98/All the Ends of the Earth

REFRAIN

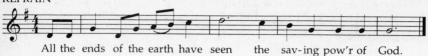

All the ends of the earth have seen the sav-ing pow'r of God.

VERSES

1. Sing to the Lord a new song,
   for he has done wondrous deeds;
   His right hand has won vict'ry for him,
   his holy arm. **R/.**

2. The Lord has made his salvation known:
   in the sight of the nations he has revealed his justice.
   He has remembered his kindness and faithfulness
   toward the house of Israel. **R/.**

3. All the ends of the earth have seen
   the salvation by our God.
   Sing joyfully unto the Lord, all you lands;
   break into song; sing praise. **R/.**

4. Sing praise to the Lord with the harp,
   with the harp and melodious song.
   With trumpets and the sound of the horn
   sing joyfully before the King, the Lord.
   Sing joyfully before the King, the Lord. **R/.**

233 Psalm 98/All the Ends of the Earth

REFRAIN 1

Cantor/All

To Verses

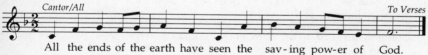

All the ends of the earth have seen the sav-ing pow-er of God.

REFRAIN 2

Cantor/All

To Verses

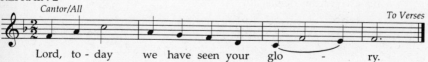

Lord, to-day we have seen your glo - ry.

VERSES

1. O sing a new song to the___ Lord, to
2. The Lord has shown, the Lord has___ shown the
3. Through all the earth, through all the___ earth, God's
4. Make mu - sic for the Lord on the harp, play

1. God, who does mar-vel-ous things. God's___ might-y hand and___
2. pow-er of heav-en to save. In___ faith-ful-ness and___
3. vic-to-ries are___ made known. Tell it near and far, let the
4. beau-ti-ful songs___ of praise. With the sound of horn and___

To Refrain

1. pow'r - ful arm have___ won the vic - to - ry.
2. stead - fast love re - mem-b'ring Is - ra - el.
3. whole world join sing-ing songs of thanks and praise.
4. trum - pets bold, make a joy - ful, joy - ful noise.

Mary Kay Beall

Text (ref.) © 1969, ICEL

Text (vss.) and music © 1994, WLP

All the Ends of the Earth/Psalm 98 234

OSTINATO REFRAIN

All the ends of the earth___ have seen the sav - ing

pow - er,___ the sav - ing pow - er of God.

VERSES

1. Sing a new song to the Lord, for he has done wonderful deeds.
   His right hand and holy arm have won the vict'ry for him. **R/.**

2. The Lord has made his salvation known, has shown the nations his justice.
   He has remembered his truth and his love for the house of Israel. **R/.**

3. All the ends of the earth have seen the salvation of God.
   Shout to the Lord, all the earth, sing out for joy. **R/.**

4. Sing psalms to the Lord with the harp, with harp and melodious song.
   With trumpet and the sound of the horn acclaim the King, the Lord. **R/.**

Text (ref.) © 1969, ICEL

Text (vss.) © 1963, Ladies of the Grail (England). GIA, exclusive agent

James J. Chepponis

Music © 1990, WLP

235 Psalm 100/Let All the Earth Cry Out

REFRAIN

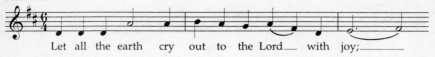

Let all the earth cry out to the Lord___ with joy;___

give thanks, and bless___ God's ho - ly name.

VERSES

1. Let all the earth cry out to the Lord with joy;
   with gladness give your service to the Lord;
   come, seek God's face with joyful hearts. **R/.**

2. Know this: the Lord is God,
   who made us, to whom we belong;
   we are God's people, the sheep of one pasture. **R/.**

3. Now enter the royal gates with songs of praise,
   God's holy courts with hymns;
   give thanks and bless God's holy name. **R/.**

4. Indeed the Lord is good, with mercy everlasting;
   from age to age endures the Lord's faithfulness. **R/.**

5. Give glory to the Father and the Son;
   give glory to the Holy Spirit, with them one;
   as in the beginning, so now, and evermore, throughout eternity. **R/.**

Stephen F. Sommerville
Text and music © 1960, 1961, WLP

Bless the Lord, O My Soul/Psalm 103 **236**

REFRAIN

Cantor/Choir/All

Bless the Lord, O my soul! All my be- ing bless God's ho- ly name.___ Bless the Lord, O my soul! And do not for- get all God's ben - e - fits.

VERSES

Cantor

1. God par - dons your sins, and heals your ill - ness - es,
2. The Lord is gra - cious, the Lord is___ mer - ci - ful,
3. For as the heav - ens are high a - bove the earth,
4. Sing, all you an - gels, give praise; sing to the Lord,

Choir/All

Praise the Lord, O my soul!

Cantor

1. God res - cues your life,___ re -
2. Is slow to an - ger,___ a -
3. So great your kind - ness___ for
4. With those who min - is - ter a -

1. deems it from de - struc - tion,
2. bound - ing in stead - fast love,
3. all who wor - ship your name,
4. dor - ing God's ho - ly name,

Choir/All

Praise the Lord, O my soul!

Cantor

1. And crowns you with great love,
2. Keeps us in lov - ing care,___
3. For those who trust your word,___
4. Sing to the Lord, my soul,___

To Refrain

1. kind - ness___ and___ ten - der - ness.
2. par - dons___ all in - iq - ui - ties.
3. keep - ing___ your___ cov - e - nant.
4. praise___ God___ through e - ter - ni - ty.

Lucien Deiss
Text and music © 1995, WLP

237 Psalm 104/Lord, Send Out Your Spirit

Text (ref.) © 1969, ICEL

C. Neil Blunt
Text (v.35.) and music © 1978, 1979, WLP

Envia tu Espíritu/Salmo 104 **238**
Send Forth Your Spirit/Psalm 104

ESTRIBILLO/REFRAIN

Cantor/Todos/All

Español: En - ví - a   tu   Es - pí - ri - tu,   Se - ñor,
English: Send   forth_____   your   Spir - it,   O   Lord,
Tagalog: Pa - da - la   i - yong   Es - pí - ri - tu,   Po - on,

y   re - nue - va   la   faz   de   la   tie - rra.
and   re - new_____   the   face   of   the   earth._____
ba - go - hin ang muk - ha   ng   mon - do._____

ESTROFAS/VERSES

Cantor

1. Ben - di - ce,   al - ma   mí - a,_____   al   Se - ñor   de
1. *Give   glo - ry   to   the   Lord,_____   call   u - pon   God's*

2. Cuán - tas   son   tus   o - bras,   la   tie - rra es - tá_____
2. *Man - y   are   God's works.__   The   earth   shines forth   with*

3. Glo - ria a   Dios   por   siem - pre._____   Go - ce   el   Se -
3. *Glo - ry   to   the   Lord._____   Sing   to   God   al -*

1. glo - ria._____   Dios   mí - o,   que   gran - de,
1. *name._____   How   great   is   our   God.____*

2. lle - na____   de   tus   cria - tu - ras,   Se - ñor,_____
2. *splen - dor_____   that   comes from   God's   crea - tures.*

3. ñor_____   con   sus   o - bras   tan   gran - des;
3. *might - y._____   Re - joice   in   God's   won - ders.*

To Refrain

1.–3. gran - de   e - res   tú.
1.–3. *Ho - ly   is   the   Lord.*

REFRAIN

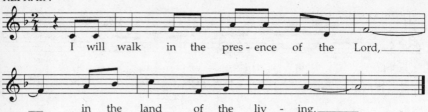

I will walk in the pres - ence of the Lord, ___ ___ in the land of the liv - ing. ___

VERSES

1. I love the Lord, I love the Lord because he has heard
   my voice in supplication,
   Because he has inclined his ear to me
   the day I called.

2. The cords of death encompassed me;
   the snares of the nether world seized upon me;
   I fell into distress and sorrow,
   And I called upon the name of the Lord,
   "O Lord, save my life!"

3. Gracious is the Lord and just;
   yes, our God is merciful.
   The Lord keeps little ones;
   I was brought low, and he saved me.

4. For he has freed my soul from death,
   my eyes from tears, my feet from stumbling.
   I shall walk before the Lord
   in the land of the living.

Howard L. Hughes
Music © 1994, WLP

240 Psalm 116/Our Blessing Cup

REFRAIN

Our bless-ing cup ___ is a com- mun - ion in the blood of Christ. Our bless-ing cup ___ is a com- mun - ion in the blood of Christ.

VERSES

1. How shall I make a return to God for all the good that is done for me?
The cup of salvation I will raise and call upon my God.

2. Precious in your eyes, O God, is the death of one who serves you.
I am your servant, child of your faithful one, you have set me free.

3. I will call upon your name, and offer sacrifice and praise to you.
Before all nations I will show my vows of love to my God.

Text (ref.) © 1969, ICEL

Marcy Weckler
Text (vss.) and music © 1994, WLP

The Cup of Salvation/Psalm 116 241

REFRAIN

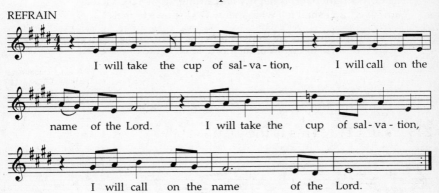

I will take the cup of sal-va-tion, I will call on the
name of the Lord. I will take the cup of sal-va-tion,
I will call on the name of the Lord.

VERSES

1. How can I repay the Lord for his goodness to me?
The cup of salvation I will raise; I will call on the Lord's name.

2. O precious in the eyes of the Lord is the death of the faithful.
Your servant, Lord, your servant am I; you have loosened my bonds.

3. A thanksgiving sacrifice make; I will call on the Lord's name.
My vows to the Lord I will fulfill before all the people.

Text (ref.) © 1969, 1981, ICEL
Text (vss.) © 1993, Ladies of the Grail (England). GIA Pub., Inc., Exclusive agent.

Steven R. Janco
Music © 1996, WLP

242 Psalm 118/This Is the Day

REFRAIN

This is the day the Lord___ has made;

let us re-joice and be glad!___ glad!___

VERSES

1. O tell the Lord how thankful you are, for love which lasts forever.
   Let the house of Israel shout, "God's mercy will last forever!"

2. The Lord's right hand is mighty and strong, to win the victory.
   I am saved, so I shall tell what mercy God shows to me!

3. The stone the builders set aside is now the cornerstone.
   This is the work, the work of the Lord, amazing to our eyes!

243 Psalm 118/This Is the Day

REFRAIN

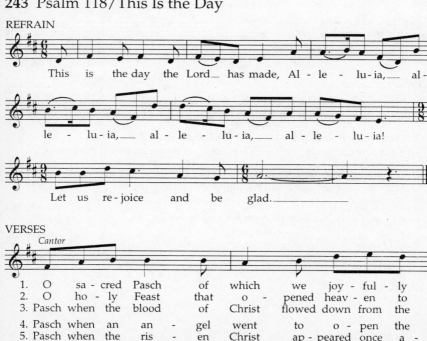

This is the day the Lord_ has made, Al - le - lu - ia, al -

le - lu - ia,___ al - le - lu - ia,___ al - le - lu - ia!

Let us re-joice and be glad.___

VERSES

Cantor

1. O	sa - cred	Pasch	of	which	we	joy - ful - ly
2. O	ho - ly	Feast	that	o -	pened heav - en	to
3. Pasch when the	blood	of	Christ	flowed down from	the
4. Pasch when an	an -	gel	went	to	o - pen	the
5. Pasch when the	ris -	en	Christ	ap - peared once	a -
6. Pasch when the	liv -	ing	Christ	re - stored us	to

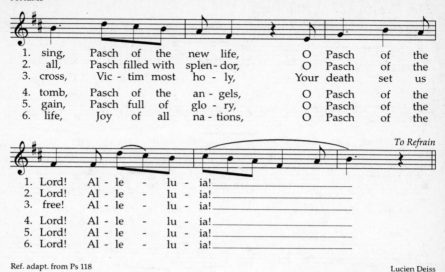

1. sing, Pasch of the new life, O Pasch of the
2. all, Pasch filled with splen-dor, O Pasch of the
3. cross, Vic-tim most ho-ly, Your death set us
4. tomb, Pasch of the an-gels, O Pasch of the
5. gain, Pasch full of glo-ry, O Pasch of the
6. life, Joy of all na-tions, O Pasch of the

To Refrain

1. Lord! Al-le-lu-ia!_____
2. Lord! Al-le-lu-ia!_____
3. free! Al-le-lu-ia!_____
4. Lord! Al-le-lu-ia!_____
5. Lord! Al-le-lu-ia!_____
6. Lord! Al-le-lu-ia!_____

Ref. adapt. from Ps 118

Lucien Deiss
Text and music © 1970, 1995, WLP

Lord, to Whom Shall We Go/Psalm 119 **244**

REFRAIN

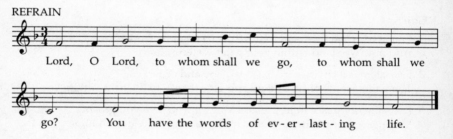

Lord, O Lord, to whom shall we go, to whom shall we go? You have the words of ev-er-last-ing life.

VERSES

1. To do your will is my delight; your law is in my heart.

2. As the deer longs for the waters, so my soul longs for you, O God.

3. Only in you is my soul at rest; from you comes my salvation.

4. My soul clings fast to you, my God; your strong right hand upholds me.

5. With all my heart I desire you. O Lord, do not forsake me.

Ps 40, 42, 63, 119; Jn 6:68

Eugene Englert
Text and music © 1981, WLP

245 Psalm 122/I Rejoiced

REFRAIN

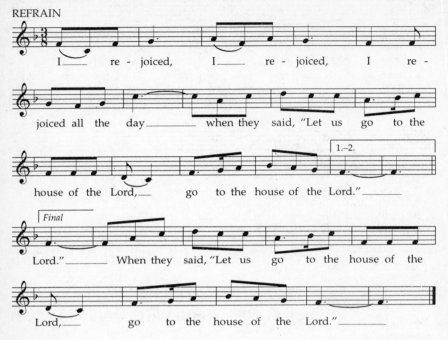

I___ re - joiced, I___ re - joiced, I re -
joiced all the day_____ when they said, "Let us go to the
house of the Lord,___ go to the house of the Lord."_____
Lord."_____ When they said, "Let us go to the house of the
Lord,___ go to the house of the Lord."_____

VERSES

1. I rejoiced when they said to me, "Let us go up to God's house."
   And now we stand within your gates, O Jerusalem.

2. Jerusalem is a city restored, a city of joy and order.
   There the people of God go up and give thanks to the name of the Lord.

3. Pray now for peace in Jerusalem! May all who love you prosper.
   May peace abound in your holy walls, security in your buildings.

Paul A. Lisicky
Text and music © 1989, WLP

246 Psalm 128/Blessed Are You

REFRAIN

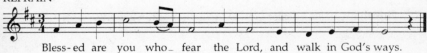

Bless-ed are you who_ fear the Lord, and walk in God's ways.

VERSES

1. Blessed are those who fear the Lord and walk in God's ways.
   By the labor of your hands you shall eat.
   You will be happy and prosper.

2. Your spouse like a fruitful vine in the heart of the house.
Children like shoots of the olive, around the table.

3. Indeed, thus shall be blest those who fear the Lord.
May you see your children's children in a happy Jerusalem.

Ron Rendek
Music © 1985, WLP

With Our God There Is Mercy/Psalm 130 **247**

REFRAIN

With our God there is mer - cy
and___ full - ness of___ re - demp - tion.

VERSES

1. From the depths I call to you,
Lord, hear my cry.
Catch the sound of my voice raised up, pleading, pleading.

2. If you record our sins,
Lord, who could survive?
But because you forgive
we stand in awe.

3. I trust in God's word,
I trust in the Lord.
More than sentries for dawn
I watch for the Lord.

4. More than sentries for dawn
let Israel watch.
The Lord will bring mercy
and grant pardon.
The Lord will free Israel
from all its sins.

Robert M. Hutmacher
Text (ref.) and music © 1995, WLP

248 Psalm 130/Out of the Depths

REFRAIN

Out of the depths I cry__ to you, O Lord._____

VERSES

1. If you, O Lord, mark our sins,
   O Lord, who can stand?
   But with you is forgiveness
   that you may be revered.

2. I trust in the Lord,
   my soul trusts in God's word.
   My soul waits for the Lord
   more than those who wait for the dawn.

3. For with the Lord is kindness
   and plentiful redemption.
   Our God will redeem Israel
   from all their iniquities.

249 Psalm 134/Into Your Hands

REFRAIN
Cantor/All

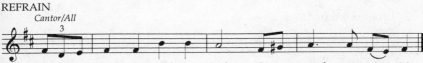

In- to your hands, O Lord my God, I com- mend my spir - it!

VERSES
Cantor

1. A - rise and draw near, to sing__ the
2. You serv - ants who wait at mid - night
3. To courts of the Lord, lift up__ your
4. Pray bless - ings from God who dwells__ on
5. To Fa - ther and Son and Spir - it

To Refrain

1. praise__ of God, You serv - ants of the Lord.
2. in__ God's house, Your lips shall praise God's name.
3. hands__ in praise, And bless the Lord our God.
4. Si - on's height, The Lord of heav'n and earth.
5. sing__ your praise, And seek God's last - ing peace.

We Will Rest in You/Psalm 134 **250**

REFRAIN

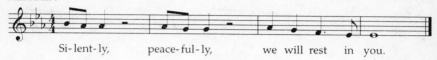

Si-lent-ly,   peace-ful-ly,   we will rest   in   you.

VERSES

1. O come, bless the Lord, all you who serve the Lord, who stand in the courts of the Lord. O come, bless the Lord, all you who serve the Lord, who stand in the courts of the house of our God.

2. Lift up your hands to the holy place and bless the Lord through the night. May the Lord bless you from Zion, the God who made both heaven and earth.

3. Glory to the Father and to the Son, and to the Holy Spirit. As always before so now and evermore. Amen.

Mike Hay
Text and music © 1993, WLP

Let My Tongue Be Silenced/Psalm 137 **251**

REFRAIN

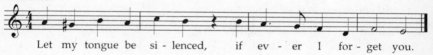

Let   my tongue be   si - lenced,   if   ev - er   I   for - get you.

VERSES

1. By the rivers of Babylon, there we sat and wept, remembering Zion. On the willows that grew there, we hung up our harps.

2. Our captors asked us for the lyrics of our songs,
   songs from our home, Zion.
   Yet how could we sing songs, sing the songs of Zion in a foreign land?

3. If I forget you, Jerusalem, if I forget you, Jerusalem, may my right hand wither, may my right hand wither, may I never speak again.

Text (ref.) © 1969, 1981, ICEL

Mike Hay
Text (vss.) and music © 1996, WLP

252 Psalm 138/Your Love Is Everlasting

REFRAIN

Lord, your love is ev - er - last - ing; do not for - sake the work of your hands! Lord, your love is ev - er - last - ing; do not for - sake the work of your hands!

VERSES

1. I thank you, Lord, with all my heart,
   for you have heard the words of my mouth!
   In the sight of the angels I bless you,
   I will adore you in your holy temple.

2. I thank you, Lord, for your faithful love,
   greater than all our wildest dreams!
   At the moment I cried out, you answered,
   and you increased the strength of my soul.

3. Lord, you stretch out your hand and save me;
   your hand will bring me all that I need.
   Your love, O Lord, is eternal;
   do not abandon the work of your hands!

4. All the rulers of the earth shall praise you,
   when they hear the words of your mouth;
   they shall sing of the ways of the Lord,
   singing "How great is the glory of the Lord!"

You Graced Me with Life/Psalm 138 253

REFRAIN

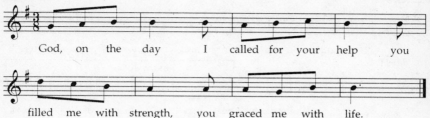

God, on the day I called for your help you

filled me with strength, you graced me with life.

VERSES

1. I give thanks to you, God, for you heard the words,
   the words of my mouth.
   In sight of the angels, I offer you thanks.
   I bow to your temple, I worship your name.

2. I chant praise to you, God, because of your kindness,
   because of your truth,
   for great is your name above all the earth,
   your word filled with grace, your promise of life.

3. Lord God, exalted and great, you stand by your people;
   you save us from harm.
   Though danger surrounds me I keep to your path.
   You raise high your hand against all my foes.

4. Lord God, my safety, my shield, you bless and uphold me;
   you guide and assure.
   Your mercy, O God, endures for all time.
   Oh, do not desert the works of your hands.

Paul A. Lisicky
Text and music © 1996, WLP

254 Psalm 139/Secrets of My Heart

REFRAIN

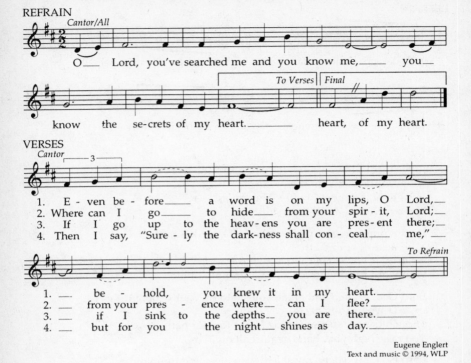

O — Lord, you've searched me and you know me, _____ you _____ know the se-crets of my heart. _____ heart, of my heart.

VERSES

1. E - ven be - fore _____ a word is on my lips, O Lord, _____
2. Where can I go _____ to hide _____ from your spir - it, Lord; _____
3. If I go up to the heav-ens you are pres-ent there; _____
4. Then I say, "Sure - ly the dark-ness shall con - ceal _____ me," _____

1. _____ be - hold, you knew it in my heart. _____
2. _____ from your pres - ence where _____ can I flee? _____
3. _____ if I sink to the depths _____ you are there. _____
4. _____ but for you the night _____ shines as day. _____

Eugene Englert
Text and music © 1994, WLP

255 Psalm 139/Search Me, O God

REFRAIN

Search me, O God, and know my heart; test me and know my in - most thoughts; seek in my soul for paths that are wrong, and lead me, lead me in the ways that are ev - er - last - ing.

VERSES

1. O Lord, you know me through and through, you know my rising, sitting down; you discern my thoughts from far away; you search me out, you know my soul, you know my walking, lying down; all my ways, all my ways lie open to you.

2. Before a word is on my tongue, you know, O Lord, the whole of it; you hem me in from ev'ry side, your hand is always laid on me. This knowledge is too great for me, too wonderful, too high, beyond my reach.

3. Oh, where can I escape your love, where can I flee your presence here? If I ascend to heaven, you are there; if I sleep in Sheol, you are there.

4. And if I fly on wings of dawn and dwell beyond the farthest seas, even there your hand would lead me and guide me; your strong right hand would hold me firmly.

5. And if I ask the dark to hide me, light around me be as night, even darkness is not dark for you; the night becomes as bright as day, for they are both the same in your sight.

Paul Inwood
Text and music © 1991, 1992, Paul Inwood, pub. and dist. by WLP

Like Incense before You/Psalm 141 256

REFRAIN

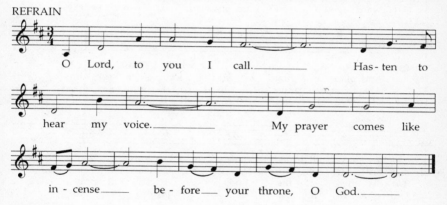

O Lord, to you I call. Has-ten to hear my voice. My prayer comes like in-cense be-fore your throne, O God.

VERSES

1. With a loud voice I cry to the Lord.
My prayer, like incense, comes before you.
Watch me, O Lord, direct what I say.
Form ev'ry word in my mouth as I pray.

2. Let not my eyes be drawn from your gaze.
Lord, let me see your goodness always.
Kindness and truth will follow my ways.
Though sinners strike me, your name I will praise.

3. Let my head never be blest by the foe;
Lord, watch my footsteps wherever I go.
For to you, Lord, shall my eyes ever turn.
Guide me, O Lord, so your ways I may learn.

Paul F. Page
Text and music © 1995, WLP

257 Psalm 141/My Prayers Rise Like Incense

REFRAIN

Cantor/All

My prayers___ rise like in - cense, my
hands like an eve - ning of - fer - ing.___

VERSES

Cantor

1. O___ Lord, to you I call; has-ten to me.___
2. O___ Lord,___ set a watch be-fore my mouth,
3. You_ let the just strike___ me, _ that is kind-ness.
4. Toward you, O Lord my God, I turn my eyes.___

1. Heark-en to my voice ___ when I call to you.
2. _ And place a guard at the door___ of my lips.
3. _ Let them re - prove me, it is oil___ for my head.
4. _ To you I flee; ___ strip me not of life.

1. Let my prayer, like in - cense, come be - fore___ you; the
2. Let my heart not be in-clined _ to wick-ed deeds;___
3. Un - der these af - flic - tions _ I still will pray. Their
4. Glo - ry to the Fa - ther, _ and to the Son, and

To Refrain

1. lift - ing of my hands, like an eve - ning sac - ri - fice.
2. Let me not par - take in the feasts of e - vil ones.
3. judg - es were cast down when they heard my pleas-ant words.
4. to the Ho - ly Spir - it,___ praise for - ev - er - more.

Donald J. Reagan
Text and music © 1982, WLP

Keep Us in Your Sight/Psalm 145 **258**

REFRAIN
Cantor/All

Come, God of un-end-ing love;— come, God of new light.

Come, kin-dle our hopes and dreams; keep us in your

sight, keep us in your sight.———

VERSES
Cantor

1. — Let cre-a-tion give thanks to you, and let—— your faith-ful
2. The eyes of all look to you with hope; you nour-ish them in due
3. The Lord is just—— in ev-'ry way and ho-ly in all good

1. sing.—— O let them tell of your won-drous reign——
2. time.—— You o-pen up—— your hand, O Lord,——
3. works.—— The Lord is near—— to those who call——

2 To Refrain

1. — and speak of your might.————
2. — and fill their de-sire.————
3. — and seek out the truth.————

259 Psalm 145/I Will Praise Your Name

REFRAIN

I will praise your name, my King— and my God.

I will praise your name, my King— and my God._____

VERSES

1. I will give you glory, my God above, and I will bless your name forever.
   Ev'ry day I will bless and praise your name forever.

2. The Lord is full of grace and mercy, who is kind and slow to anger,
   God is good in ev'ry way and full of compassion.

3. Let all your works give you thanks, O Lord, and let all the
   faithful bless you.
   Let them speak of your might, O Lord, the glory of your kingdom.

4. The Lord is faithful in word and deed and always near.
   God's name is holy,
   Lifting up all those who fall, God raises up the lowly.

David Haas
Text and music © 1983, GIA

260 Psalm 145/I Will Praise Your Name

REFRAIN

I__ will praise your name for - ev -

er, my____ King and my God.

VERSES

1. I will extol you, O my God and King,
   and I will bless your name forever and ever.
   Every day will I bless you, and I will praise your name forever.

2. The Lord is gracious and merciful,
   slow to anger and of great kindness.
   The Lord is good to all
   and compassionate toward all his works.

3. Let all your works give you thanks, O Lord,
   and let your faithful ones bless you.
   Let them discourse of the glory of your kingdom
   and speak of your might.

4. The Lord is faithful in all his words
   and holy in all his works.
   The Lord lifts up all who are falling
   and raises up all who are bowed down.

Whenever You Serve Me/Psalm 146 261

REFRAIN

VERSES

1. Put no trust in the powerful, mere mortals in whom there is no help.
   Take their breath, they return to clay and their plans that day come
   to nothing.

2. They are happy who are helped by Jacob's God, whose hope is in
   the Lord their God,
   who alone made heaven and earth, the seas and all they contain.

3. It is the Lord who keeps faith forever, who is just to those who
   are oppressed.
   It is God who gives bread to the hungry, the Lord who sets prisoners free.

4. The Lord who gives sight to the blind, who raises up those who are
   bowed down,
   the Lord who protects the stranger and upholds the widow and orphan.

5. It is the Lord who loves the just but thwarts the path of the wicked.
   The Lord will reign forever, Zion's God from age to age.

262 Psalm 150/Praise God

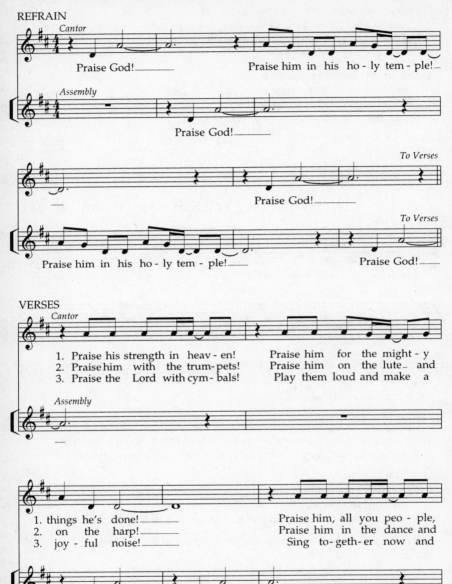

REFRAIN

Cantor
Praise God!___ Praise him in his ho-ly tem-ple!___

Assembly
Praise God!___

Praise God!___ *To Verses*

Praise him in his ho-ly tem-ple!___ Praise God!___ *To Verses*

VERSES

Cantor
1. Praise his strength in heav-en! Praise him for the might-y
2. Praise him with the trum-pets! Praise him on the lute___ and
3. Praise the Lord with cym-bals! Play them loud and make a

Assembly

1. things he's done!___
2. on the harp!___
3. joy-ful noise!___

Praise him, all you peo-ple,
Praise him in the dance and
Sing to-geth-er now and

Praise God! Praise God!___

To Refrain
(Last time to Final Refrain)

1. for the Lord our God is___ great!___
2. praise the Lord with flute and___ drum!___
3. lift your voice un - to the___ Lord!___

To Refrain
(Last time to Final Refrain)

FINAL REFRAIN

Cantor

Praise God!___ Praise him in his ho - ly tem - ple!_

Assembly

Praise God!___

Praise God!___

Praise him in his ho - ly tem - ple! Praise God!___

Praise God!___

Praise God!___

Paul Tate
Text and music © 1996, WLP

263 Psalm 150/Praise God in This Holy Dwelling

Al - le - lu - ia! Al - le - lu - ia! Al - le - lu - ia!

VERSES

1. Praise God   in this ho - ly dwell - ing;
2. Praise God   with the blast of trum - pet;
3. Praise God   with re - sound - ing cym - bals;
4. Praise God, the al - might - y Fa - ther;

1. Praise God   on the might - y throne;
2. Bring praise   now with lyre and harp;
3. With cym - bals that crash, give praise;
4. Praise Christ, the be - lov - ed Son;

1. Prais - ing   for all won - der - ful deeds;
2. Prais - ing   with the tim - brel and dance;
3. O let   ev - 'ry - thing that has breath,
4. Give praise   to the Spir - it of love;

1. Sing praise   to our Sov - 'reign Maj - es - ty.
2. With the   gen - tle sound of string and reed.
3. Let all   liv - ing crea - tures praise the Lord.
4. For - ev - er the tri - une God be praised.

Al - le - lu - ia! Al - le - lu - ia!

1.–3. / *To Verses* ‖ *Final*

Al - le - lu - ia! lu - ia!

Omer Westendorf

Jan M. Vermulst, 1925–1994
Text and music © 1964, WLP

Canticle of Zechariah 264

FOREST GREEN   CMD

1. Blest be the God of Is - ra - el, The
2. Through ho - ly proph - ets did you speak Your
3. Of old you gave your sol - emn oath To
4. O ti - ny Child, your name shall be The
5. The ris - ing sun shall shine on us To

1. ev - er - liv - ing Lord, You come in pow'r to
2. word in days of old, That you would save us
3. fa - ther A - bra - ham: Whose seed a might - y
4. proph - et of the Lord; The way of God you
5. bring the light of day To all who dwell in

1. save your own, Your peo - ple Is - ra - el.
2. from our foes And all who bear us ill.
3. race should be And blest for - ev - er - more.
4. shall pre - pare To make God's com - ing known.
5. dark - est night And shad - ow of the grave.

1. For Is - ra - el you now raise up Sal -
2. To our an - ces - tors did you give Your
3. You vowed to set your peo - ple free From
4. You shall pro - claim to Is - ra - el Sal -
5. Our foot - steps God shall safe - ly guide To

1. va - tion's tow'r on high, In Da - vid's house, who
2. cov - e - nant of love; So with us all you
3. fear of ev - 'ry foe, That we might serve you
4. va - tion's dawn - ing day, When God shall wipe a -
5. walk the ways of peace; Whose name for - ev - er -

1. reigned as king And ser - vant of the Lord.
2. keep your word In love that knows no end.
3. all our days In good - ness, love, and peace.
4. way all sins With mer - cy and with love.
5. more be blest, Who lives and loves and saves.

Lk 1:69–79
James Quinn
Text © James Quinn, Selah Publishing Co. Inc., North American agent.

Surrey folk melody

265 I Praise You, O God

1. I praise you, O God, Lord of heav-en and earth,
2. Mag - nif - i - cent things in my life you have done,
3. You scat - ter the proud, but you gath - er the meek;
4. Re - call - ing your prom - ise made a - ges a - go,

1. My Sav - ior, my Mak - er, who called me from birth!
2. And blest is your name, O Com - pas - sion - ate One!
3. You top - ple the might - y, but strength- en the weak.
4. You vis - it your peo - ple, new life to be - stow.

1. Yes, I, through all a - ges, re - mem-bered shall be,
2. From past gen - er - a - tions to those yet to be,
3. The rich you ig - nore, send them emp - ty a - way,
4. On all of your chil - dren you show - er your care,

1. For you, God of love, have tru - ly blessed me!
2. Your mer - ci - ful love ex - tends like the sea!
3. But fill with good things the hun - gry each day.
4. With mer - ci - ful love be - yond all com - pare!

Becket G. Senchur
Text and music © 1994, WLP

266 Hail, Blessed Lady/Salve, Regina

SALVE REGINA

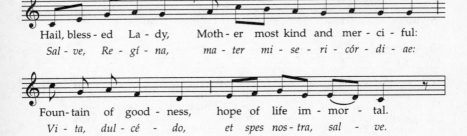

Hail, bless - ed La - dy, Moth - er most kind and mer - ci - ful:
Sal - ve, Re - gí - na, ma - ter mi - se - ri - cór - di - ae:

Foun- tain of good - ness, hope of life im - mor - tal.
Vi - ta, dul - cé - do, et spes nos - tra, sal - ve.

We are but sin-ners, chil-dren of Eve still in ex-ile.
Ad te cla-má-mus, éx-su-les, fí-li-i He-vae.

To you we send our sighs, the trials that be-fall us,
Ad te su-spi-rá-mus, ge-mén-tes et flen-tes

pass-ing through this vale of sor-row. Hear then our plea as our
in hac la-cri-má-rum val-le. E-ia er-go, Ad-vo-

in-ter-ces-sor, turn then to us those lov-ing eyes com-
cá-ta no-stra, il-los tu-os mi-se-ri-cór-des

pas-sion-ate to give us com-fort. Then, ho-ly Maid,
ó-cu-los ad nos con-vér-te. Et Je-sum,

when our ex-ile here on earth is end-ed, lead us to Je-sus
be-ne-dí-ctum fru-ctum ven-tris tu-i, no-bis post hoc ex-

Christ, your Son in glo-ry. O gen-tle, O
sí-li-um o-stén-de. O cle-mens: O

lov-ing, O gra-cious, O Vir-gin Mar-y.
pi-a: O dul-cis Vir-go Ma-rí-a.

Latin, 11th cent.
English text by Omer Westendorf
English text © 1966, WLP

Chant, Mode V

267 My Soul Flies Free

ST. BRENDAN'S   Irregular

1. My soul flies free on pinions of laud, My spirit, too, soars forth like wind, rejoicing in my Savior. Oh, what a tender gaze enfolds and elevates This child of time to timeless state of blessing evermore.

2. The hand which wrought creation in pow'r Caresses me with holiness, this love is named eternal; The arm which holds the earth disperses arrogance And empties thrones, while lifting up the lowly, long forgot.

3. All hunger-filled are led to a feast, All empty affluence cast out by heaven's loving kindness; The mercy pledged will blaze as generations join Eternity's posterity to raise one voice and sing:

4. In rapture sing to Almighty God, To Christ, who died and rose to reign in never-ending glory; And to the Spirit, sing with grateful heart and tongue. Come, prophets, martyrs, sinners, saints, unite in ageless song:

Magnificat! My heart pours out its praise! Magnificat! To God I sing Magnificat!

Luke 1:46–55, adapt.
Alan J. Hommerding

Steven C. Warner
Text and music © 1995, WLP

Canticle of Our Lady 268

REFRAIN

My soul gives glo-ry to the Lord;

My spir-it re-joic-es in God, my Sav-ior.

VERSES

1. My soul gives glory to the Lord; My spirit rejoices in God, my Savior.

2. He has looked on the lowliness of his servant,
   and henceforth all generations shall call me blessed.

3. The almighty has done wonders for me, And holy is his name.

4. From age to age is his mercy, to those who fear him.

5. He shows the might of his arm, and scatters the proud of heart.

6. He casts down the mighty from their thrones, and raises up the lowly.

7. The hungry he fills with good things and the rich he sends away empty.

8. He gives help to Israel, his servant, who remembers his mercy.

9. The mercy he promised to our fathers, to Abraham and all his
   posterity forever.

10. All praise to the Blessed Trinity, both now and forever. Amen.

Luke 1:46-55, *Magnificat*
Omer Westendorf

Jan M. Vermulst, 1925-1994
Text and music © 1964, WLP

Canticle of Simeon 269
CREATOR ALME SIDERUM

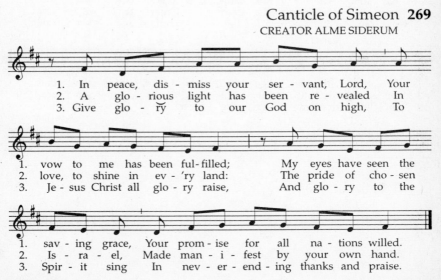

1. In peace, dis-miss your ser-vant, Lord, Your
2. A glo-rious light has been re-vealed In
3. Give glo-rӯ to our God on high, To

1. vow to me has been ful-filled; My eyes have seen the
2. love, to shine in ev-'ry land: The pride of cho-sen
3. Je-sus Christ all glo-ry raise, And glo-ry to the

1. sav-ing grace, Your prom-ise for all na-tions willed.
2. Is-ra-el, Made man-i-fest by your own hand.
3. Spir-it sing In nev-er-end-ing thanks and praise.

Alan J. Hommerding
Text © 1994, WLP

Chant, Mode IV

270 Mary's Song of Praise

PLEADING SAVIOR   87 87 D

1. Sing, my soul, sing out your prais-es; Sing, for God ex-alt-ed me. Look-ing on this low-ly ser-vant, All shall bless me ten-der-ly. Might-y God has shown great fa-vor, Ho-ly is that won-drous name. Mer-ci-ful to all earth's chil-dren, Age to age, God loves the same.

2. Hearts of pride our God will scat-ter, Haught-y ones will be cast down, Rais-ing those who once were low-ly, Feed-ing all who are God's own. Is-ra-el, up-held in mer-cy, Knows the heav'n-ly, prom-ised grace Giv'n to A-bra-ham and Sa-rah, Par-ents of our cho-sen race.

3. Glo-ry be to God al-might-y, Guid-ing us in per-fect love. Glo-ry be to Je-sus, Sav-ior, God's own Word from heav'n a-bove. Glo-ry be to God the Spir-it, Might-y wind and burn-ing fire. Saints and sin-ners, join in sing-ing With the blest, ce-les-tial choir.

Alan J. Hommerding
Text © 1994, WLP

Joshua Leavitt's *Christian Lyre*, 1830

Hymns and Songs

When we are sad and sing a sad song, we mourn more soulfully. When we are overjoyed and sing a joyful song, the joy is made stronger, deeper, wider.

We sing our liturgy to express and deepen praise. Think of the acclamations that we sing, strange and simple words set to music: Amen. Alleluia. Holy, holy, holy. To speak these words is somehow deficient, so much so that the Church has a rule: The "Alleluia" before the gospel must be sung. "Alleluia" is a song, our song, the song of the Church, the song of heaven itself. And even if I do not feel like praising God right now, if I join in singing "Alleluia" with the rest of God's people, the singing carries my heart heavenward.

Singing together not only does something inside of me and you; it does something for us as a body. It unites us. A single, communal voice is lifted up, and that is precisely why we sing the liturgy. The singing makes us one. The body of Christ—many though its members—lifts up one voice to God, and the Church makes the amazing claim that this voice is the very voice of Christ. Consider, for example, the communion song: The singing and the walking and the eating and the drinking, done together, help proclaim our communion, the union that we share with each other through, with, and in Christ.

If we sing the liturgy, if we at least make the effort to join in the song, we do our part. We carry our weight. But if we do not sing, we mute the voice of the body of Christ. Like any human activity, the ability to sing is learned gradually, and there's no better way to learn than by trying. Even if your abilities are weak, keep in mind that together we are strong. Together we are the voice of Christ.

Have you ever heard the prayer of Jews, or Muslims, or Hindus? Have you ever taken part in Byzantine Catholic worship? These different peoples have something in common: They sing their prayer. Speaking it can seem awkward and irreverent. What happened to cause some Roman Catholic communities to give up singing their liturgy? One answer is that, in some places, Catholics were forced to worship in secret. Oppression gave rise to a spoken or even silent liturgy. In our own day, we can give thanks for the right to sing our prayer. Our singing gives witness to the Church's faith and freedom.

Sometimes we sing just for the sheer delight of singing together before God. That's where hymns come into the liturgy. Most hymns are poems set to music; some are stories told in stanzas. Would you ever tell a joke without its punch line? Or begin a story and then refuse to tell its conclusion? That's what can happen with hymns when we skip verses to save time. The sense can be lost. In any case, hurrying is never a virtue at worship. What is it like when you love someone, and want to say how much, only to be told to hurry up?

Sing the liturgy. Sing it with patience and perseverance, with reverence and respect. Singing will do something for our communal prayer—making it lovely and engaging, and making it true to our tradition that the word of God is a sung word. This word tunes the soul and sets it singing.

Singing also will do something for us—draw us together, center us in our heart, give voice to our deepest joys and pains. Singing will delight God, who created the choirs of angels so that songs would never cease.

301 When Morning Gilds the Skies

LAUDES DOMINI 666 D

1. When morn - ing gilds the skies,___ My heart, a - wak-ing, cries,
2. To God, the Word, on high___ The hosts of an - gels cry:
3. Let earth's wide cir - cle round___ In joy - ful notes re - sound:
4. Be this, while life is mine,___ My can - ti - cle di - vine:

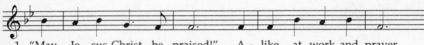

1. "May Je - sus Christ be praised!" A - like at work and prayer
2. "May Je - sus Christ be praised!" Let mor - tals, too, up - raise
3. "May Je - sus Christ be praised!" Let air, and sea, and sky,
4. "May Je - sus Christ be praised!" Be this th' e - ter - nal song,

1. To Je - sus I re - pair: "May Je - sus Christ be praised!"
2. Their voice in hymns of praise: "May Je - sus Christ be praised!"
3. From depth to height, re - ply: "May Je - sus Christ be praised!"
4. Through all the a - ges long: "May Je - sus Christ be praised!"

Katholisches Gesangbuch, 1828
Tr. by Edward Caswall, 1814–1878

Joseph Barnby, 1838–1896

302 Hid in You

ROJAS Irregular

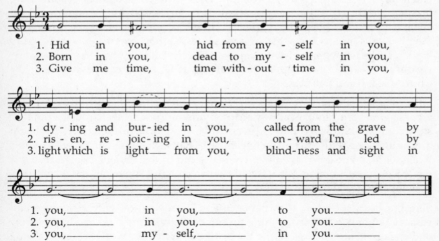

1. Hid in you, hid from my - self in you,
2. Born in you, dead to my - self in you,
3. Give me time, time with - out time in you,

1. dy - ing and bur - ied in you, called from the grave by
2. ris - en, re - joic - ing in you, on - ward I'm led by
3. light which is light___ from you, blind-ness and sight in

1. you,_____ in you,_____ to you._____
2. you,_____ in you,_____ to you._____
3. you,_____ my - self,_____ in you._____

Anders Frostenson, tr. by Paul B. Austin
Swedish text © AF-Foundation, Hymns and Songs/Verbum

Michael Bogdan
Tr. and music © 1976, 1994, WLP

Morning Has Broken 303

BUNESSAN 55 54 D

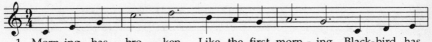

1. Morn-ing has bro - ken Like the first morn - ing, Black-bird has
2. Sweet the rain's new fall Sun - lit from heav - en, Like the first
3. Mine is the sun - light; Mine is the morn - ing Born of the

1. spo - ken Like the first bird. Praise for the sing - ing; Praise for the
2. dew - fall On the first grass. Praise for the sweet- ness Of the wet
3. one light E - den saw play. Praise with e - la - tion, Praise ev - 'ry

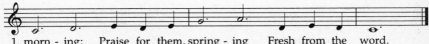

1. morn - ing; Praise for them, spring - ing Fresh from the word.
2. gar - den, Sprung in com- plete - ness Where God has passed.
3. morn - ing, God's re - cre - a - tion Of the new day.

Ps 30:5

Scots Gaelic melody

Eleanor Farjeon, 1881–1965; text © David Higham Assoc. Ltd.

This Day God Gives Me 304

BUNESSAN 55 54 D

1. This day God gives me Strength of high heaven,
   Sun and moon shining, Flame in my hearth,
   Flashing of light'ning, Wind in its swiftness,
   Deeps of the ocean, Firmness of Earth.

2. This day God sends me Strength as my mainstay,
   Might to uphold me, Wisdom as guide.
   Your eyes are watchful, Your ears are list'ning,
   Your lips are speaking, Friend at my side.

3. God's way is my way, God's shield is 'round me,
   God's host defends me, Saving from ill.
   Angels of heaven, Drive from me always,
   All that would harm me, Stand by me still.

4. Rising, I thank you, Mighty and strong One,
   King of creation, Giver of rest,
   Firmly confessing Threeness of Persons,
   Oneness of Godhead, Trinity blest.

Ascr. to St. Patrick, 372–466

Adapt. by James Quinn, text © 1993, James Quinn, Selah Publishing Co., Inc., North American agent

305 Day Is Done

AR HYD Y NOS   84 84 88 84

1. Day   is done, but   Love un - fail - ing   Dwells   ev - er   here;
2. Dark de-scends, but Light un - end - ing   Shines through our night;
3. Eyes will close, but you   un-sleep-ing   Watch   by   our side;

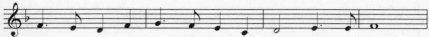

1. Shad - ows fall, but hope, pre - vail - ing, Calms ev - 'ry fear.
2. You   are with us,   ev - er lend - ing   New strength to sight.
3. Death may come, in Love's safe-keep-ing   Still   we   a - bide.

1. Lov-ing   Fa - ther, none for- sak - ing, Take our hearts, of Love's own mak-ing;
2. One in love, your truth con-fess-ing, One in   hope of heav - en's bless-ing,
3. God of love, all   e - vil quell-ing, Sin for - giv-ing, fear dis - pel - ling:

1. Watch our sleep-ing, guard our wak-ing, Be   al - ways near.
2. May we see, in   love's pos-sess-ing, Love's end - less light!
3. Stay with us, our hearts in-dwell-ing, This   e - ven-tide.

James Quinn
Text © James Quinn, Selah Publishing Co. Inc., North American agent

Traditional Welsh melody

306 To the Hills We Lift Our Eyes

AR HYD Y NOS   84 84 88 84

1. To the hills we lift our eyes when
   we are afraid,
   To the ever-living God who
   heav'n, earth has made.
   God keeps watch o'er one and all,
   We shall not stumble, slip nor fall
   For God is present when we call,
   To strengthen and aid.

2. Shelt'ring us in cooling shade, our
   God, always near,
   Keep us from the path of sin, from
   sorrow and tears.
   All our days the Lord shall lead us,
   Heal our wounds and richly feed us,
   Coming, going, God will heed us,
   We cannot fear.

3. Glory be to God in heav'n, for
   mercy outpoured,
   Glory be to Jesus Christ, the true,
   living Word,
   To the Spirit glory be,
   And thankful praise eternally,
   Our living God, the One in Three,
   Forever adored.

Adapt. from Ps 121
Alan J. Hommerding
Text © 1993, WLP

Evening Hymn 307
WONDER 87 87 87

1. Filled with wear - i - ness and won - der,
2. Emp - tied of more hours for liv - ing,
3. Fear - ful, fraught with dis - il - lu - sion,
4. Con - fi - dent of new cre - a - tion

1. Fond re - mem - brance and re - grets,
2. Worn by each de - mand - ing task,
3. As the dark on us de - scends,
4. Which your dream - ing strokes will paint

1. Bring we now un - to the night - fall
2. Bowed and bur - dened by mis - giv - ings,
3. Wres - tling with the vain il - lu - sion
4. Ra - diant in its truth and beau - ty,

1. Dai - ly rich - es, dai - ly debts;
2. Grant new vig - or as we ask
3. That we know what life por - tends;
4. Built by sin - ners, built by saints;

1. Re - con - ciled and rent a - sun - der,
2. For your mer - cy and for - giv - ing.
3. Wake our hearts be - yond con - fu - sion,
4. Guide our slum - ber to sal - va - tion,

1. God of light, now hear___ our___ prayer.
2. Sun of Jus - tice, hear___ our___ prayer.
3. Fie - ry Spir - it, hear___ our___ prayer.
4. Dawn E - ter - nal, hear___ our___ prayer.

Alan J. Hommerding

Steven R. Janco
Text and music © 1995, WLP

308 Now It Is Evening

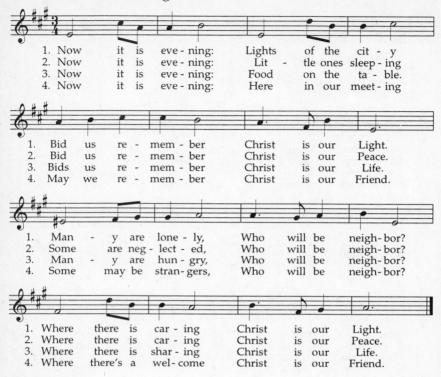

1. Now it is eve-ning: Lights of the cit-y
2. Now it is eve-ning: Lit-tle ones sleep-ing
3. Now it is eve-ning: Food on the ta-ble.
4. Now it is eve-ning: Here in our meet-ing

1. Bid us re-mem-ber Christ is our Light.
2. Bid us re-mem-ber Christ is our Peace.
3. Bids us re-mem-ber Christ is our Life.
4. May we re-mem-ber Christ is our Friend.

1. Man-y are lone-ly, Who will be neigh-bor?
2. Some are neg-lect-ed, Who will be neigh-bor?
3. Man-y are hun-gry, Who will be neigh-bor?
4. Some may be stran-gers, Who will be neigh-bor?

1. Where there is car-ing Christ is our Light.
2. Where there is car-ing Christ is our Peace.
3. Where there is shar-ing Christ is our Life.
4. Where there's a wel-come Christ is our Friend.

Fred Pratt Green
Text © 1974, Hope Publishing Co.

Mike Hay
Music © 1994, WLP

309 God of Day and God of Darkness
BEACH SPRING 87 87 D

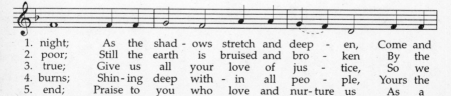

1. God of day and God of dark-ness, Now we stand be-fore the
2. Still the na-tions curse the dark-ness, Still the rich op-press the
3. Show us Christ in one an-oth-er, Make us ser-vants strong and
4. You shall be the path that guides us, You the light that in us
5. Praise to you in day and dark-ness, You our source and you our

1. night; As the shad-ows stretch and deep-en, Come and
2. poor; Still the earth is bruised and bro-ken By the
3. true; Give us all your love of jus-tice, So we
4. burns; Shin-ing deep with-in all peo-ple, Yours the
5. end; Praise to you who love and nur-ture us As a

1. make   our   dark-ness   bright.   All   cre - a - tion   still   is
2. ones   who   still   want   more.   Come   and   wake   us   from   our
3. do   what   you   would   do.   Let   us   call   all   peo - ple
4. love   that   we   must   learn.   For   our   hearts   shall   wan - der
5. fa - ther,   moth - er,   friend.   Grant   us   all   a   peace - ful

1. groan - ing   For   the   dawn - ing   of__ your   might,   When   the
2. sleep - ing,   So   our   hearts   can - not   ig - nore   All   your
3. ho - ly,   Let   us   pledge   our   lives   a - new;   Make   us
4. rest - less   Till   they   safe   to   you   re - turn;   Find - ing
5. rest - ing,   Let   each   mind   and   bod - y   mend,   So   we

1. Sun   of   peace and   just - ice   Fills   the   earth   with   ra - diant   light.
2. peo - ple   lost   and   bro - ken,   All   your   chil - dren   at   our   door.
3. one   with   all   the   low - ly,   Let   us   all   be   one   in   you.
4. you   in   one   an - oth - er,   We   shall   all   your   face   dis - cern.
5. rise   re - freshed   to - mor - row,   Hearts   re- newed   to   king-dom   tend.

Marty Haugen
Text © 1985, 1994, GIA

The Sacred Harp, Philadelphia, 1844

Stay with Us 310

REFRAIN
Cantor/All

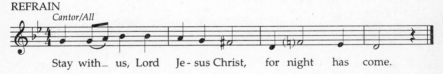

Stay with__ us, Lord   Je - sus Christ,   for   night   has   come.

VERSES

1. All day long, O Lord, I have waited patiently for you on my doorstep.
   And behold, you were living in my house, next to me.

2. All day long, O Lord, I have looked both near and far for you in each
   stranger.
   And behold, you were dwelling in my brothers and sisters.

3. All day long, O Lord, I have kept my joy closed in my hands for protection.
   And behold, I found happiness in reaching out to you.

4. All day long, O Lord, I have sought your word in human thoughts and in
   wisdom.
   And behold, they were present in the depths of my own heart.

Lk 24:29

Lucien Deiss
Text and music © 1995, WLP

311 The Day You Gave Us

ST. CLEMENT 98 98

1. The day you gave us, Lord, is
2. We thank you that your Church, un -
3. A - cross each con - ti - nent and
4. The sun that bids us rest is
5. So be it, Lord; your throne shall

1. end - ed, The dark - ness falls at your be -
2. sleep - ing While earth rolls on - ward in - to
3. is - land As dawn leads on an - oth - er
4. wak - ing Your friends be - neath the west - ern
5. nev - er, Like earth's proud em - pires, pass a -

1. hest; To you our morn - ing hymns as -
2. light, Through all the world its watch - is
3. day, The voice of prayer is nev - er
4. sky, And hour by hour fresh lips are
5. way: Your king - dom stands, and grows for

1. cend - ed, Your praise shall sanc - ti - fy our rest.
2. keep - ing, And rests not now by day or night.
3. si - lent, Nor dies the strain of praise a - way.
4. mak - ing Your won - drous do - ings heard on high.
5. ev - er, Till all on earth your will o - bey.

John Ellerton, 1826–1893, alt.

Clement C. Scholefield, 1839–1904

Heal Us, Lord **312**
HEAL US, LORD CM

1. Lord Je - sus, as we turn from sin
2. We call on you whose liv - ing Word
3. Your glance at Pe - ter helped him know
4. Reach out and touch with heal - ing pow'r
5. Then stay with us when eve - ning comes

1. With strength and hope re - stored,
2. Has made the Fa - ther___ known.
3. The love he had de - nied;
4. The wounds we have re - ceived,
5. And dark - ness makes us___ blind;

1. Re - ceive the hom - age that we bring
2. O Shep - herd, we have wan - dered far;
3. Now gaze on us and heal us, Lord,
4. That in for - give - ness we may love
5. O stay un - til the light of dawn

1. To you, our ris - en Lord.
2. Find us and lead us home.
3. Of self - ish - ness and pride.
4. And may no long - er grieve.
5. May fill both heart and mind.

Ralph Wright
Text © 1980, ICEL

Howard L. Hughes
Music © 1989, WLP

VERSES

1. I have made a cov - e - nant___ with___ my
2. Yah - weh, the as - sem - bly of those___ who
3. Hap - py the peo - ple who learn to ac -
4. I___ have re - vealed___ my cho - sen
5. He will call to me,___ "My Fa - ther! My

1. cho - sen,___ Giv - en my ser - vant my
2. love you Ap - plaud___ your mar - vel - ous
3. claim you.___ They___ re - joice in your
4. ser - vant And he can re - ly on___
5. God!" For I make him my first - born___

1. word.___ I have made your
2. word.___ Who___ in the
3. light.___ You___ are our
4. me;___ Giv - en him my
5. Son.___ I can - not take

1. name___ to last___ for - ev - er,
2. skies can com - pare___ with Yah - weh?___
3. glo - ry and you are our cour - age. Our
4. love___ to last___ for - ev - er.___
5. back___ my giv - en prom - ise. I've

To Refrain

1. built to out - last___ all time.___
2. Who___ can ri - val him?___
3. hope___ be - longs___ to you.___
4. He___ shall rise in my name.___
5. called him to shine like the sun.___

REFRAIN

All

I will cel - e - brate your love for - ev - er, Yah - weh.

Age on age,___ my words pro - claim your love.

For I claim that love is built to last for -

ev - er, Found - ed firm_____ your faith - ful -

1.–5. *To Verses* | *Final*

ness._____ ness._____

Ps 89

Karen M. Barrie
Text and music © 1973, Karen M. Barrie

I Will Sing to the Lord **314**

REFRAIN

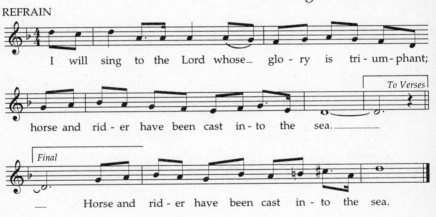

I will sing to the Lord whose_ glo - ry is tri - um - phant;

To Verses

horse and rid - er have been cast in - to the sea._____

Final

_ Horse and rid - er have been cast in - to the sea.

VERSES

1. My strength and my courage is the Lord, God has been my savior,
The Lord is my God, I will praise him, the God of my father I extol.

2. God is a warrior, Lord is his name, Pharoah's army God hurled into the
sea, Pharoah's warriors submerged in the Red Sea.

3. Flood waters covered them, they sank like a stone, Your right hand, O
Lord, is magnificent with power, the enemies are shattered by your might.

4. The people you redeemed are planted on your mountain, the place where
you set your throne which your hands established, forever the Lord shall
reign.

Ex 15:1–18

Gael Berberick
Text and music © 1997, WLP

315 All Things Bright and Beautiful

ROYAL OAK   76 76 with Refrain

All things bright and beau - ti - ful, All crea-tures great and small,

All things wise and won - der - ful, The Lord God made them all.

1. Each lit - tle flow'r that__ o - pens, Each
2. The pur - ple - head - ed__ moun - tain, The
3. The cold wind in the__ win - ter, The
4. God gave us eyes to__ see them, And

1. lit - tle bird that sings, God made their glow - ing__
2. riv - er run - ning by, The sun - set, and the__
3. plea - sant sum - mer sun, The__ ripe fruits in the__
4. lips that we__ might tell How great is God Al -

D.C.

1. col - ors, and__ made their ti - ny__ wings.
2. morn - ing That bright - ens up the__ sky.
3. gar - den, God__ made them ev - 'ry__ one.
4. might - y, Who has made all things well.

Cecil F. Alexander, 1818–1898, alt.   English melody

God, Who Made the Earth and Heaven 316

AR HYD Y NOS   84 84 88 84

1. God, who made the earth and heav-en, Dark-ness and
2. And when morn a-gain shall call us To run life's
3. Guard us wak-ing, guard us sleep-ing, And, when we
4. Ho-ly Fa-ther, throned in heav-en, All ho-ly

1. light: You the day for work have giv-en,
2. way, May we still what-e'er be-fall us,
3. die, May we in your might-y keep-ing
4. Son, Ho-ly Spir-it free-ly giv-en,

1. For rest the night. May your an-gel
2. Your will o-bey. From the pow'r of
3. All peace-ful lie. When the trump-et's
4. Blest Three in One: Grant us grace we

1. guards de-fend us, Slum-ber sweet your mer-cy send us,
2. e-vil hide us, In the nar-row path-way guide us,
3. call shall wake us, Then, O Lord, do not for-sake us,
4. now im-plore you, Till we lay our crowns be-fore you

1. Ho-ly dreams and hopes at-tend us, All through the night.
2. Nev-er be your smile de-nied us All through the day.
3. But to reign in glo-ry take us With you on high.
4. And in wor-thier strains a-dore you While ag-es run.

Text vs. 1: Reginald Heber, 1783–1826
Text vss. 2, 4: William Mercer, 1811–1871; text vs. 3: Richard Whately, 1787–1863, alt.

Traditional Welsh melody

317 God, Our God of Distant Ages

NETTLETON   87 87 D

1. God, our God of dis-tant a-ges, God, our God, now pres-ent
2. Pres-ent in the words once spo-ken By the proph-ets, saints of
3. Might-y Lord of all cre-a-tion, Three-fold is your pres-ence

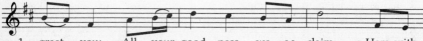

1. here,   God of pro-phets, seers, and sa-ges,   Ev-er
2. old,   Lord, your tes-ta-ments un-bro-ken   By our
3. known: Bread and word and con-gre-ga-tion   Are the

1. pres-ent,   ev-er near.   Great and might-y Lord, we
2. lips   are   here re-told.   O-pen, Lord, our hearts to
3. sym-bols   you have shown.   Time and space can-not con-

1. greet you; All your good-ness we ac-claim. Here with-
2. hear_ you; Sa-cred are the words you speak. In the
3. fine_ you, Nor the earth nor heav'n a-bove. Yet our

1. in   our midst we meet you   As we ga-ther in your name.
2. Good News we are near you, You, the liv-ing News we seek.
3. hum-ble hearts en-shrine you, In-fi-nite, great God of love.

Omer Westendorf
Text © 1984, WLP

John Wyeth's *Repository of Sacred Music, Part Second,* 1813

318 Immortal, Invisible, God Only Wise

ST. DENIO   11 11 11 11

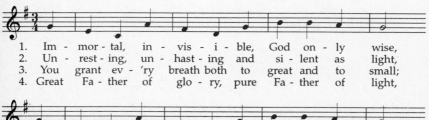

1. Im-mor-tal, in-vis-i-ble, God on-ly wise,
2. Un-rest-ing, un-hast-ing and si-lent as light,
3. You grant ev-'ry breath both to great and to small;
4. Great Fa-ther of glo-ry, pure Fa-ther of light,

1. In light in-ac-ces-si-ble hid from our eyes,
2. Not want-ing nor wast-ing, you rule day and night;
3. You save us from death, you, the true life of all.
4. Your an-gels a-dor-ing, all veil-ing their sight;

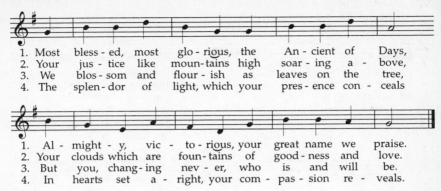

1. Most bless - ed, most glo - rious, the An - cient of Days,
2. Your jus - tice like moun-tains high soar - ing a - bove,
3. We blos - som and flour - ish as leaves on the tree,
4. The splen- dor of light, which your pres - ence con - ceals

1. Al - might - y, vic - to - rious, your great name we praise.
2. Your clouds which are foun- tains of good - ness and love.
3. But you, chang-ing nev - er, who is and will be.
4. In hearts set a - right, your com - pas - sion re - veals.

Walter C. Smith, 1824–1908, alt.

Welsh melody
Adapt. from *Caniadau y Cyssegr*, 1839

Many and Great, O God 319

LACQUIPARLE Irregular

1. Man - y and great, O God, are your works,
2. Give to us all com - mu - nion with you,

1. Mak - er of earth and sky. Your hands have
2. Who with the stars a - bide, Come_____ to

1. set the heav'ns with_ stars; Your fin- gers spread the
2. us and dwell with_ us; With you are found the

1. hills and_ plains. And at your word the seas were
2. gifts of_ life. Bless us with life that has no_

1. formed; O - ceans o - bey your voice.
2. end, E - ter - nal life with you.

Wakantanka tuku nitawa
Joseph R. Renville, 1779–1846
Tr. by Philip Frazier, 1892–1964

Dakota Hymn
Dakota Odowan, 1879

320 Bring Many Names

RIDGEVIEW 9 10 11 9

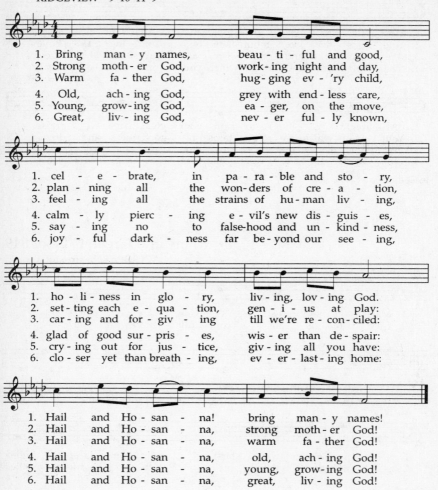

1. Bring man-y names, beau-ti-ful and good,
2. Strong moth-er God, work-ing night and day,
3. Warm fa-ther God, hug-ging ev-'ry child,

4. Old, ach-ing God, grey with end-less care,
5. Young, grow-ing God, ea-ger, on the move,
6. Great, liv-ing God, nev-er ful-ly known,

1. cel-e-brate, in pa-ra-ble and sto-ry,
2. plan-ning all the won-ders of cre-a-tion,
3. feel-ing all the strains of hu-man liv-ing,

4. calm-ly pierc-ing e-vil's new dis-guis-es,
5. say-ing no to false-hood and un-kind-ness,
6. joy-ful dark-ness far be-yond our see-ing,

1. ho-li-ness in glo-ry, liv-ing, lov-ing God.
2. set-ting each e-qua-tion, gen-i-us at play:
3. car-ing and for-giv-ing till we're re-con-ciled:

4. glad of good sur-pris-es, wis-er than de-spair:
5. cry-ing out for jus-tice, giv-ing all you have:
6. clo-ser yet than breath-ing, ev-er-last-ing home:

1. Hail and Ho-san-na! bring man-y names!
2. Hail and Ho-san-na, strong moth-er God!
3. Hail and Ho-san-na, warm fa-ther God!

4. Hail and Ho-san-na, old, ach-ing God!
5. Hail and Ho-san-na, young, grow-ing God!
6. Hail and Ho-san-na, great, liv-ing God!

Brian Wren

Donna B. Kasbohm

O Worship the King 321

HANOVER   10 10 11 11

1. O   wor - ship   the   King,   all   glo - rious   a - bove!
2. O   tell   of   God's   might   and   won - der - ful   grace!
3. The   earth with its   store   of   won - ders un - told,

4. Your boun - ti - ful   care,   what   tongue can   re - cite?
5. Frail chil - dren of   dust   and   fee - ble   as   frail,
6. O   meas - ure - less   might,   in -   ef - fa - ble   love,

1. O   grate - ful - ly   sing   God's   pow - er__ and   love!
2. Whose robe   is   the   light,   whose   can - o - py   space.
3. Al - might - y,   your   pow'r   has   found - ed__ of   old,

4. It   breathes in the   air;   it   shines in__   the   light;
5. In   you   do   we   trust   nor   find you_ to   fail;
6. While an - gels de - light   to   hymn you_ a - bove,

1. Our   shield and de - fend - er,   the   an - cient of   days,
2. Whose char - iots of might the   deep   thun - der - clouds form,
3. Es - tab - lished it fast by   a   change - less de - cree,

4. It   streams from the hills; it   de - scends to   the   plain,
5. Your mer - cies, how ten - der,   how   firm to the   end!
6. The   hum - bler cre - a - tion,though fee - ble their lays,

1. Pa - vil - ioned in splen - dor   and   gird - ed   with praise.
2. And   straight is God's path on   the   wings of   the   storm.
3. And   'round it has cast, like   a   man - tle, the   sea.

4. And   sweet - ly dis - tills in   the   dew and   the   rain.
5. Our   Mak - er, De - fen - der,   Re -   deem - er, and   Friend.
6. With true ad - o - ra - tion shall sing to your praise.

Ps 104:1–2, 6–7, 10, 13, 24, 29, 33–34   Attr. to William Croft, 1678–1727
Robert Grant, 1779–1838, alt.

322 Glorious Things of You Are Spoken

ABBOT'S LEIGH 87 87 D

1. Glo - rious things of you__ are spo - ken, Zi - on,
2. See, the streams of liv - ing wa - ters, Spring - ing
3. 'Round each hab - i - ta - tion hov- 'ring, See the
4. Blest in - hab - it - ants__ of Zi - on, Washed in

1. ci - ty of__ our God; God whose word can -
2. from__ e - ter - nal love, Well sup - ply your
3. cloud__ and fire__ ap - pear For a glo - ry
4. the__ Re - deem - er's blood! Je - sus, whom their

1. not__ be bro - ken, Formed you as__ the saints' a - bode;
2. sons_ and daugh-ters, And all fear__ of want re - move.
3. and _ a cov - 'ring, Show - ing that__ the Lord_ is near.
4. souls re - ly on, Makes them mon - archs, priests to God.

1. On the Rock of A - ges found - ed, What can
2. Who can faint while such__ a riv - er Ev - er
3. Thus de - riv - ing from__ their ban - ner, Light by
4. Them, by his great love,__ he rais - es, Rul - ers

1. shake_ your sure re - pose? With__ sal - va - tion's
2. will__ their thrist as - suage? Grace_ which, like the
3. night__ and shade by day, Safe__ they feed up -
4. o - ver self to reign, And__ as priests, his

1. walls sur- round-ed, You_ may smile at all your foes.
2. Lord, the giv - er, Nev - er fails_ from age to age.
3. on__ the man - na Which God gives them on their way.
4. sol - emn prais - es Each for thank - ful of - f'ring brings.

Ps 87:3
John Newton, 1725–1807, alt.

Cyril V. Taylor, 1907–1991
Music © 1942, 1970, Hope Publishing Co.

God, Who Stretched the 323 Spangled Heavens

HOLY MANNA   87 87 D

1. God, who stretched the span - gled heav - ens In - fi - nite in
2. We have ven - tured worlds un - dreamed of_ Since the child-hood
3. As each far ho - ri - zon beck - ons, May it_ chal - lenge

1. time and place, Flung the_ suns in burn - ing_ ra - diance
2. of our race; Known the_ ec - sta - sy of_ wing - ing_
3. us a - new: Chil - dren of cre - a - tive pur - pose,

1. Through the_ si - lent fields of space: We, your chil - dren
2. Through un - trav - eled realms of space; Probed the se - crets
3. Serv - ing_ oth - ers, hon - 'ring you. May our dreams prove

1. in your like - ness, Share in - ven - tive_ pow'rs with you;
2. of the_ at - om, Yield - ing un - i - mag - ined pow'r,
3. rich with prom - ise; Each en - deav - or_ well be - gun;

1. Great Cre - a - tor, still cre - at - ing,_
2. Fac - ing_ us with life's de - struc - tion_
3. Great Cre - a - tor, give us_ guid - ance_

1. Show us_ what we yet may do.
2. Or our_ most tri - um - phant hour.
3. Till our_ goals and yours are one.

Catherine Cameron
Text © 1967, Hope Publishing Co.

William Moore's *Columbian Harmony*, 1825

324 Sea and Islands, All Are Laughing

RADUJTE SA, Ó KREŠŤANIA   87 87 77 87

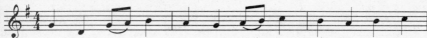

1. Sea and is - lands, all are laugh-ing; Earth is glad with
2. Fire will sweep and flash be - fore_ God; En - e - mies will
3. Ju - dah's cit - ies shout their glad - ness; Lord, you are so

1. joy - ful cry. God is King and lives in splen - dor;
2. burn a - way; E - vil scat - ters in the whirl- wind;
3. good and great. Zi - on's heard it: you are Sav - ior,

1. Shout your praise as God goes by! Cloud and mist God's
2. Moun-tains melt like wax a - way; God will rule_ from
3. Free - ing from a dis - mal fate; All the loved ones

1. throne en - fold; Trum - pets thun - der bright and bold.
2. sea to sea; Al - ways Lord and Mas - ter be.
3. will be free; God's own friends a light will see.

Al - le - lu - ia, al - le - lu - ia, God, our God, is Lord and King!

Ps 97:1–3, 5, 8–11
Willard F. Jabusch; text © 1979, Willard F. Jabusch

Traditional Slovak hymn tune

325 Thanks Be to Christ

AUGHTON   LMD

1. Your bod - y, Lord, we now re - ceive. We strive by faith to_
2. In this, your leg - a - cy of love, Your liv - ing pres - ence
3. Each time you give your - self to us, You sanc - ti - fy our_

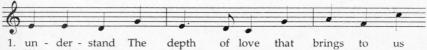

1. un - der - stand The depth of love that brings to us
2. fills each soul. O help us, Christ, so near us now,
3. lives a - new. In grate - ful ad - o - ra - tion, Lord,

1. Di - vin - i - ty___ at___ your com - mand.
2. And___ lead us to___ our___ com - mon goal.
3. We___ now re - turn___ our___ lives to you.

Thanks be to Christ, God's on - ly___ Son, The ev - er ho - ly,___

bless - ed One, May he be praised in song and___ prayer,

For won - drous works___ known___ ev - 'ry - where!

Rose Weber
Text © 1970, WLP

William B. Bradbury, 1816–1868

You Are the Way 326
MORNING SONG CM

1. You are the way; through you a - lone Can
2. You are the truth; your___ word a - lone True
3. You are the life; the___ rend - ing___ tomb Pro -
4. You are the way, the___ truth, the___ life; Grant

1. we the Fa - ther find; In___ you O___ Christ, has
2. wis - dom can im - part; You___ on - ly___ can in -
3. claims your con - qu'ring arm; And those who put their
4. us that way to know, That truth to___ keep, that

1. God re - vealed His heart, his will,___ his mind!
2. form the___ mind And pu - ri - fy___ the heart.
3. trust in___ you Not death nor hell___ shall harm.
4. life to___ win, Whose joys e - ter - nal flow.

George W. Doane, 1799–1859, alt.

Ananias Davisson's *Kentucky Harmony*, 1816

327 Jesus in the Morning

JESUS IN THE MORNING Irregular

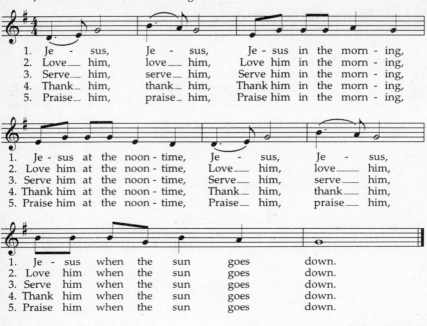

1. Je - sus,   Je - sus,   Je - sus in the morn - ing,
2. Love__ him,   love__ him,   Love him in the morn - ing,
3. Serve__ him,   serve__ him,   Serve him in the morn - ing,
4. Thank__ him,   thank__ him,   Thank him in the morn - ing,
5. Praise__ him,   praise__ him,   Praise him in the morn - ing,

1. Je - sus at the noon - time,   Je - sus,   Je - sus,
2. Love him at the noon - time,   Love__ him,   love__ him,
3. Serve him at the noon - time,   Serve__ him,   serve__ him,
4. Thank him at the noon - time,   Thank__ him,   thank__ him,
5. Praise him at the noon - time,   Praise__ him,   praise__ him,

1. Je - sus when the sun goes down.
2. Love him when the sun goes down.
3. Serve him when the sun goes down.
4. Thank him when the sun goes down.
5. Praise him when the sun goes down.

Traditional American

328 Glory and Praise to You

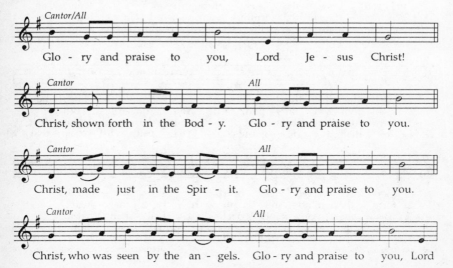

Cantor/All

Glo - ry and praise to you, Lord Je - sus Christ!

Cantor   All

Christ, shown forth in the Bod - y.   Glo - ry and praise to you.

Cantor   All

Christ, made just in the Spir - it.   Glo - ry and praise to you.

Cantor   All

Christ, who was seen by the an - gels. Glo - ry and praise to you, Lord

Cantor

Je - sus Christ! Christ, pro- claimed a - mong the na - tions.

All Glo - ry and praise to you. *Cantor* Christ, re- ceived in faith through-out the

All whole world. Glo - ry and praise to you. *Cantor* Christ, ex - alt - ed in

All glo - ry. Glo - ry and praise to you, Lord Je - sus Christ!

Lucien Deiss
Text and music © 1965, 1966, 1968, 1973, WLP

Rejoice, the Lord Is King 329

DARWALL'S 148TH   66 66 88

1. Re - joice, the Lord is King! Your Lord and King a - dore!
2. The Lord, our Sav - ior, reigns, The God of truth and love;
3. God's king-dom can - not fail, Christ rules o'er earth and heav'n;
4. Re - joice in glo-rious hope! For Christ, the Judge, shall come

1. Re - joice, give thanks and sing, Ex - ul - tant ev - er - more.
2. For Christ has purged our sins And reigns, en- throned a - bove.
3. The keys of death and hell To Christ the Lord are giv'n.
4. To take all those who love To their e - ter - nal home.

Lift up your heart, lift up your voice!

Re - joice, a - gain I say, re - joice!

Ps 95:2–3; Heb 1:3; Rv 1:18
Charles Wesley, 1707–1788, alt.

John Darwall, 1731–1789

330 Jesu, Joy of Our Desiring/Come with Us

WERDE MUNTER   87 87 76 86

1. Je - su, joy of our de - sir - ing,
2. Through the way where hope is guid - ing,

1. Come with us, O bless - ed Je - sus,
2. You are God from ev - er - last - ing,

1. Ho - ly wis - dom, love most bright,
2. Hark, what peace - ful mu - sic rings;

1. With a faith for - ev - er new
2. God of God and Light of Light;

1. Drawn by you, our souls as - pir - ing,
2. Where the flocks in you con - fid - ing,

1. And in leav - ing now your al - tar,
2. You are God, your glo - ry veil - ing,

1. Soar to un - cre - a - ted Light.
2. Drink of joy from death - less springs!

1. Let us nev - er - more leave you.
2. That we all may bear the sight.

1. Word of God, our flesh that fash - ioned
2. Theirs is beau - ty's fair - est pleas - ure;

1. O let your an - gel cho - rus
2. Sus - tain us, Lord, and help us,

1. With the fire of life im - pas - sioned,
2. Theirs is wis - dom's ho - liest treas - ure;

1. Cease not the heaven - ly strain;
2. Our dai - ly life to bear,

1. Striv - ing still to truth un - known,
2. You for - ev - er lead your own,

1. But in us, your lov - ing chil - dren,
2. That through us, your ho - ly teach - ing

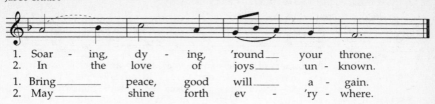

1. Soar - ing, dy - ing, 'round___ your throne.
2. In the love of joys___ un - known.

1. Bring___ peace, good will___ a - gain.
2. May___ shine forth ev - 'ry - where.

Jesu, Joy of Man's Desiring, Martin Jahn, c. 1620–1682
Tr. by Robert S. Bridges, 1844–1930, alt.
Come with Us, O Blessed Jesus, John H. Hopkins, Jr., 1820–1891, alt.

Himmlische Lieder, 1642
Johann P. Schop, c. 1590–1664

All Hail the Power of Jesus' Name 331
DIADEM 86 86 66 86

1. All hail the pow'r of Je - sus' name! Let an - gels pros-trate
2. Crown him, you mar - tyrs of our God, In heav-en's loft - y
3. O seed of Is - rael's chos - en race, Now ran-somed from the
4. Hail Christ, you heirs of Da - vid's line, Whom Da - vid Lord did

1. fall; Bring forth the roy - al di - a - dem, And
2. hall; Praise Christ whose way_ of pain you trod, And
3. fall, Hail Christ who saves you by his grace, And
4. call, The God - made - flesh, yet God di - vine, And

1. crown him Lord of all; And crown him Lord of
2. crown him Lord of all; And crown him Lord of
3. crown him Lord of all; And crown him Lord of
4. crown him Lord of all; And crown him Lord of

1. all; And_ crown him Lord of all; Bring
2. all; And_ crown him Lord of all; Praise
3. all; And_ crown him Lord of all; Hail
4. all; And_ crown him Lord of all; The

1. forth the roy - al di - a - dem, And crown him Lord of all.
2. Christ whose way of pain you trod, And crown him Lord of all.
3. Christ who saves you by his grace, And crown him Lord of all.
4. God - made - flesh, yet God di - vine, And crown him Lord of all.

Edward Perronet, 1726–1792
Alt. by John Rippon, 1751–1836, alt.

The Primitive Baptist Hymn and Tune Book, 1902

332 All Hail the Power of Jesus' Name

CORONATION 86 86 86

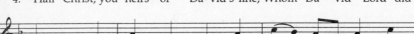

1. All hail the pow'r of Je - sus' name! Let an - gels pros - trate
2. Crown him, you mar - tyrs of our God, In heav - en's loft - y
3. O seed of Is - rael's chos - en race, Now ran - somed from the
4. Hail Christ, you heirs of Da - vid's line, Whom Da - vid Lord did

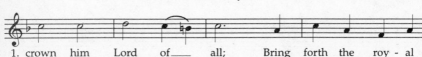

1. fall; Bring forth the roy - al di - a - dem, And
2. hall; Praise Christ whose way of pain_ you trod, And
3. fall, Hail Christ who saves you by_ his_ grace, And
4. call, The God - made - flesh, yet God_ di - vine, And

1. crown him Lord of__ all; Bring forth the roy - al
2. crown him Lord of__ all; Praise Christ whose way of
3. crown him Lord of__ all; Hail Christ who saves you
4. crown him Lord of__ all; The God - made - flesh, yet

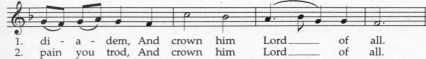

1. di - a - dem, And crown him Lord____ of all.
2. pain you trod, And crown him Lord____ of all.
3. by_ his_ grace, And crown him Lord____ of all.
4. God di - vine, And crown him Lord____ of all.

Edward Perronet, 1726–1792
Alt. by John Rippon, 1751–1836, alt.

Oliver Holden, 1765–1844

333 Somebody's Knockin' at Your Door

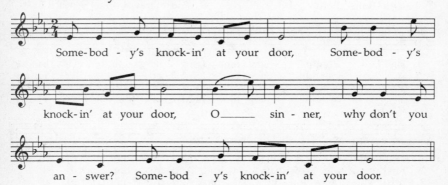

Some - bod - y's knock - in' at your door, Some - bod - y's

knock - in' at your door, O____ sin - ner, why don't you

an - swer? Some - bod - y's knock - in' at your door.

1. Knocks like— Je - sus,
2. Can't you— hear him?
3. Je - sus— calls you,
4. Can't you— trust him?

Some - bod - y's knock-in' at your door;

1. Knocks like— Je - sus,
2. Can't you— hear him?
3. Je - sus— calls you,
4. Can't you— trust him?

Some - bod - y's knock-in' at your door.

O_____ sin - ner, why don't you an - swer?

Some - bod - y's knock - in' at your door.

African-American

Christ Be beside Me 334
BUNESSAN 55 54 D

1. Christ be be - side me, Christ be be - fore me, Christ be be -
2. Christ on my right hand, Christ on my left hand, Christ all a -
3. Christ be in all hearts Think-ing a - bout me; Christ be on

1. hind me, King of my heart. Christ be with - in me, Christ be be -
2. round me, Shield in the strife. Christ in my sleep - ing, Christ in my
3. all tongues Tell-ing of me. Christ be the vis - ion In eyes that

1. low me, Christ be a - bove me, Nev - er to part.
2. sit - ting, Christ in my ris - ing, Light of my life.
3. see me; In ears that hear me, Christ ev - er be.

Attr. to St. Patrick, 372–466
Tr. by James Quinn
Tr. © 1969, James Quinn, Selah Publishing Co., North American agent.

Gaelic melody

335 Jesus Shall Reign

DUKE STREET LM

1. Je - sus shall reign wher - e'er the___ sun
2. Peo - ple and realms of___ ev - 'ry___ tongue
3. Bless - ings a - bound wher - e'er he___ reigns,
4. Let ev - 'ry crea - ture___ rise and___ bring

1. Does its suc - ces - sive jour - neys run;
2. Dwell on his love with sweet - est song,
3. The pris - 'ners leap to lose their chains;
4. Their joy - ful prais - es to our King;

1. His king - dom stretch from___ shore___ to___ shore,
2. And chil - dren's voic - es___ shall___ pro - claim
3. The wea - ry find___ e - ter - nal___ rest,
4. An - gels de - scend with___ songs___ a - gain,

1. Till moons shall wax and wane no more.
2. Their ear - ly bless - ings on his name.
3. And all who suf - fer want are blest.
4. And earth re - peat the loud A - men!

Ps 72
Isaac Watts, 1674–1748, alt.

Henry Boyd's *Psalm and Hymn Tunes*, 1793
Attr. to John C. Hatton, c. 1720–1793

336 I Know That My Redeemer Lives

DUKE STREET LM

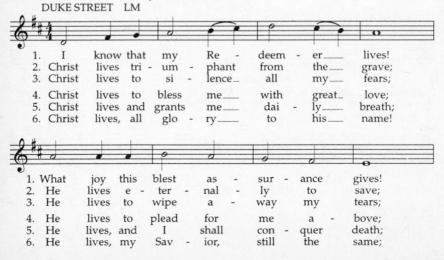

1. I know that my Re - deem - er___ lives!
2. Christ lives tri - um - phant from the___ grave;
3. Christ lives to si - lence___ all my___ fears;

4. Christ lives to bless me___ with great___ love;
5. Christ lives and grants me___ dai - ly___ breath;
6. Christ lives, all glo - ry___ to his___ name!

1. What joy this blest as - sur - ance gives!
2. He lives e - ter - nal - ly to save;
3. He lives to wipe a - way my tears;

4. He lives to plead for me a - bove;
5. He lives, and I shall con - quer death;
6. He lives, my Sav - ior, still the same;

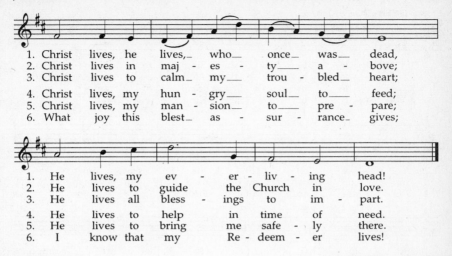

1. Christ lives, he lives, who once was dead,
2. Christ lives in maj - es - ty a - bove;
3. Christ lives to calm my trou - bled heart;
4. Christ lives, my hun - gry soul to feed;
5. Christ lives, my man - sion to pre - pare;
6. What joy this blest as - sur - ance gives;

1. He lives, my ev - er - liv - ing head!
2. He lives to guide the Church in love.
3. He lives all bless - ings to im - part.
4. He lives to help in time of need.
5. He lives to bring me safe - ly there.
6. I know that my Re - deem - er lives!

Jb 19:23
Samuel Medley, 1738–1799, alt.

Attr. to John Hatton, c. 1710–1793

Alleluia No. 1 337

ALLELUIA NO. 1   88 with Refrain

REFRAIN

Al - le - lu - ia, al - le - lu - ia, give thanks to the ris-en Lord.

Al - le - lu - ia, al - le - lu - ia, give praise to his name.

VERSES

1. Je - sus is Lord of all the earth;
2. Spread the Good News o'er all the earth;
3. We have been cru - ci - fied with Christ;
4. Come, let us praise the liv - ing God;

To Refrain

1. He is the King of cre - a - tion.
2. Je - sus has died and has ris - en.
3. Now we shall live for - ev - er.
4. Joy - ful - ly sing to our Sav - ior.

Phil 2:10; Mk 16:15; Rom 6:6, 8; 2 Tm 2:11

Donald E. Fishel
Text and music © 1973, Word of God Music

338 Alleluia! Sing to Jesus

HYFRYDOL 87 87 D

1. Al - le - lu - ia! Sing to Je - sus,
2. Al - le - lu - ia! Not as or - phans
3. Al - le - lu - ia! Bread of an - gels,
4. Al - le - lu - ia! King e - ter - nal,

1. His the scep - ter, his___ the throne;
2. Are we left in sor - row now;
3. You on earth our food,___ our stay;
4. You the Lord of lords___ we own;

1. Al - le - lu - ia! His the tri - umph,
2. Al - le - lu - ia! He is near___ us,
3. Al - le - lu - ia! Here the sin - ful
4. Al - le - lu - ia! Son of Ma - ry,

1. His the vic - to - ry___ a - lone;
2. Faith be - lieves, nor ques - tions how;
3. Flee to you from day___ to day;
4. Son of God from heav - en's throne;

1. Hark! the songs___ of peace - ful Zi - on
2. Though the cloud___ from sight re - ceived___ him
3. In - ter - ces - sor, friend of sin - ners,
4. Our sal - va - tion you ac - com - plished,

1. Thun - der like___ a might - y flood,
2. When the for - ty days___ were o'er,
3. Earth's Re - deem - er, plead___ for me,
4. Robed in flesh,___ our great___ High Priest;

1. Je - sus out___ of ev - 'ry na - tion
2. Shall___ our hearts for - get___ his prom - ise,
3. Where the songs___ of all___ the sin - less
4. Here___ on earth___ both priest___ and vic - tim

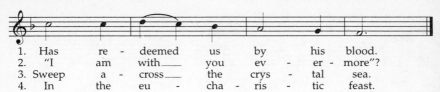

1. Has re - deemed us by his blood.
2. "I am with___ you ev - er - more"?
3. Sweep a - cross___ the crys - tal sea.
4. In the eu - cha - ris - tic feast.

William C. Dix, 1837–1898, alt.

Rowland H. Prichard, 1811–1887

To Jesus Christ, Our Sovereign King 339
ICH GLAUB AN GOTT   87 87 with Refrain

1. To Je - sus Christ, our sov - 'reign King Who
2. Your reign ex - tend, O King be - nign, To
3. To you and to___ your Church, great King, We

1. is the world's sal - va - tion, All praise and hom - age
2. ev - 'ry land and na - tion; For in your king - dom,
3. pledge our hearts' ob - la - tion; Un - til be - fore_ your

1. do we bring And thanks and ad - o - ra - tion.
2. Lord di - vine, A - lone we find sal - va - tion.
3. throne we sing In end - less ju - bi - la - tion.

Christ Je - sus, Vic - tor! Christ Je - sus, Rul - er!

Christ Je - sus, Lord and Re - deem - er!

Martin B. Hellriegel, 1890–1981
Text © 1978, Irene C. Mueller

Mainzer Gesangbuch, 1870

340 The King of Glory

KING OF GLORY   75 75 with Refrain

REFRAIN

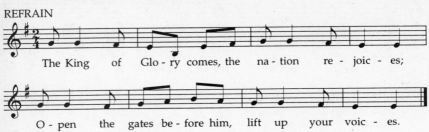

The King   of   Glo - ry comes, the   na - tion   re - joic - es;

O - pen   the   gates be - fore him,   lift   up   your   voic - es.

VERSES

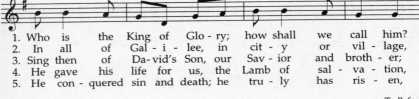

1. Who   is   the   King of   Glo - ry;   how shall   we   call   him?
2. In   all   of   Gal - i - lee, in   cit - y   or   vil - lage,
3. Sing then   of   Da - vid's Son, our   Sav - ior   and   broth - er;
4. He gave   his   life for   us, the   Lamb of   sal - va - tion,
5. He con - quered sin and death; he   tru - ly   has   ris - en,

To Refrain

1. He   is   Em - man - u - el, the   prom - ised   of   a - ges.
2. He goes   a - mong his peo - ple   cur - ing   their   ill - ness.
3. In   all   of   Gal - i - lee was   nev - er   an - oth - er.
4. He took   up - on him - self the   sins   of   the   na - tion.
5. And he   will   share with us   his   heav - en - ly   vi - sion.

Willard F. Jabusch
Text © 1967, 1984, Willard F. Jabusch

Israeli folk song

341 Christ, the Word before Creation

SHIRLEY   87 87 87

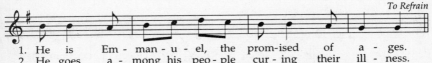

1. Christ, the   Word   be - fore   cre - a - tion;   Christ, the   Lord   of
2. Christ, who walked   a - mong the   low - ly;   Christ, who   with the
3. Christ,   up - on   the   cross sus - pend - ed;   Christ, your   bod - y
4. Christ, whose Word brings hope and glad - ness;   Christ, the   name in

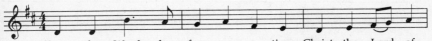

1. time   and space;   Christ, who came   for   our   sal - va - tion;
2. out - cast dined;   Christ, who sought   the   lost   and   lone - ly;
3. tombed   in   stone;   Christ,   a - live,   to   God   as - cend - ed;
4. which   we   pray;   Christ, whose com - fort   con - quers   sad - ness;

1. Christ, in - car - nate truth and grace: Fill the Church, your
2. Christ, who healed the sick, the blind: Send your Church with
3. Christ, for - ev - er with your own: Help your Church in
4. Christ, our Life, our Truth, our Way: Through your Church - 's

1. liv - ing Bod - y, With your Spir - it's en - er - gy.
2. true com - pas - sion Where the peo - ple cry in pain.
3. ev - 'ry na - tion Bear to all your ris - en life!
4. pro - cla - ma - tion, Tell a - broad your Word to - day!

Herman G. Stuempfle, Jr.

Perry Nelson
Text and music © 1997, WLP

Hail, Redeemer, King Divine 342
ST. GEORGE'S WINDSOR 77 77 D

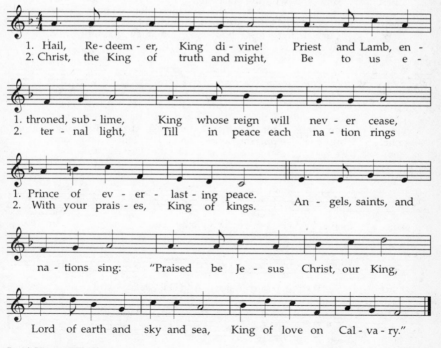

1. Hail, Re - deem - er, King di - vine! Priest and Lamb, en -
2. Christ, the King of truth and might, Be to us e -

1. throned, sub - lime, King whose reign will nev - er cease,
2. ter - nal light, Till in peace each na - tion rings

1. Prince of ev - er - last - ing peace. An - gels, saints, and
2. With your prais - es, King of kings.

na - tions sing: "Praised be Je - sus Christ, our King,

Lord of earth and sky and sea, King of love on Cal - va - ry."

Patrick Brennan, 1877–1951, alt.
Text © Burns & Oates, Ltd.

George J. Elvey, 1816–1893, alt.

343 Lord of the Dance

SIMPLE GIFTS Irregular

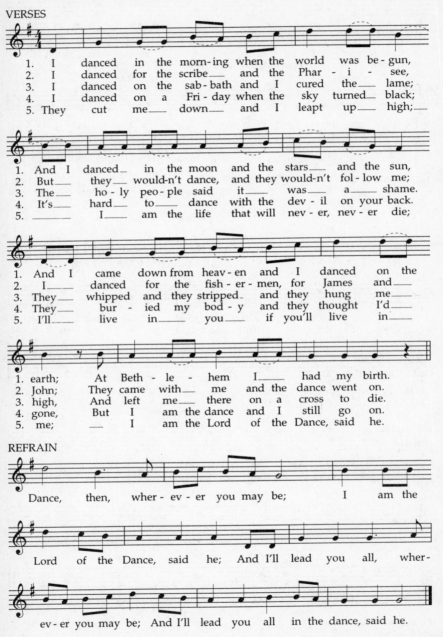

VERSES

1. I danced in the morn-ing when the world was be-gun,
2. I danced for the scribe___ and the Phar - i - see,
3. I danced on the sab-bath and I cured the___ lame;
4. I danced on a Fri - day when the sky turned___ black;
5. They cut me___ down___ and I leapt up___ high;___

1. And I danced___ in the moon and the stars___ and the sun,
2. But___ they___ would-n't dance, and they would-n't fol - low me;
3. The___ ho - ly peo - ple said it___ was___ a___ shame.
4. It's___ hard___ to___ dance with the dev - il on your back.
5. ___ I___ am the life that will nev - er, nev - er die;

1. And I came down from heav - en and I danced on the
2. I___ danced for the fish - er - men, for James and___
3. They___ whipped and they stripped___ and they hung me___
4. They___ bur - ied my bod - y and they thought I'd___
5. I'll___ live in___ you___ if you'll live in___

1. earth; At Beth - le - hem I___ had my birth.
2. John; They came with___ me and the dance went on.
3. high, And left me___ there on a cross to die.
4. gone, But I am the dance and I still go on.
5. me; ___ I am the Lord of the Dance, said he.

REFRAIN

Dance, then, wher - ev - er you may be; I am the

Lord of the Dance, said he; And I'll lead you all, wher-

ev - er you may be; And I'll lead you all in the dance, said he.

Sydney Carter
Text © 1963, Stainer and Bell Ltd.

Shaker melody

Crown Him with Many Crowns 344

DIADEMATA SMD

1. Crown him with man - y crowns, The Lamb up - on the
2. Crown him the Lord of life, Who tri - umphed o'er the
3. Crown him the Lord of love, Be - hold his hands and
4. Crown him the Lord of peace, Whose pow'r a scep - ter
5. Crown him the Lord of years, The ris - en Lord sub -

1. throne; Hark! how the heav'n - ly an - them drowns
2. grave, And rose vic - to - rious in the__ strife
3. side, Rich wounds yet vis - i - ble a - bove
4. sways From pole to pole, that wars may__ cease,
5. lime, Cre - a - tor of the roll - ing__ spheres,

1. All mu - sic but its own. A - wake, my soul, and
2. For those he came to save. His glo - ries now we
3. In beau - ty glo - ri - fied. No an - gel in the
4. Ab - sorbed in prayer and praise. His reign shall know no
5. The Mas - ter of all time. All hail, Re - deem - er,

1. sing To Christ, who set us free,
2. sing, Who died and rose on high,
3. sky Can full - y bear that sight,
4. end, And 'round his pierc - ed feet
5. hail! For you have died for me;

1. And hail him as your heav'n - ly King
2. Who died, e - ter - nal life to bring,
3. But down - ward bends his burn - ing eye
4. Fair flow'rs of Par - a - dise ex - tend
5. Your praise and glo - ry shall not fail

1. Through all e - ter - ni - ty.
2. And lives that death may die.
3. At mys - ter - ies so bright.
4. Their fra - grance ev - er sweet.
5. Through - out e - ter - ni - ty.

Vss. 1, 3–5: Matthew Bridges, 1800–1894, alt.
Vs. 2: Godfrey Thring, 1823–1903

George J. Elvey, 1816–1893

345 Come, Holy Ghost

LAMBILLOTTE LM

1. Come, Ho - ly Ghost, Cre - a - tor blest,
2. O Com - fort - er, to thee we cry,
3. Praise be to thee, Fa - ther and Son,

1. And in our hearts take up thy rest;
2. Thou heav'n - ly gift of God most high,
3. And Ho - ly Spir - it, with them one;

1. Come with thy grace and heav'n - ly aid
2. Thou font of life and fire of love,
3. And may the Son on us be - stow

1.
1. To fill the hearts which thou hast made.
2. And sweet a - noint - ing from a - bove.
3. The gifts that from the Spir - it flow.

2.
made.
bove.
flow.

Veni, Creator Spiritus, attr. to Rabanus Maurus, c. 776–856
Tr. by Edward Caswall, 1814–1878, alt.

Louis Lambillotte, 1796–1855, alt.

346 The Holy Spirit and the Church

LAUDES DOMINI 666 D

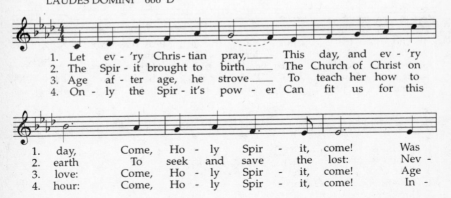

1. Let ev - 'ry Chris - tian pray, This day, and ev - 'ry
2. The Spir - it brought to birth The Church of Christ on
3. Age af - ter age, he strove To teach her how to
4. On - ly the Spir - it's pow - er Can fit us for this

1. day, Come, Ho - ly Spir - it, come! Was
2. earth To seek and save the lost: Nev -
3. love: Come, Ho - ly Spir - it, come! Age
4. hour: Come, Ho - ly Spir - it, come! In -

1. not the Church we love — Com - mis - sioned from a -
2. er has he with drawn, — Since that tre - men - dous
3. af - ter age, a - new, — She proved the gos - pel
4. struct, in - spire, u - nite; — And make us see the

1. bove? Come, Ho - ly Spir - it, come!
2. dawn, His gifts at Pen - te - cost.
3. true: Come, Ho - ly Spir - it, come!
4. light: Come, Ho - ly Spir - it, come!

Fred Pratt Green
Text © 1971, Hope Publishing Co.

Joseph Barnby, 1836–1896

Spirit Divine, Attend Our Prayer 347
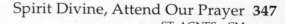
ST. AGNES   CM

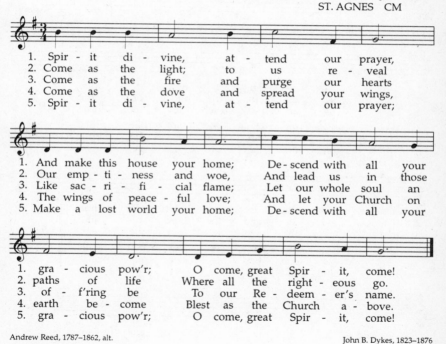

1. Spir - it di - vine, at - tend our prayer,
2. Come as the light; to us re - veal
3. Come as the fire and purge our hearts
4. Come as the dove and spread your wings,
5. Spir - it di - vine, at - tend our prayer;

1. And make this house your home; De - scend with all your
2. Our emp - ti - ness and woe, And lead us in those
3. Like sac - ri - fi - cial flame; Let our whole soul an
4. The wings of peace - ful love; And let your Church on
5. Make a lost world your home; De - scend with all your

1. gra - cious pow'r; O come, great Spir - it, come!
2. paths of life Where all the right - eous go.
3. of - f'ring be To our Re - deem - er's name.
4. earth be - come Blest as the Church a - bove.
5. gra - cious pow'r; O come, great Spir - it, come!

Andrew Reed, 1787–1862, alt.

John B. Dykes, 1823–1876

348 O Holy Spirit, by Whose Breath

LASST UNS ERFREUEN   88 8 88   with Refrain

1. O Ho - ly Spir - it, by whose breath
2. You are the seek - er's sure re - source,
3. In you God's en - er - gy is shown,
4. Flood our dull sens - es with your light;
5. From in - ner strife grant us re - lease;
6. Praise to the Fa - ther, Christ the Word,

1. Life ris - es vi - brant out of death;
2. Of burn - ing love the liv - ing source,
3. To us your var - ied gifts make known,
4. In mu - tual love our hearts u - nite.
5. Turn na - tions to the ways of peace,
6. And to the Spir - it, God the Lord,

Al - le - lu - ia, al - le - lu - ia,

1. Come to cre - ate, re - new, in - spire;
2. Pro - tec - tor in the midst of strife,
3. Teach us to speak, teach us to hear;
4. Your pow'r the whole cre - a - tion fills;
5. To ful - ler life your peo - ple bring
6. To whom all hon - or, glo - ry be,

1. Come, kin - dle in our hearts your fire.
2. The giv - er and the Lord of life.
3. Yours is the tongue and yours the ear.
4. Con - firm our weak, un - cer - tain wills.
5. That as one bod - y we may sing:
6. Both now and for e - ter - ni - ty.

Al - le - lu - ia, al - le - lu - ia, al - le - lu - ia,

al - le - lu - ia, al - le - lu - ia!

Text attr. to Rabanus Maurus, 776–865; tr. by John W. Grant   *Geistliche Kirchengesänge*, Cologne, 1623
Text reprinted with permission of John W. Grant

O Holy Spirit, Enter In 349

WIE SCHÖN LEUCHTET   887 887 48 48

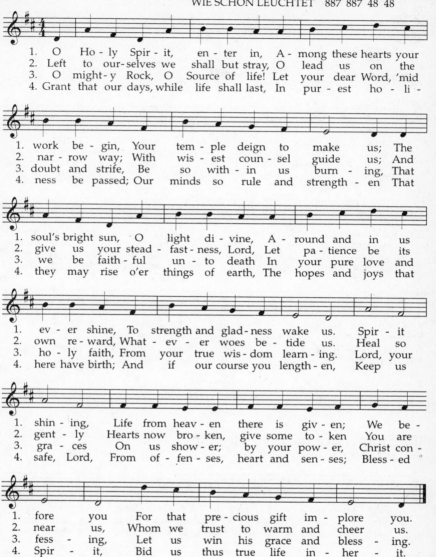

1. O Ho-ly Spir-it, en-ter in, A-mong these hearts your
2. Left to our-selves we shall but stray, O lead us on the
3. O might-y Rock, O Source of life! Let your dear Word, 'mid
4. Grant that our days, while life shall last, In pur-est ho-li-

1. work be-gin, Your tem-ple deign to make us; The
2. nar-row way; With wis-est coun-sel guide us; And
3. doubt and strife, Be so with-in us burn-ing, That
4. ness be passed; Our minds so rule and strength-en That

1. soul's bright sun, O light di-vine, A-round and in us
2. give us your stead-fast-ness, Lord, Let pa-tience be its
3. we be faith-ful un-to death In your pure love and
4. they may rise o'er things of earth, The hopes and joys that

1. ev-er shine, To strength and glad-ness wake us. Spir-it
2. own re-ward, What-ev-er woes be-tide us. Heal so
3. ho-ly faith, From your true wis-dom learn-ing. Lord, your
4. here have birth; And if our course you length-en, Keep us

1. shin-ing, Life from heav-en there is giv-en; We be-
2. gent-ly Hearts now bro-ken, give some to-ken You are
3. gra-ces On us show-er; by your pow-er, Christ con-
4. safe, Lord, From of-fen-ses, heart and sen-ses; Bless-ed

1. fore you For that pre-cious gift im-plore you.
2. near us, Whom we trust to warm and cheer us.
3. fess-ing, Let us win his grace and bless-ing.
4. Spir-it, Bid us thus true life in-her-it.

Michael Schirmer, 1606–1673
Tr. by Catherine Winkworth, 1827–1878, alt.

Philipp Nicolai, 1556–1608

350 Come, Our Almighty King

ITALIAN HYMN   664 6664

1. Come, our al - might - y King, Help us your
2. Come, O in - car - nate Word, By heav'n and
3. Come, ho - ly Com - fort - er, Your sa - cred
4. To the great One in Three, E - ter - nal

1. name to sing, Help us to praise.
2. earth a - dored. Our prayer at - tend;
3. wit - ness bear In this glad hour!
4. prais - es be Hence ev - er - more;

1. Fa - ther all glo - ri - ous, Ev - er vic - to - ri - ous,
2. Come and your peo - ple bless, And give your word suc - cess;
3. Your grace to us im - part; Now rule in ev - 'ry heart,
4. You sov - 'reign maj - es - ty May we in glo - ry see,

1. Come and reign o - ver us, An - cient of Days.
2. Spir - it of ho - li - ness, On us de - scend.
3. Nev - er from us de - part, Spir - it of pow'r!
4. And to e - ter - ni - ty Love and a - dore!

Anon., *Collection of Hymns*, 1757, alt.   Felice de Giardini, 1716–1796

351 Sing Your Praises to the Father

PLEADING SAVIOR   87 87 D

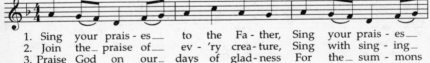

1. Sing your prais - es to the Fa - ther, Sing your prais - es
2. Join the praise of ev - 'ry crea - ture, Sing with sing - ing
3. Praise God on our days of glad - ness For the sum - mons

1. to the Son, Sing your prais - es to the Spir - it,
2. birds at dawn; When the stars shine forth at night - fall,
3. to re - joice; Praise God in our times of sad - ness

1. Liv - ing and e - ter - nal One. God has made us,
2. Hear their heav'n-ly an - ti - phon. Join in praise for
3. For the help of heav-en's voice. God our Fa - ther,

1. God has blessed us, God has called us to be true;
2. light of sum - mer, Au - tumn glo - ries, win - ter snows,
3. strong and lov - ing, Christ our Sav - ior, Lead - er, Lord,

1. God is Lord of all cre - a - tion,
2. For the com - ing of the spring - time,
3. Liv - ing God, Cre - a - tor Spir - it,

1. Dai - ly mak - ing all things new.
2. And the life of all that grows.
3. Be your ho - ly name a - dored.

Robert B. Y. Scott
Text used by permission of Robert B. Y. Scott

Joshua Leavitt's *Christian Lyre*, 1831

All Hail, Adored Trinity 352
OLD HUNDREDTH LM

1. All hail, a - dor - ed Trin - i - ty; All
2. Three Per - sons praise we ev - er - more, One
3. O Trin - i - ty, O U - ni - ty, Be

1. praise, e - ter - nal U - ni - ty: O God the Fa - ther,
2. on - ly God our hearts a - dore: In your sure mer - cy
3. pres - ent as we wor - ship thee; And to the an - gels'

1. God the Son, And God the Spir - it, ev - er one.
2. ev - er kind, May we our strong pro - tec - tion find.
3. songs in light Our prayers and prais - es now u - nite.

Latin, c. 11th cent.
Tr. by John D. Chambers, 1805–1893

Pseaumes octante trois de David, 1551
Louis Bourgeois, c. 1510–1561

353 Hymn to the Trinity

ST. BERNADETTE 76 65 with Refrain

1. O Fa - ther, whose might-y arm Em - brac - es us
2. Christ Je - sus, the Son of God, Pure fount of pure
3. O Spir - it, our Par - a - clete, Con - firm and in -
4. All praise to the Fa - ther be, All praise to the

1. all, We praise you in glo - ry And an - swer your call.
2. love, The cause of our yearn-ing For heav - en a - bove.
3. spire; Re - new in God's peo - ple The flame of your fire.
4. Son; All praise to the Spir - it While cen - tur - ies run.

Ho - ly, ho - ly, blest be the Tri - ni - ty,

Three - in - One and One - in - Three.

Robert E. Kreutz, 1922–1996
Text and music © 1980, WLP

354 How Wonderful the Three-in-One

PROSPECT 8 8 8 8

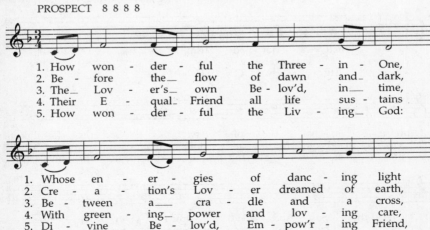

1. How won - der - ful the Three - in - One,
2. Be - fore the flow of dawn and dark,
3. The Lov - er's own Be - lov'd, in time,
4. Their E - qual Friend all life sus - tains
5. How won - der - ful the Liv - ing God:

1. Whose en - er - gies of danc - ing light
2. Cre - a - tion's Lov - er dreamed of earth,
3. Be - tween a cra - dle and a cross,
4. With green - ing power and lov - ing care,
5. Di - vine Be - lov'd, Em - pow'r - ing Friend,

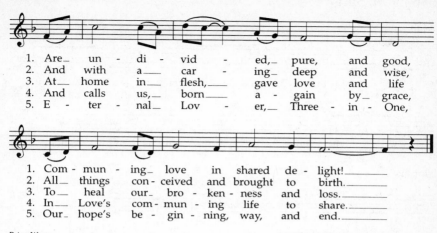

1. Are un - di - vid - ed,_ pure, and good,
2. And with a_ car - ing_ deep and wise,
3. At_ home in_ flesh,_ gave love and life
4. And calls us,_ born_ a - gain by_ grace,
5. E - ter - nal_ Lov - er,_ Three - in - One,

1. Com - mun - ing_ love in shared de - light!___
2. All_ things con - ceived and brought to birth.___
3. To_ heal our_ bro - ken - ness and loss.___
4. In_ Love's com - mun - ing life to share.___
5. Our_ hope's be - gin - ning, way, and end.___

Brian Wren
Text © 1989, Hope Publishing Co.

William Walker's *Southern Harmony*, 1835

Sing Praise to Our Creator 355
GOTT VATER! SEI GEPRIESEN   76 76 with Refrain

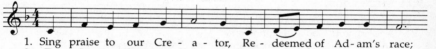

1. Sing praise to our Cre - a - tor, Re - deemed of Ad - am's race;
2. To Je - sus Christ give glo - ry, God's co - e - ter - nal Son;
3. Now praise the Ho - ly Spir - it Poured forth up - on the earth,

1. God's chil - dren by a - dop - tion, Bap - tized in liv - ing grace.
2. As mem - bers of his Bod - y We are_ in Christ made one.
3. Who sanc - ti - fies and guides us, Con - firmed in our re - birth.

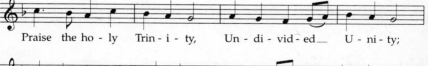

Praise the ho - ly Trin - i - ty, Un - di - vid - ed_ U - ni - ty;

Ho - ly God, might - y God, God im - mor - tal, be a - dored.

Omer Westendorf
Text © 1962, WLP

Maintzisch Gesangbuch, 1661

356 Sion, Sing

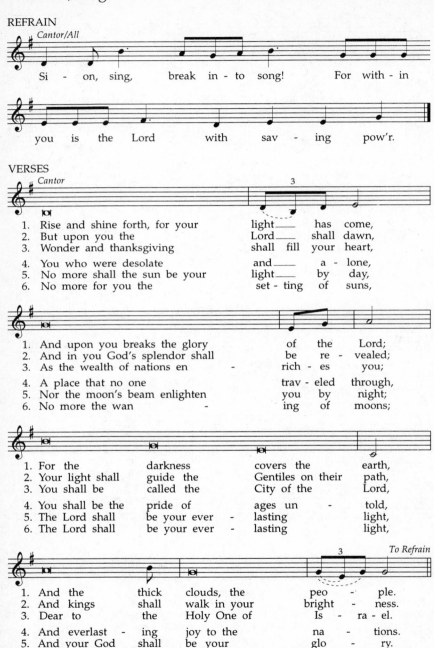

REFRAIN

Cantor/All

Si - on, sing, break in - to song! For with - in you is the Lord with sav - ing pow'r.

VERSES

Cantor

1. Rise and shine forth, for your light___ has come,
2. But upon you the Lord___ shall dawn,
3. Wonder and thanksgiving shall fill your heart,
4. You who were desolate and___ a - lone,
5. No more shall the sun be your light___ by day,
6. No more for you the set - ting of suns,

1. And upon you breaks the glory of the Lord;
2. And in you God's splendor shall be re - vealed;
3. As the wealth of nations en - rich - es you;
4. A place that no one trav - eled through,
5. Nor the moon's beam enlighten you by night;
6. No more the wan - ing of moons;

1. For the darkness covers the earth,
2. Your light shall guide the Gentiles on their path,
3. You shall be called the City of the Lord,
4. You shall be the pride of ages un - told,
5. The Lord shall be your ever - lasting light,
6. The Lord shall be your ever - lasting light,

To Refrain

1. And the thick clouds, the peo - ple.
2. And kings shall walk in your bright - ness.
3. Dear to the Holy One of Is - ra - el.
4. And everlast - ing joy to the na - tions.
5. And your God shall be your glo - ry.
6. And the days of your mourning shall come to an end.

Zep 3:14–17; Lk 1:28–35
Vss.: Is 60:1–5, 15, 19–20

Lucien Deiss
Text and music © 1965, WLP

We Form One Church 357

CLEANSING FOUNTAIN 86 86 76 86

1. We___ form one Church, one Chris - tian folk, Re -
2. We___ know the kind - ness of Christ's love, We___
3. Our___ hope is strong in Je - sus Christ, Our___

1. deemed by God's own Son; Re - freshed by clear and
2. know his will___ to___ save; We___ know he won the
3. faith is in___ his___ name; We___ know he seeks the

1. sav - ing streams, We___ share in grac - es won.
2. vic - to - ry O'er___ sin and o'er the grave.
3. sin - ful one, For___ that is why Christ came;

1. We___ break the bread of heav - en To
2. To___ each of us is giv - en The
3. To___ care for those who suf - fer, And

1. feed us on___ our___ way; We___ take the cup that
2. full - ness of___ his___ grace, To___ live in joy a
3. love both young and old, A___ man of sor - rows,

1. brings us life To___ cel - e - brate this day.
2. life of love Un - til we see his face.
3. ris - en now, As___ he him- self fore - told!

Willard F. Jabusch
Text © 1976, Willard F. Jabusch

American melody

358 The Church's One Foundation

AURELIA 76 76 D

1. The Church's one foun - da - tion Is Je - sus
2. E - lect from ev - 'ry na - tion, Yet one o'er
3. Though with a scorn - ful won - der The world sees
4. 'Mid toil and trib - u - la - tion, And tu - mult
5. Yet she on earth has un - ion With God, the

1. Christ her Lord; She is his new cre - a - tion
2. all the earth, Her char - ter of sal - va - tion,
3. her op - pressed, By schisms rent a - sun - der,
4. of her war, She waits the con - sum - ma - tion
5. Three - in - One, And mys - tic, sweet com - mun - ion

1. By wa - ter and the Word. From heav'n he
2. One Lord, one faith, one birth; One ho - ly
3. By her - e - sies dis - tressed; Yet saints their
4. Of peace for - ev - er - more, Till with the
5. With those whose rest is won. O hap - py

1. came and sought her To be his ho - ly bride; With
2. name she bless - es, Par - takes one ho - ly food, And
3. watch are keep - ing, Their cry goes up, "How long?" And
4. vi - sion glo - rious Her long - ing eyes are blest, And
5. ones and ho - ly! Lord, give us grace that we Like

1. his own blood he bought her, And for her life he died.
2. to one hope she press - es, With ev - 'ry grace en - dued.
3. soon the night of weep - ing Shall be the morn of song.
4. the great Church vic - to - rious Shall be the Church at rest.
5. them, the meek and low - ly, May live e - ter - nal - ly.

Samuel J. Stone, 1839–1900, alt.

Samuel S. Wesley, 1810–1876

Baptized in Living Waters 359

AURELIA   76 76 D

1. Baptized in living waters,
   On Christ we firmly stand,
   Are made one living body
   In ev'ry time and land,
   In dying and in rising,
   We join the endless song,
   With saints throughout the ages,
   All heaven's holy throng.

2. With living bread Christ feeds us,
   A banquet is prepared;
   To pastures green he leads us,
   To rich and bounteous fare;
   To one cup of salvation,
   Refreshing as the dew,
   Inscribed upon our hearts as
   The covenant anew.

3. Anointed with one Spirit,
   Confirmed with oil of joy,
   The Church proclaims the gospel
   Of sin and death destroyed;
   With wisdom's understanding,
   With knowing judgment right,
   With rev'rence, courage, wonder,
   The gifts of heav'nly light.

4. With healing touch we reach out
   To those in pain and grief,
   As living signs embracing
   All those who seek relief.
   And, reconciled with others,
   We reconcile with Christ,
   Returning through the pow'r of
   His cross and sacrifice.

5. Through word and prayer and worship,
   Through deed and sacrament,
   We are the living witness,
   And to the world are sent.
   As God's own holy people,
   On Christ we firmly stand,
   Empow'red by one same Spirit
   In ev'ry time and land.

Alan J. Hommerding
Text © 1994, WLP

360 At the Font We Start Our Journey

WESTMINSTER ABBEY 87 87 87

1. At the font we start our jour - ney,
2. At the pul - pit we are fash - ioned,
3. At the al - tar we are nour - ished
4. At the or - gan we are shar - ers,
5. At the door we are com - mis - sioned,

1. In the Eas - ter faith bap - tized;
2. By the Eas - ter tale re - told
3. With the Eas - ter gift of bread;
4. As the Eas - ter an - thems ring,
5. Now the Eas - ter vic - t'ry's won,

1. Doubts and fears no long - er blind us,
2. In - to wit - nes - ses and proph - ets,
3. In our break - ing it to piec - es
4. In a joy - ful cel - e - bra - tion
5. To re - store a world di - vid - ed

1. By the light of Christ sur - prised.
2. By the pow'r of Christ made bold.
3. See the love of Christ out - spread.
4. Of the reign of Christ the King.
5. To the peace of Christ as one.

1. Al - le - lu - ia, al - le - lu - ia!
2. Al - le - lu - ia, al - le - lu - ia!
3. Al - le - lu - ia, al - le - lu - ia!
4. Al - le - lu - ia, al - le - lu - ia!
5. Al - le - lu - ia, al - le - lu - ia!

1. Hope held out and re - al - ized.
2. Faith pro - claimed, yet still un - told.
3. Life em - braced, yet free - ly shed.
4. Praise re - sounds and prayer takes wing.
5. Eas - ter's work must still be done.

Jeffery W. Rowthorn
Text © 1991, Hope Publishing Co.

Henry Purcell, 1659–1695

Lord, You Give the Great Commission 361

ABBOT'S LEIGH   87 87 D

1. Lord, you give the great com-mis-sion: "Heal the
2. Lord, you call us to your ser-vice: "In my
3. Lord, you make the com-mon ho-ly: "This my
4. Lord, you show us love's true meas-ure: "Fa-ther,
5. Lord, you bless with words as-sur-ing: "I am

1. sick and preach the word." Lest the Church ne-
2. name bap-tize and teach." That the world may
3. bod-y, this my blood." Let us all, for
4. what they do, for-give." Yet we hoard as
5. with you to the end." Faith and hope and

1. glect its mis-sion, And the gos-pel go un-heard,
2. trust your prom-ise, Life a-bun-dant meant for each,
3. earth's true glo-ry, Dai-ly lift life heav-en-ward,
4. pri-vate trea-sure All that you so free-ly give.
5. love re-stor-ing, May we serve as you in-tend,

1. Help us wit-ness to your pur-pose With re-
2. Give us all new fer-vor, draw us Clos-er
3. Ask-ing that the world a-round us Share your
4. May your care and mer-cy lead us To a
5. And, a-mid the cares that claim us, Hold in

1. newed in-teg-ri-ty;
2. in com-mu-ni-ty;
3. child-ren's lib-er-ty; With the Spir-it's
4. just so-ci-e-ty;
5. mind e-ter-ni-ty;

gifts em-pow'r us For the work of min-is-try.

Jeffery W. Rowthorn

Cyril V. Taylor, 1907–1991
Text and music © 1942, 1970, 1978, Hope Publishing Co.

362 Christ Is Made the Sure Foundation

REGENT SQUARE 87 87 87

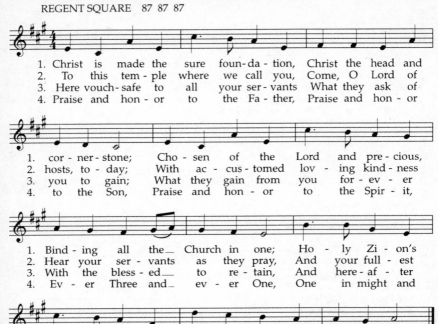

1. Christ is made the sure foun-da-tion, Christ the head and
2. To this tem-ple where we call you, Come, O Lord of
3. Here vouch-safe to all your ser-vants What they ask of
4. Praise and hon-or to the Fa-ther, Praise and hon-or

1. cor-ner-stone; Cho-sen of the Lord and pre-cious,
2. hosts, to-day; With ac-cus-tomed lov-ing kind-ness
3. you to gain; What they gain from you for-ev-er
4. to the Son, Praise and hon-or to the Spir-it,

1. Bind-ing all the Church in one; Ho-ly Zi-on's
2. Hear your ser-vants as they pray, And your full-est
3. With the bless-ed to re-tain, And here-af-ter
4. Ev-er Three and ev-er One, One in might and

1. help for-ev-er, And our con-fi-dence a-lone.
2. ben-e-dic-tion Shed with-in its walls al-ways.
3. in your glo-ry Ev-er-more with you to reign.
4. One in glo-ry, While un-end-ing ag-es run.

Angularis fundamentum, 7th or 8th cent.   Henry T. Smart, 1813–1879
Tr. by John M. Neale, 1818–1866, alt.

363 Lovely Is Your Dwelling Place

VERSES

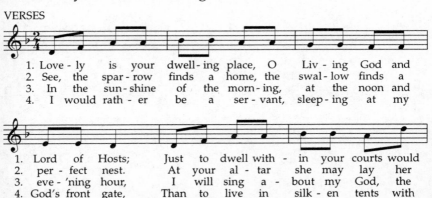

1. Love-ly is your dwell-ing place, O Liv-ing God and
2. See, the spar-row finds a home, the swal-low finds a
3. In the sun-shine of the morn-ing, at the noon and
4. I would rath-er be a ser-vant, sleep-ing at my

1. Lord of Hosts; Just to dwell with-in your courts would
2. per-fect nest. At your al-tar she may lay her
3. eve-'ning hour, I will sing a-bout my God, the
4. God's front gate, Than to live in silk-en tents with

REFRAIN

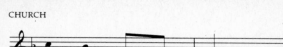

```
1. be    my    proud - est    boast.    One    day    in    your
2. lit - tle   ones   to      rest.
3. God   of    love   and    pow'r.
4. those who   scheme and    hate.
```

```
courts  is  bet - ter  than  a  thou - sand  oth - er  days.
```

```
I would live with - in your house and  ev - er  sing your praise!
```

Ps 84
Willard F. Jabusch
Text © 1997, WLP

Traditional Jewish melody

You Shall Be My People 364

VERSES

```
1. I    will take your hearts of  stone  and give you hearts of  flesh;
2. I    will take clean wa  -  ter   and pour it  o - ver  you;
3. Through you will  my  ho - li - ness  and glo - ry  be  re - vealed,
4. I    will take what was de - stroyed and build it  up  a - gain;
5. I    will breathe my  life  in  you   and raise you from your graves;
6. I    will make  a  cov - e - nant  of  last - ing peace with you;
```

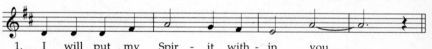

```
1. I    will put  my   Spir - it  with - in    you._____
2. From your sins will  I   pur - i - fy    you._____
3. As   I    gath - er  you   from the   na - tions._____
4. I    will bring forth life  in   the  waste - land._____
5. Then you  shall know I   am   the  Lord  God._____
6. I    will dwell for - ev - er  a - mong  you._____
```

REFRAIN

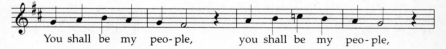

```
You shall be  my  peo - ple,    you shall be  my  peo - ple,
```

```
you shall be  my  peo - ple,  and  I  will be your God.
```

Ez 36:23–28

Michael Ward
Text and music © 1989, WLP

365 We Are Your People

SINE NOMINE   10 10 10 with Alleluias

1. We are your peo - ple, called from man - y
2. Root - ed in faith and nour - ished by your
3. We find in font and cross our u - ni -
4. Stir us to hear your call, O Christ, and
5. Make us your light in dark - ened cit - y
6. Christ, be the truth by whom our feet are

1. lands, Known by your name, up -
2. word, Firm in the hope your
3. ty, Yet cel - e - brate our
4. rise, Striv - ing for right where
5. streets, Bear - ing your hope where
6. led; Christ, be the bread by

1. held by your strong hands, Bear - ing your
2. prom - ise has se - cured, We bring our
3. rich di - ver - si - ty. Bind us as
4. jus - tice, fal - len, lies, Serv - ing in
5. e - vil still de - feats, Tell - ing of
6. whom our hearts are fed; Christ, be our

1. cross and led by your com - mands.
2. love, our lives to you, our Lord.
3. one in peace and char - i - ty.
4. love where pain for heal - ing cries.
5. grace till ev - 'ry voice re - peats:
6. life, our strength through years a - head.

Al - le - lu - ia! Al - le - lu - ia!

Herman G. Stuempfle, Jr.
Text © 1994, WLP

Ralph Vaughan Williams, 1872–1958

Lord, I Want to Be a Christian 366

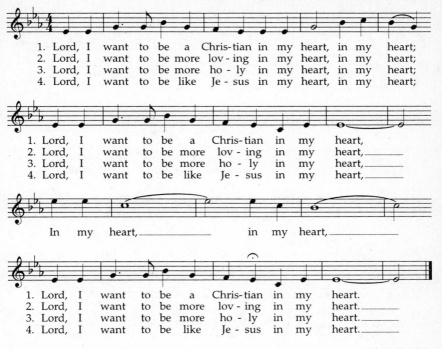

1. Lord, I want to be a Chris-tian in my heart, in my heart;
2. Lord, I want to be more lov-ing in my heart, in my heart;
3. Lord, I want to be more ho-ly in my heart, in my heart;
4. Lord, I want to be like Je-sus in my heart, in my heart;

1. Lord, I want to be a Chris-tian in my heart,
2. Lord, I want to be more lov-ing in my heart,_____
3. Lord, I want to be more ho-ly in my heart,_____
4. Lord, I want to be like Je-sus in my heart,_____

In my heart,_____ in my heart,_____

1. Lord, I want to be a Chris-tian in my heart.
2. Lord, I want to be more lov-ing in my heart._____
3. Lord, I want to be more ho-ly in my heart._____
4. Lord, I want to be like Je-sus in my heart._____

African-American

When to the Sacred Font We Came 367

ST. ANNE CM

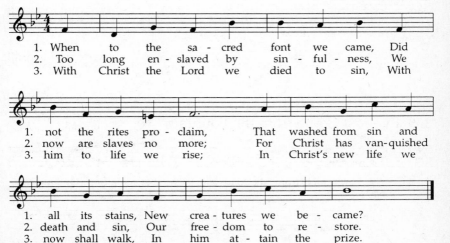

1. When to the sa-cred font we came, Did
2. Too long en-slaved by sin-ful-ness, We
3. With Christ the Lord we died to sin, With

1. not the rites pro-claim, That washed from sin and
2. now are slaves no more, For Christ has van-quished
3. him to life we rise; In Christ's new life we

1. all its stains, New crea-tures we be-came?
2. death and sin, Our free-dom to re-store.
3. now shall walk, In him at-tain the prize.

Rom 6:3, 4
Scottish Translations and Paraphrases, 1781, alt.

William Croft, 1678–1727

368 Waters of Love

FINLANDIA 10 10 10 10 with Refrain

1. Wa-ters of love, God's pow-er now de-clare;___
2. God calls us to the foun-tain of re-birth,___
3. Joined to the Church, formed by God's ho-ly hand,___

1. Born to new life, di-vin-i-ty we share.___
2. And dig-ni-fies all crea-tures with new worth;___
3. Each one is freed to fol-low God's com-mand.___

1. Fa-ther and Son and Ho-ly Spir-it, come,___
2. And by the Spir-it's ac-tion in the soul,___
3. Love and as-sur-ance give, all you who guide,___

1. Bring-ing the light of faith that Je-sus won.___
2. God lifts us up by love and makes us whole.___
3. And bring this new-born Chris-tian to God's side.___

Most gra-cious God, your glo-ry ev-er show___

When-ev-er these re-deem-ing wa-ters flow.___

Rose Weber
Text © 1976, WLP

Jean Sibelius, 1865–1957

369 I've Just Come from the Fountain

I've just come from the foun-tain, I've just come from the foun-tain,

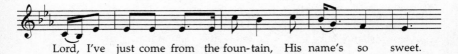

Lord, I've just come from the foun-tain, His name's so sweet.

1. O broth-ers, I love Je-sus, O broth-ers, I love Je-sus,
2. O sis-ters, I love Je-sus, O sis-ters, I love Je-sus,
3. Been drink-ing from the foun-tain, Been drink-ing from the foun-tain,

1. O broth-ers, I love Je-sus,
2. O sis-ters, I love Je-sus, His name's so sweet.
3. Been drink-ing from the foun-tain,

African-American

A Living Hope 370
PACIFICA 87 87 87

1. Bless the Fa-ther of our Sav-ior, Sing in praise for
2. From the ris-en Christ's own prom-ise New birth draws its
3. From the wa-ter of sal-va-tion, We a-rise to

1. gra-cious love. We are washed in liv-ing wa-ter,
2. faith-ful life. Guard-ed for us, we in-her-it
3. prom-ised life. By the Spir-it's pow'r un-fad-ing,

1. Made new peo-ple in God's joy. Here we cel-e-
2. Liv-ing hope that con-quers death, Gifts of grace for
3. Look-ing toward the fi-nal age, We a-wait God's

1. brate God's mer-cy. Let us pray and be re-newed!
2. our sal-va-tion. Now re-joice and be re-freshed!
3. fi-nal king-dom. Now give thanks; we are re-ceived!

Michael W. Jones, alt.

John H. Olivier
Music © 1982, WLP

371 Church of God

CHURCH OF GOD   Irregular with Refrain

REFRAIN

Church of God, cho - sen peo - ple, sing your praise to God.

He has called you out of dark - ness in - to his mar - vel-ous light.

VERSES

1. Come, people of God, with joyful song; Praise God the Father of all.
   Baptized in Christ, reborn in him, Our hearts are filled with joy.
   He cleanses our sin, Renewing our lives.

2. The Church is built with living stones, With Christ as cornerstone.
   In him we trust who makes us one, Uniting us in love.
   We build on the rock Of faith in Christ.

3. As heirs of Christ, redeemed by love, We wait for his return;
   A priestly people off'ring praise To God, the source of hope.
   For Jesus is Lord, Our Savior and God.

4. As water springing from the rock Once brought God's people life,
   The living water giv'n by Christ Creates our lives anew.
   So come, you who thirst, To springs of new life.

5. We gather here to worship God, Our eucharist to share.
   We give God thanks and celebrate The myst'ry of this love;
   The Word is made flesh And given for us.

6. May fragrant smoke of incense rise To fill this house of prayer.
   May we who gather find true peace, God's presence filling our lives.
   Our hearts lift with praise, Our lips sing in joy.

7. The light of Christ has come to us, Dispelling all our fears.
   His light reveals the path of life; We follow him with joy.
   The glory of God, The light of the world.

Pamela Stotter

Margaret Daly
Text and music © 1980, ICEL

Sweet, Sweet Spirit 372

SWEET, SWEET SPIRIT   9 11 9 11 with Refrain

1. There's a sweet, sweet Spir - it in this place,_____
2. There are bless - ings you can - not re - ceive_____
3. If you say he saved you from your sin,_____

1. And I know that it's the Spir - it of__ the Lord;_____
2. Till you know him in his full - ness and__ be - lieve;_____
3. Now you're weak, you're bound, and can - not en - ter in,_____

1. There are sweet ex - pres - sions on each face,_____
2. You're the one to prof - it when you say,_____
3. You can make it right if you will yield;_____

1. And I know they feel the pres - ence of__ the Lord.
2. "I am going to walk with Je - sus all__ the way."_____
3. You'll en - joy the Ho - ly Spir - it that__ we feel._____

Sweet Ho - ly Spir - it, sweet heav - en - ly Dove,

Stay right here with__ us, fill - ing us with__ your love;

And for these bless - ings we lift our hearts in

praise._____ With - out a doubt we'll know__ that we have

been re - vived__ When we shall leave this place._____

Doris Akers
Text and music © 1962, Manna Music, Inc.

373 Creating Spirit, Holy Lord

PUER NOBIS LM

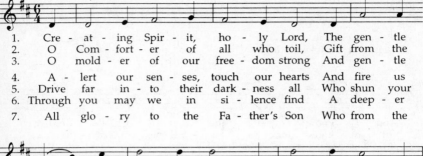

1. Cre - at - ing Spir - it, ho - ly Lord, The gen - tle
2. O Com - fort - er of all who toil, Gift from the
3. O mold - er of our free - dom strong And gen - tle
4. A - lert our sen - ses, touch our hearts And fire us
5. Drive far in - to their dark - ness all Who shun your
6. Through you may we in si - lence find A deep - er
7. All glo - ry to the Fa - ther's Son Who from the

1. breeze, the might - y wind, With warmth and pow'r and
2. foun - tain - head of light, O Spir - it of all
3. fin - ger of God's hand, Come, lead our words with -
4. with your gift of love, That proud and fall - en,
5. liv - ing gifts of peace; Pro - tect us deep with -
6. knowl - edge of God's Son; Through you we know the
7. grave has ris'n on high; His Spir - it makes us

1. gra - cious - ness In grace re - fash - ion heart and mind.
2. love and fire, A - noint - ing chri - sm of all might.
3. in the paths That wis - dom in your love has planned.
4. weak and blind, Your light may lead us from a - bove.
5. in your calm And keep us safe till dan - gers cease.
6. Fa - ther's love And live by faith till night is gone.
7. sing with joy And praise our God e - ter - nal - ly.

Veni, Creator Spiritus
Tr. by Ralph Wright
Tr. © 1989, GIA

Adapt. by Michael Praetorius, 1571–1621

374 Litany for the Holy Eucharist

REFRAIN

Ag - nus De - i, mi - se - re - re no - bis.
or: Ho - ly Lamb of God, in your mer - cy, hear us.

Alan J. Hommerding
Text (English) and music © 1994, WLP

Here around This Table Gathered 375

ADORO TE   75 75 65 65   with Refrain

REFRAIN

Here a-round this ta-ble gath-ered, we re-joice to share your feast,

faith-ful friend of saint and sin-ner, Christ, our gra-cious host!

VERSES

1. Let the hun-gry come to me, Let the poor be fed.
2. I my-self am liv-ing bread; Feed on me and live.
3. Here a-mong you shall I dwell, Mak-ing all things new.
4. Nour-ished by the Word of God, Now we eat the bread.
5. Man-y grains be-come one loaf, Man-y grapes, the wine.
6. Ris-en Sav-ior, walk with us, Lead us by the hand.

1. Let the thirst-y come and drink, Share my wine and bread.
2. In this cup, my blood for you; Drink the wine I give.
3. You shall be my ver-y own, I, your God-with-you.
4. With the gift of God's own life Hun-gry hearts are fed.
5. So shall we one bod-y be, Who to-geth-er dine.
6. Heal our blind-ed eyes and hearts, Help us un-der-stand.

1. Though you have no mon-ey, Come to me and eat.
2. All who eat my bod-y, All who drink my blood
3. Blest are you in-vit-ed To my wed-ding feast.
4. Man-na in the des-ert, In our dark-est night!
5. As the bread is bro-ken, As the wine is shared:
6. Lord make known your pres-ence At this ta-ble blest.

To Refrain

1. Drink the cup I of-fer; Feed on fin-est wheat!
2. Shall have joy for-ev-er, Share the life of God.
3. You shall live for-ev-er, All your joys in-creased.
4. Food for pil-grim peo-ple, Pledge of glo-ry bright!
5. So must we be giv-en, Car-ing as Christ cared.
6. Stay with us for-ev-er, God, our host and guest!

Delores Dufner

Ref.: Terri Nehl and Christine Manderfeld
Vss.: Chant, Mode V
Text and music © 1985, 1989, 1996, Sisters of St. Benedict

376 Shepherd of Souls, Refresh and Bless

ST. AGNES CM

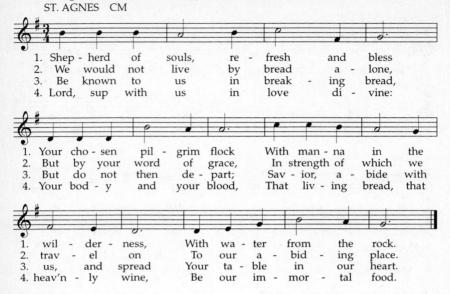

1. Shep - herd of souls, re - fresh and bless
2. We would not live by bread a - lone,
3. Be known to us in break - ing bread,
4. Lord, sup with us in love di - vine:

1. Your cho - sen pil - grim flock With man - na in the
2. But by your word of grace, In strength of which we
3. But do not then de - part; Sav - ior, a - bide with
4. Your bod - y and your blood, That liv - ing bread, that

1. wil - der - ness, With wa - ter from the rock.
2. trav - el on To our a - bid - ing place.
3. us, and spread Your ta - ble in our heart.
4. heav'n - ly wine, Be our im - mor - tal food.

James Montgomery, 1771–1854, alt.

John B. Dykes, 1823–1876

377 Father, We Thank Thee, Who Hast Planted

RENDEZ À DIEU 98 98 D

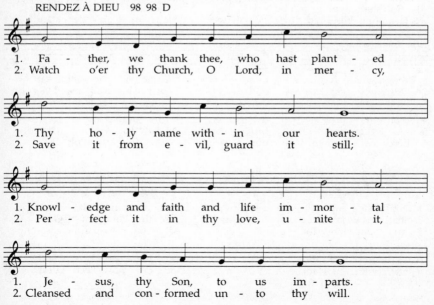

1. Fa - ther, we thank thee, who hast plant - ed
2. Watch o'er thy Church, O Lord, in mer - cy,

1. Thy ho - ly name with - in our hearts.
2. Save it from e - vil, guard it still;

1. Knowl - edge and faith and life im - mor - tal
2. Per - fect it in thy love, u - nite it,

1. Je - sus, thy Son, to us im - parts.
2. Cleansed and con - formed un - to thy will.

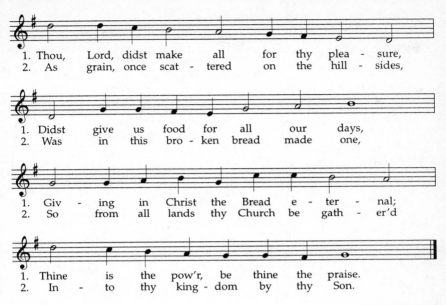

1. Thou, Lord, didst make all for thy plea - sure,
2. As grain, once scat - tered on the hill - sides,

1. Didst give us food for all our days,
2. Was in this bro - ken bread made one,

1. Giv - ing in Christ the Bread e - ter - nal;
2. So from all lands thy Church be gath - er'd

1. Thine is the pow'r, be thine the praise.
2. In - to thy king - dom by thy Son.

Didache, c. 110
Tr. by F. Bland Tucker, 1895–1984, alt.
Text © The Church Pension Fund

Genevan Psalter, 1551
Attr. to Louis Bourgeois, c. 1510–1561

Let Us Break Bread Together 378
LET US BREAK BREAD TOGETHER   10 10 with Refrain

1. Let us break bread to - geth - er on our knees;
2. Let us drink wine to - geth - er on our knees;
3. Let us praise God to - geth - er on our knees;

1. Let us break bread to - geth - er on our knees.
2. Let us drink wine to - geth - er on our knees.
3. Let us praise God to - geth - er on our knees.

When I fall on my knees, with my face to the ris - ing

sun, O Lord, have mer - cy on me.

African-American

379 I Am the Bread of Life

BREAD OF LIFE   Irregular with Refrain

1. I am the bread of life. You who
2. The bread that I will give is my
3. Un - less you eat of the
4. I am the res - ur - rec - tion,
5. Yes, Lord, I be - lieve that

1. come to me shall not hun - ger; and who be -
2. flesh for the life of the world, and if you
3. flesh of the Son of Man and
4. I am the life. If you be -
5. you are the Christ, the

1. lieve in me shall not thirst. No one can come to
2. eat of this bread, you shall live for -
3. drink of his blood, and drink of his
4. lieve in me, ev - en though you
5. Son of God, who have

1. me un - less the Fa - ther beck - ons.
2. ev - er, you shall live for - ev - er.
3. blood, you shall not have life with - in you.
4. die, you shall live for - ev - er.
5. come in - to the world.

And I will raise you up, and I will

raise you up, and I will raise you

up on the last day.

Jn 6

Suzanne Toolan
Text and music © 1971, 1982, 1986, GIA

We Remember 380

REFRAIN

We re-mem-ber how you loved us_____ to your death,

and still we cel-e-brate, for you are with us here;_____

And we be-lieve_ that we will see you_____ when you come

in your glo-ry, Lord._____ We re-mem-ber,_____ we

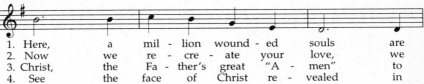

cel-e-brate, we be-lieve._____

VERSES

1. Here, a mil - lion wound - ed souls are
2. Now we re - cre - ate your love, we
3. Christ, the Fa - ther's great "A - men" to
4. See the face of Christ re - vealed in

1. yearn-ing just to touch you and be healed;_____
2. bring the bread and wine to share a meal;_____
3. all the hopes and dreams of ev - 'ry heart;_____
4. ev - 'ry per - son stand - ing by your side;_____

To Refrain

1. Gath - er all your peo - ple and hold them to your heart.
2. Sign of grace and mer - cy, the pres - ence of the Lord.
3. Peace be - yond all tell - ing and free - dom from all fear.
4. Gift to one an - oth - er and tem - ples of your love.

Marty Haugen
Text and music © 1980, GIA

381 Eucharistic Litany

REFRAIN

Cantor/All

Bread of life, sav - ing cup, feed our hun - gry souls with

you. Nour - ish us, strength-en us; by your pres - ence in this

Last time to Final — 3 — *To Verses* | *Final*

meal may we be one. one.

Cantor

All — 3 —

By your pres - ence in this meal may we be one.

VERSES

Cantor *All*

1. Be - hold the Lamb of God,
2. Be - hold the meal of heav'n,
3. Be - hold the way of truth,
4. Be - hold the cov - e - nant,

Bread of life, sav - ing cup,

Cantor *All*

1. Who takes a - way our sins,
2. A feast for rich and poor,
3. Our source of hope and peace,
4. The sac - ri - fice of Love,

Nour - ish us, strength - en us.

Cantor *All*

1. We're blest and called to dine,
2. O Christ, our gra - cious host,
3. How great a gift of love,
4. The cup of last - ing life,

Bread of life, sav - ing cup,

Cantor *All* *To Refrain*

1. At the ban - quet of the Lord.
2. At the ban - quet of the Lord.
3. Our__ trea - sure and our joy.
4. Our__ pro - mise of your love.

Nour - ish us, strength - en us.

Paul Hillebrand
Text and music © 1994, WLP

Take and Eat 382

10 10 10 10 with Refrain

REFRAIN

Cantor/All

Take and eat; take and eat; this is my bod-y giv-en up for you. Take and drink; take and drink: this is my blood giv-en up for you.

VERSES

Cantor

1. I am the Word that spoke and light was made;
2. I am the way that leads the ex-ile home;
3. I am the Lamb that takes a-way your sin;
4. I am the cor-ner-stone that God has laid;
5. I am the light that came in-to the world;
6. I am the first and last, the Liv-ing One;

1. I am the seed that died to be re-born;
2. I am the truth that sets the cap-tive free;
3. I am the gate that guards you night and day;
4. A cho-sen stone and pre-cious in his eyes;
5. I am the light that dark-ness can-not hide;
6. I am the Lord who died that you might live;

1. I am the bread that comes from heav'n a-bove;
2. I am the life that rais-es up the dead;
3. You are my flock: you know your shep-herd's voice;
4. You are God's dwell-ing place, on me you rest;
5. I am the morn-ing star that nev-er sets;
6. I am the bride-groom, this my wed-ding song;

To Refrain

1. I am the vine that fills your cup with joy.
2. I am your peace, true peace my gift to you.
3. You are my own: your ran-som is my blood.
4. Like liv-ing stones, a tem-ple for God's praise.
5. Lift up your face, in you my light will shine.
6. You are my bride, come to the mar-riage feast.

Text (vss.) James Quinn
Text (ref.) J. Michael Joncas
Text (vss.) © 1989, James Quinn, Selah Publishing Co., Inc., North American agent

J. Michael Joncas
Text (ref.) and music © 1989, GIA

REFRAIN

Eat this bread, drink this cup, come to me and nev-er be hun-gry.

Eat this bread, drink this cup, trust in me and you will not thirst.

VERSES

1. I am the bread of life, the true bread sent from the Father.

2. Your ancestors ate manna in the desert, but this is the bread come down from heaven.

3. Eat my flesh and drink my blood, and I will raise you up on the last day.

4. Anyone who eats this bread will live forever.

5. If you believe and eat this bread, you will have eternal life.

Jn 6:35
Adapt. by Robert J. Batastini and the Taizé Community

Jacques Berthier, 1923–1994
Text and music © 1984, Les Presses de Taizé
Pub. by GIA

384 In the Breaking of the Bread

1. In the walk-ing on the road, we saw him.
2. We set out to find his friends to tell them.
3. But then we be-came a fraid with-out him.
4. We ran out in-to the street to tell them,

1. In the tell-ing of our hopes, we saw him.
2. We went to Je-ru-sa-lem to tell them;
3. In the dark-ened room we stayed with-out him,
4. Ev-'ry-one that we could meet, to tell them,

1. In the burn-ing of our hearts, we saw the
2. And with joy we told them, "We have seen the
3. Wait-ing for the one he said that he would
4. "God has raised him up and we have seen the

1. Lord.
2. Lord!"
3. send.
4. Lord!"

At the meal he took the
And as we were speak-ing,
Then the Spir-it of the
We took bread as he had

1. bread and then he blessed it, broke it,
2. there he stood a - mong us, blessed us,
3. Lord came down up - on us, fill - ing us,
4. done and then we blessed it, broke it,

1. of - fered it. In the break-ing of the bread,
2. said to us, "Now my peace I leave with you."
3. chang - ing us, Giv - ing us the strength to say:
4. of - fered it. In the break-ing of the bread,

Last time to Final

We saw him! Sud-den-ly our eyes were o - pened,

And we knew he was a - live!

Final

There with-in our midst was Je - sus, And we knew he was a-

live! In the break - ing of the bread,

He is here with us a - gain. And we know he is a-

live! Al - le - lu - ia!

Al - le - lu - ia, al - le - lu - ia! Al - le - lu - ia, al - le -

lu - ia! Al - le - lu - ia!

Michael Ward
Text and music © 1988, WLP

385 This Is My Body

MADSEN 87 87 with Refrain

This is my bod - y giv - en for your free - dom.

This is my blood which was shed for all my peo - ple.

Take, all, and eat, till the day of my re - turn.

1. On your jour - ney to the king - dom You will
2. Come to me, all you, who la - bor Come, and
3. I am Way and Truth and Life, come Fol - low
4. Hear, my flock, now hear me call - ing For I

1. find the strength you need At this ta - ble
2. I will give you rest. Join your fam - 'ly
3. me, be - lieve and live. Know that I am
4. know you all by name. Come with me, the

D.C.

1. of re - mem - brance Of my ris - ing from the dead.
2. at my ban - quet; Food and drink are all the best.
3. al - ways with you, Giv - ing all I have to give.
4. bless - ed shep - herd, To the new Je - ru - sa - lem.

Anon., rev. by Charles G. Frischmann
Text © 1968, 1973, 1976, WLP

Anon.

386 O Blessed Savior

REFRAIN

O bless - ed Sav - ior, now be - hold the grate - ful

gath - 'ring of your fold in joy - ful med - i -

ta - tion. Our thirst-ing souls, our hun-gry

hearts now seek the food which life im-parts,

the bread__ of our__ sal - va - tion.

VERSES

Cantor

1. O Lord, our God, the source of love,
2. To us you say, "Take this and eat!"
3. O lov - ing God, the source of life,
4. As once you fed the mul - ti - tude
5. O Lord, you know our hu - man plight;

1. All good gifts come__ from you,_____
2. Now yearn - ing hearts__ are fed;_____
3. You are the Ho - ly One_____
4. When loaves and fish__ were few,_____
5. You bid us come__ to you;_____

1. Who once sent man - na from__ a - bove
2. Come, fill us with the best__ of wheat;
3. Who gives to us the sav - ing cup,
4. O feed us now with bread__ and wine
5. Your yoke is mild, your bur - den light;

To Refrain

1. To feed your cho - sen few._____
2. Give us the liv - ing bread._____
3. Je - sus, your on - ly Son._____
4. That makes us one__ in you._____
5. Re - fresh our souls__ a - new._____

Omer Westendorf
Text © 1990, Omer Westendorf

Jerry R. Brubaker
Music © 1990, Jerry R. Brubaker, dist. by WLP

387 Take Our Bread

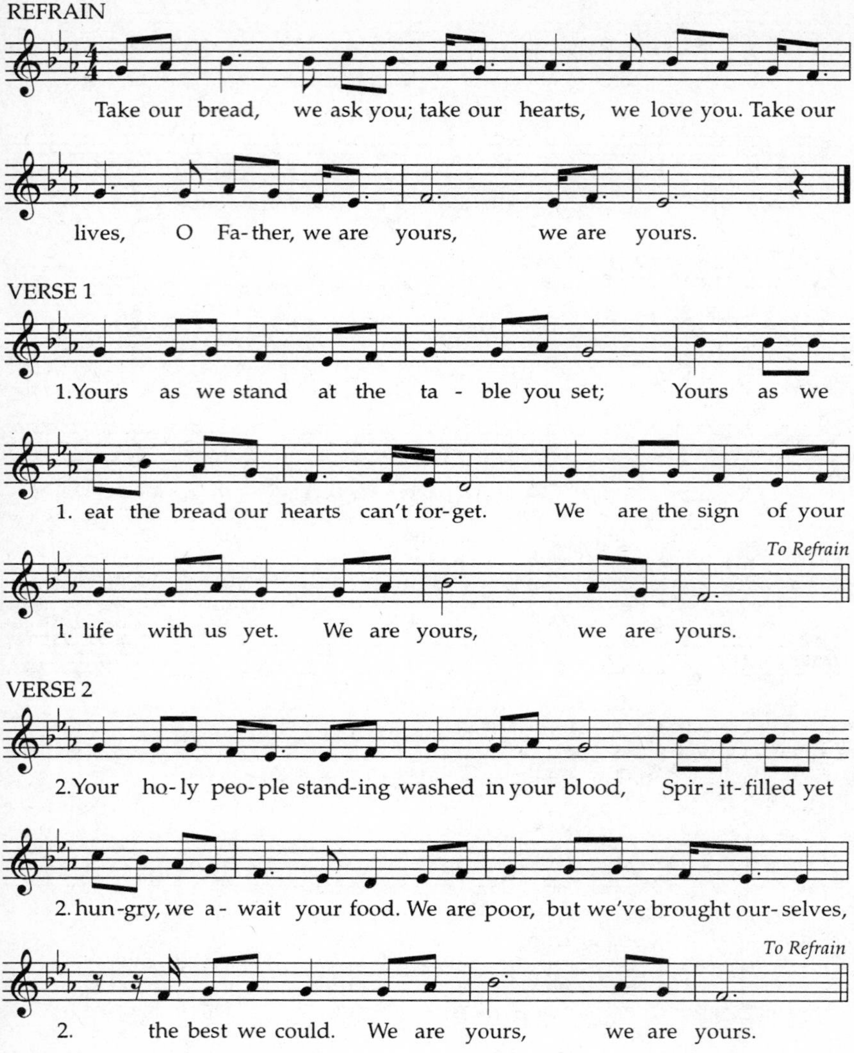

REFRAIN

Take our bread, we ask you; take our hearts, we love you. Take our lives, O Fa-ther, we are yours, we are yours.

VERSE 1

1. Yours as we stand at the ta-ble you set; Yours as we eat the bread our hearts can't for-get. We are the sign of your life with us yet. We are yours, we are yours.

To Refrain

VERSE 2

2. Your ho-ly peo-ple stand-ing washed in your blood, Spir-it-filled yet hun-gry, we a-wait your food. We are poor, but we've brought our-selves, the best we could. We are yours, we are yours.

To Refrain

Joe Wise
Text and music © 1967, 1968, Joe Wise, dist. by GIA

388 Remember Me

REFRAIN

Cantor/All

Re-mem-ber me, re-mem-ber me, when you

eat this bread, when you drink this cup, re - mem - ber me,

re - mem - ber me un - til I come a - gain.

VERSES

Cantor/Choir

1. When you feed those in need, re - mem-ber me, when you
2. When you quench thirst-y souls, re - mem-ber me, when you
3. When you seek out the truth, re - mem-ber me, when you

4. When you shine in the dark, re - mem-ber me, when you
5. When you gath - er in peace, re - mem-ber me, when you
6. When you hon - or the earth, re - mem-ber me, when you

7. When you lift the op-pressed, re - mem-ber me, when you
8. When you care for the sick, re - mem-ber me, when you
9. When you dance with the lame, re - mem-ber me, when you

10. When you cher - ish your faith, re - mem-ber me, when you

1. come to the ta - ble and you share with the world, re-mem-ber me,
2. drink of the king-dom and you pour out your life, re-mem-ber me,
3. speak what is wise, and you walk in my way, re-mem-ber me,

4. search out the lost, and you wel-come them home, re-mem-ber me,
5. pray in the Spir-it and you lift up your voice, re-mem-ber me,
6. join with cre - a - tion and you tend my gifts, re-mem-ber me,

7. chal - lenge the might-y and you give to the poor, re-mem-ber me,
8. com - fort the dy - ing and you ease their pain, re-mem-ber me,
9. sing with the mute, and you see with the blind, re-mem-ber me,

10. hope for my com-ing and you trea - sure love, re-mem-ber me,

To Refrain

1. be my liv - ing bread, un - til I come a - gain.
2. be my sav - ing cup, un - til I come a - gain.
3. be my shin - ing word, un - til I come a - gain.

4. be my light for the world, un - til I come a - gain.
5. be my song of joy, un - til I come a - gain.
6. be my gen - tle hand, un - til I come a - gain.

7. be my jus - tice for all, un - til I come a - gain.
8. be my heal - ing balm, un - til I come a - gain.
9. be my ten - der touch, un - til I come a - gain.

10. be my pres-ence ev-'ry-where, un - til I come a - gain.

Alan J. Hommerding
Text and music © 1992, WLP

389 Do This in Remembrance of Me

REMEMBRANCE   87 87 with Refrain

1. Lord, we gath - er 'round your ta - ble, First to hear your
2. Gath - er now, O Ad - am's chil - dren; Come and take the
3. Je - sus told the twelve a - pos - tles: I will give you
4. Drink this cup of your sal - va - tion, Of my blood poured
5. At this ta - ble I will give you Food that none could

1. ho - ly Word; Then par - take with one an - oth - er
2. sa - cred bread. Now we join in cel - e - bra - tion
3. liv - ing bread. Take and eat, this is my bod - y.
4. out for you. Do for those of ev - 'ry na - tion
5. give be - fore. Take of this and I can prom - ise

1. Of the eu - cha - ris - tic food.
2. Of the words that Je - sus said:
3. Then he turned to them and said: Do this in re -
4. What your Lord has done for you.
5. You will live for - ev - er - more.

mem - brance of me; Do this in re - mem - brance of me.

Lou Fortunate
Text and music © 1972, WLP

390 I Come with Joy

LAND OF REST   CM

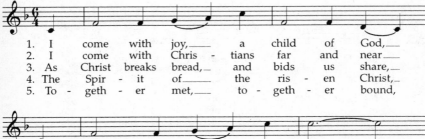

1. I come with joy,___ a child of God,___
2. I come with Chris - tians far and near___
3. As Christ breaks bread,___ and bids us share,___
4. The Spir - it of___ the ris - en Christ,___
5. To - geth - er met,___ to - geth - er bound,

1. For - giv - en, loved,___ and free,_____
2. To find, as all___ are fed,_____
3. Each proud di - vi - sion ends._____
4. Un - seen but ev - er near_____
5. By all that God___ has done,_____

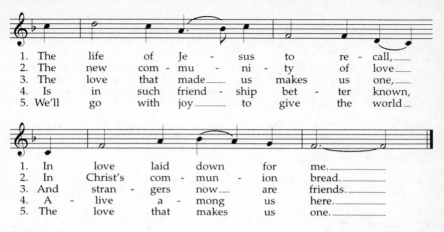

1. The life of Je - sus to re - call,___
2. The new com - mu - ni - ty of love__
3. The love that made__ us makes us one,__
4. Is in such friend - ship bet - ter known,
5. We'll go with joy___ to give the world__

1. In love laid down for me._____
2. In Christ's com - mun - ion bread._____
3. And stran - gers now__ are friends._____
4. A - live a - mong us here._____
5. The love that makes us one._____

Brian Wren
Text © 1971, 1995, Hope Publishing Co.

American folk hymn

At the Table of the World 391

1. At the ta - ble of the world, some have plen- ty, some have none.
2. At the ta - ble of the world, some have hon- or, some have scorn.
3. Set the ta - ble of our God in the Church and in the world,

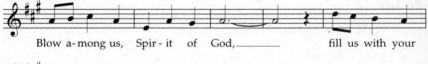

1. At the ta - ble of our God, all are plen - ti - ful-ly fed.
2. At the ta - ble of our God, all are wel- comed and ac- claimed.
3. Till the chil-dren, fed and loved, taste and see that life is good.

Blow a- mong us, Spir - it of God,___ fill us with your

cour- age and care!___ Hur- ri- cane and Breath,

take us on a jour-ney of love!___

Brian Wren
Text © 1989, Hope Publishing Co.

Carl Johengen
Music © 1993, WLP

392 Let All Mortal Flesh Keep Silence

PICARDY 87 87 87

1. Let all mor-tal flesh keep si-lence, And with fear and
2. King of kings, yet born of Ma-ry, As of old on
3. Rank on rank, the host of heav-en Spreads its van-guard
4. At his feet the six-wing'd ser-aph, Cher-u-bim with

1. trem-bling stand; Pon-der noth-ing earth-ly-mind-ed,
2. earth he stood; Lord of lords in hu-man ves-ture,
3. on the way, As the light of light de-scend-ed
4. sleep-less eye, Veil their fac-es to the Pres-ence,

1. For with bless-ing in his hand Christ, our God, to
2. In the bod-y and the blood He will give to
3. From the realms of end-less day, That the pow'rs of
4. As with cease-less voice they cry, "Al-le-lu-ia,

1. earth de-scend-ed, Our full hom-age to de-mand.
2. all the faith-ful His own self for heav'n-ly food.
3. hell may van-ish As the dark-ness clears a-way.
4. al-le-lu-ia, Al-le-lu-ia, Lord most high!"

Cherubic hymn, Liturgy of St. James, 4th cent.
Tr. by Gerard Moultrie, 1829–1885

Traditional French carol, 17th cent.

393 Gather 'Round This Supper Table

NETTLETON 87 87 D

1. Gath-er 'round this sup-per ta-ble For the bread we need to-
2. Oh, how of-ten we have wished that We were there that ho-ly
3. Now that sup-per is re-peat-ed And the cov-e-nant we

1. day, For the Sav-ior wants to feed us Lest we
2. night, When the Lord taught his dis-ci-ples How to
3. seal, As we gath-er 'round the ta-ble And par-

1. per-ish on the way. Bright the cup and plate and
2. live in joy and light, When he broke the bread of
3. take of Je-sus' meal. In his name we come to-

1. can - dles, White the lin - en cloth that's spread. It's a
2. heav - en, When he blessed the cup of wine, When he
3. geth - er, In his hon - or sing our song, In his

1. feast that Je - sus of - fers; To a ban - quet we are led.
2. shared with the a - pos - tles, Of his love the liv - ing sign.
3. mem - 'ry ev - er of - fered As our life - time flows a - long.

Willard F. Jabusch
Text © 1977, WLP

Wyeth's *Repository of Sacred Music: Part Second,* 1813

O Lord, with Wondrous Mystery 394
ANDRIESSEN 86 86 88 86

1. O___ Lord, with won - drous mys - ter - y You___
2. You___ are the same, our Christ and Lord, Who___

1. take our___ bread and wine, And___ make of these two
2. blessed the___ sup - per room; You___ are the God who

1. hum - ble things Your - self, our___ Lord di - vine.
2. died and rose Tri - umph - ant___ from the tomb.

1. Our___ wheat and drink be - come our Light, Our___
2. This___ bread bears your di - vin - i - ty, This___

1. al - tar bears your awe - some might; O Lord, we thank you
2. cup con - tains in - fin - i - ty; The mys - t'ry fills our

1. for the gift That lies be - fore our sight.
2. souls with love, O___ Ho - ly Maj - es - ty.

Michael Gannon
Text © 1955, WLP

Hendrik F. Andriessen, 1892–1981
Music reprinted by permission of the Hendrik F. Andriessen estate

395 See Us, Lord, about Your Altar

DRAKES BOUGHTON   87 87

1. See us, Lord, a - bout your al - tar,
2. Hear our prayers, O lov - ing Fa - ther,
3. Wheat and grape con - tain the mean - ing:
4. Hear us yet: so much is need - ful
5. Mem - bers of his Mys - tic Bod - y,

1. Though so man - y, we are one;
2. Hear in them your Son, our Lord;
3. Food and drink he is to all;
4. In our frail, dis - or - dered life;
5. Now we know our prayer is heard,

1. Man - y souls by love u - nit - ed
2. Hear him speak our love and wor - ship,
3. One in Christ, we come a - dor - ing,
4. Stay with us and tend our weak - ness,
5. Heard by you be - cause your chil - dren

1. In the heart of Christ, your Son.
2. As we sing with one ac - cord.
3. Gath - ered by his lov - ing call.
4. Till that day of no more strife.
5. Have re - ceived th'e - ter - nal Word.

John Greally
Text used by permission of British Province of the Society of Jesus

Edward W. Elgar, 1857–1934
Music used by permission of Burns & Oates, Ltd.

How Blest Are We 396

JESU, DULCIS MEMORIA LM

1. How blest are we who share this bread,
2. O Lord, we eat this bread of life,
3. The He - brews fed on heav'n - ly food,
4. This ban - quet brings e - ter - nal life,
5. Give thanks to Je - sus, sav - ing Lord,
6. Lord Je - sus Christ, we beg your grace;
7. Give praise to God for he is good,

1. The flesh and blood of Christ our Lord.
2. The bread you give to faith - ful ones.
3. The man - na gath - ered in the wild.
4. A life of love and u - ni - ty.
5. Our Pas - chal Vic - tim, pres - ent here,
6. We turn to you, our hope and guide.
7. To him who made us like him - self,

1. May love u - nite us grate - ful - ly,____
2. The peace of Christ your Son is ours,____
3. Your God - sent bread we now re - ceive,____
4. For we now live in Je - sus Christ____
5. Who shares the Fa - ther's love with us;____
6. This bread u - nites us all to you,____
7. To Christ, his Son, who set us free,____

1. God's cho - sen ones who live in peace.
2. U - nit - ing us who do your will.
3. Our dai - ly food of last - ing strength.
4. And share with him his ris - en might.
5. And makes us wor - thy for our God.
6. A - wait - ing per - fect u - ni - ty.
7. To God's great Gift, our Source of life. A - men.____

James G. McMullen, 1936–1989
Text used by permission of Summy-Birchard Music

Chant, Mode I

397 Humbly We Adore You/Adoro Te Devote

ADORO TE DEVOTE   65 65 D

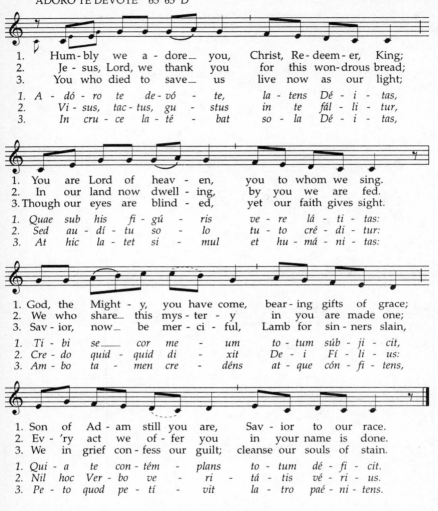

1. Hum-bly we a-dore you, Christ, Re-deem-er, King;
2. Je-sus, Lord, we thank you for this won-drous bread;
3. You who died to save us live now as our light;

1. A - dó - ro te de-vó - te, la - tens Dé - i - tas,
2. Vi - sus, tac-tus, gu - stus in te fál - li - tur,
3. In cru - ce la - té - bat so - la Dé - i - tas,

1. You are Lord of heav - en, you to whom we sing.
2. In our land now dwell - ing, by you we are fed.
3. Though our eyes are blind - ed, yet our faith gives sight.

1. Quae sub his fi - gú - ris ve - re lá - ti - tas:
2. Sed au - dí - tu so - lo tu - to cré - di - tur:
3. At hic la - tet si - mul et hu - má - ni - tas:

1. God, the Might - y, you have come, bear-ing gifts of grace;
2. We who share this mys - ter - y in you are made one;
3. Sav - ior, now be mer - ci - ful, Lamb for sin - ners slain,

1. Ti - bi se cor me - um to - tum súb - ji - cit,
2. Cre - do quid - quid di - xit De - i Fí - li - us:
3. Am - bo ta - men cre - déns at - que cón - fi - tens,

1. Son of Ad - am still you are, Sav - ior to our race.
2. Ev - 'ry act we of - fer you in your name is done.
3. We in grief con - fess our guilt; cleanse our souls of stain.

1. Qui - a te con - tém - plans to - tum dé - fi - cit.
2. Nil hoc Ver - bo ve - ri - tá - tis vé - ri - us.
3. Pe - to quod pe - tí - vit la - tro paé - ni - tens.

4. Christ, our God and brother, hear our humble plea;
   By this holy banquet grant us unity.
   Make us one in loving you, one in mind and heart,
   Till in heaven we are yours, never more to part.

5. Hail, O Word Incarnate, born from Mary's womb;
   Hail, O Strength immortal, risen from the tomb.
   Share with us your victory, Savior ever blest:
   Live more fully in our hearts; be our constant guest.

6. Faith alone reveals here bread of Paradise;
   Faith alone may witness Jesus' sacrifice.
   Therefore, Lord, as once of old Thomas gained his sight,
   Now increase our feeble faith; shed your healing light.

7. Christ, at his last supper, breaking bread, decreed:
"This, my body, take and eat;" heav'nly food indeed!
Then he blessed the cup of wine; "take and drink," he said:
"From this chalice of my blood, soon for sinners shed."

8. Now with glad thanksgiving, praise Christ glorified;
He in us is present; we in him abide.
Members of his body, we in him are one;
Hail this sacred union, heav'n on earth begun!

4. *Plagas, sicut Thomas, non intúeor: Deum tamen meum te confíteor:*
Fac me tibi semper magis crédere, In te spem habére, te dilígere.

5. *O memoriále mortis Dómini, Panis vivus vitam praestans hómini,*
Praesta meae menti de te vívere, Et te illi semper dulce sápere.

6. *Pie pellicáne, Jesu Dómine, Me immúndum munda tuo sánguine,*
Cujus una stilla salvum fácere Totum mundum quit ab omni scélere.

7. *Jesu, quem velátum nunc adspício, Oro fiat illud quod tam sítio:*
Ut te reveláta cernens fácie, Visu sim beátus tuae glóriae.

Attr. Thomas Aquinas, c. 1225–1274   Chant, Mode V
Vss. 1–4: Tr. by Melvin Farrell, 1930–1986, Vss. 5–8: Tr. by Omer Westendorf
Tr. © 1955, 1961, 1964, WLP

What You Gave Us for Our Taking 398
TUA MUNERA FUERUNT   88 77

1. What you gave us for our tak-ing, Now as
2. These our gifts, by Christ made roy-al, Come from
3. May this bread and may this wine, then, Born of
4. So may foods that quench and nour-ish Change to

1. works of hu-man mak-ing Let us, Lord, give
2. hearts con-trite and loy-al; Take them, Fa-ther,
3. earth, be made di-vine, when They be-come Christ's
4. make the spir-it flour-ish, Pledge of heav-en's

1. back to you; Let us, Lord, give back to you.
2. with our love; Take them, Fa-ther, with our love.
3. sac-ri-fice; They be-come Christ's sac-ri-fice.
4. feast of joy, Pledge of heav-en's feast of joy.

Tua munera fuerunt   *Neues…Kirchen- und Hauss Gesang der…Tochter Sion*, Cologne, 1741
Tr. by John J. Ryan, 1893–1983, alt.

399 Draw Near

10 10 10 10 with Refrain

REFRAIN *Cantor/All*

Draw near, draw__ near! Take the bod - y
of your Lord. Draw near, draw__ near!
Drink the__ blood for you out-poured.

VERSES *Cantor*

1. Draw near and take the bod - y of your Lord,
2. Christ, our Re - deem - er, God's e - ter - nal Son,
3. Let us ap-proach with faith - ful hearts sin - cere,
4. With heav'n-ly bread makes those who hun - ger whole,

1. And drink the ho - ly blood for you out-poured:
2. Has by his cross and blood the vic - t'ry won:
3. And take the pledg - es of sal - va - tion here:
4. Gives liv - ing wa - ters to the thirst - ing soul:

1. Saved by his bod - y and his ho - ly blood, With
2. He gave his life for great-est and for least, Him -
3. Christ, who in this life all the saints de-fends, Gives
4. Judge of the na - tions, to whom all must bow, In

To Refrain

1. souls re-freshed we give our thanks to God.
2. self the of - f'ring and him - self the Priest.
3. all be - liev - ers life that nev - er ends.
4. this great feast of love is with us now.

Sancti, venite, Christi corpus sumite
7th cent. hymn, tr. by John M. Neale, 1818–1866, alt.

Steven R. Janco
Music © 1992, WLP

Taste and See 400

REFRAIN

Cantor/All

Taste and see, taste and see the good - ness
of the Lord._____ O taste and see, taste and
see the good - ness of the Lord,_____ of the Lord.

VERSES

Cantor

1. I will bless the Lord___ at all times;_____ __
2. Glo - ri - fy the Lord___ with__ me;_____ to -
3. Wor-ship__ the Lord,___ all you peo-ple;_____ __

1. praise_____ shall al - ways be on my lips._____ My
2. geth-er__ let us all_____ praise God's name._____ I
3. you'll__ want for noth-ing_____ if you ask._____ __

1. soul_____ shall glo-ry_____ in the Lord_____ for
2. called_____ the Lord___ who an - swered me;_____ from
3. Taste_____ and see__ that the Lord is good;_____ in

To Refrain

1. God_____ has been__ so good to me._____
2. all_____ my trou-bles I was set free._____
3. God_____ we need__ put all our trust._____

Ps 34

James E. Moore, Jr.
Text and music © 1983, GIA

401 Now We Remain

REFRAIN

We hold the death of the Lord deep in our hearts.____

Liv-ing, now we re - main with Je-sus, the Christ.____

VERSES

1. Once we were peo - ple a - fraid, lost in the
2. Some - thing which we have known, some-thing we've
3. He chose to give of him - self, be - came our
4. We are the pres - ence of God; this is our

1. night.____ Then by your cross we were saved;
2. touched,____ What we have seen with our eyes:
3. bread,____ Bro - ken that we might live;
4. call,____ Now to be - come bread and wine:

1.–3. To Refrain

1. Dead be - came liv - ing, life from your giv - ing.____
2. This we have heard, life - giv - ing Word.____
3. Love be - yond love, pain for our pain.____
4. Food for the hun - gry, life for the wea - ry,____

4.

To Refrain

4.__ For to live with the Lord, we must die with the Lord.____

2 Cor; 1 Jn; 2 Tm

David Haas
Text and music © 1983, GIA

Gift of Finest Wheat 402

BICENTENNIAL   CM with Refrain

You sat-is-fy the hun-gry heart With gift of fin-est wheat; Come, give to us, O— sav-ing Lord, The bread of life to eat.

1. As when the shep - herd calls his sheep, They
2. With joy - ful lips we sing to you Our
3. Is not the cup we bless and share The
4. The mys - t'ry of your pres - ence, Lord, No
5. You give your - self to us, O Lord; Then

1. know and heed his voice, So when you call your
2. praise and grat - i - tude, That you should count us
3. blood of Christ out- poured? Do not one cup, one
4. mor - tal tongue can tell: Whom all the world can -
5. self - less let us be, To serve each oth - er

D.C.

1. fam - 'ly, Lord, We fol - low and re - joice.
2. wor - thy, Lord, To share this heav'n- ly food.
3. loaf, de - clare Our one - ness in the Lord?
4. not con - tain Comes in our hearts to dwell.
5. in your name In truth and char - i - ty.

Omer Westendorf

Robert E. Kreutz, 1922–1996
Text and music © 1977, Archdiocese of Philadelphia

403 Give Thanks and Remember

REFRAIN

Give thanks and re - mem - ber;____ Here is a
liv - ing sign:____ That one man's dy - ing and
ris - ing be - comes our bread and wine.____

VERSES

1. As long____ as we are God's peo - ple And earth____ has
2. As long as we live for each oth - er,____ Plant- ing the
3. God tends____ the pines and the spar - rows, And knows us and

1. fruit____ to give,____ So long____ will God be our
2. words of the Son,____ So long____ will God be our
3. all____ our ways,____ And God is the source of our

To Refrain

1. Fa - ther; Thank God for all that lives.____
2. Fa - ther; Thank God for all he's done.____
3. life and love; Thank God with sim - ple praise.____

Jack Miffleton
Text and music © 1975, WLP

404 I Am the Bread of Life

REFRAIN

I am the bread of life, I am the bread of life; Who
comes to me shall not hun-ger, Who be-lieves in me shall not thirst.

VERSES

1. O God, my God, for you I long, for you my soul is athirst. All my being
pines for you, as parched ground for the rain.

2. In the sanctuary I come to you, to behold your glory and pow'r. To know your love is better than life; my lips shall speak your praise.

3. So will I bless you all my days, in pray'r I call on your name. My soul shall feast upon your love; my heart rejoices in you, my God.

4. For you, O God, have been my help; beneath your wings I dwell secure. My soul shall ever cling to you, and your right hand shall hold me fast.

Based on Psalm 63
Text (vss.) © 1975, Oxford University Press, from *English Praise*

Eugene Englert
Text (ref.) and music © 1982, 1985, WLP

One Communion of Love 405

REFRAIN

Je - sus, in this great sac - ra - ment, you nour - ish and strength-en our ho - li - ness, that we might walk in the light of one faith, and in one com - mun - ion of love.___ *To Verses*

Final
love.___ That we might walk in the light of one faith, and in one com - mun - ion of love.___

VERSES

1. Our Lord gave him - self as an un - blem-ished of - f'ring, a
2. When we eat this meal, we re - mem - ber Christ's pas - sion, and
3. We come then to you, to be fed at your ta - ble, that

To Refrain

1. most fit - ting gift for the glo - ry of God.___
2. share in his pow'r till the end of all time.___
3. we may all grow in the like - ness of Christ.___

James V. Marchionda
Text and music © 1995, WLP

406 We Bring, You Take

REFRAIN

We bring, you take, and bless,____ and break, and all____ are fed with wine____ and bread.

VERSES

1. The night you were betrayed, good friend and Lord, you ate with friends your people's freedom meal, and gave them bread, and shared a cup of wine, to show how you would give yourself for all.

2. Upon a shingly beach, beside the sea, you met your friends again and cooked a meal of bread and fish, to show yourself alive, when all the world declared you dead and gone.

3. And ev'ry time we share this bread and wine we taste and tell how all the world should be, and dream of freedom, fairness, food, and peace, and know that you are risen and alive.

4. We bring ourselves, and offer all we have. We bring our caring for our town and land. We bring out hope that ev'ry child be fed. We taste eternal life, and dwell in love.

Brian Wren
Text © 1989, Hope Publishing Co.

Carl Johengen
Music © 1995, WLP

407 At That First Eucharist

UNDE ET MEMORES   10 10 10 10 10 10

1. At that first eu - cha - rist be - fore you died,
2. For all your Church, O Lord, we in - ter - cede;
3. We pray for those who wan - der from the fold;
4. So, Lord, at length when sac - ra-ments shall cease,

1. O Lord, you prayed that all be one in you;
2. O make our lack of char - i - ty to cease;
3. O bring them back, good shep-herd of the sheep,
4. May we be one with all your Church a - bove,

1. At this our eu - cha - rist a - gain pre - side,
2. Draw us the near - er each to each, we plead,
3. Back to the faith which saints be - lieved of old,
4. One with your saints in one un - end - ing peace,

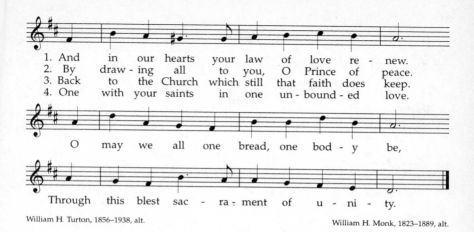

1. And in our hearts your law of love re - new.
2. By draw - ing all to you, O Prince of peace.
3. Back to the Church which still that faith does keep.
4. One with your saints in one un - bound - ed love.

O may we all one bread, one bod - y be,

Through this blest sac - ra - ment of u - ni - ty.

William H. Turton, 1856–1938, alt.

William H. Monk, 1823–1889, alt.

I Received the Living God 408

LIVING GOD   77 77 with Refrain

I re - ceived the liv - ing God, and my heart is full of joy.

I re - ceived the liv - ing God, and my heart is full of joy.

1. Je - sus said: I am the Bread Knead - ed
2. Je - sus said: I am the Vine, And my
3. Je - sus said: I am the Way; And my
4. Je - sus said: I am the Truth; If you
5. Je - sus said: I am the Life Far from

1. long to give you life; You who will par - take of
2. branch - es you shall be; Come and drink the sav - ing
3. Fa - ther longs for you; So I come to bring you
4. fol - low close to me, You will know me in your
5. whom no thing can grow, But re - ceive this bread and

D.C.

1. me Need not ev - er fear to die.
2. cup, Till the King - dom you shall see.
3. home To be one with us a - new.
4. heart, And my word shall make you free.
5. cup, And my Spir - it you shall know.

Anon.
Vs. 2: Alan J. Hommerding
Text (vs. 2) © 1994, WLP

Anon.

409 Amazing Grace
NEW BRITAIN   CM

1. A - maz - ing— grace! How sweet the sound, That
2. 'Twas grace that— taught my heart to fear, And
3. The Lord has— prom - ised good to me, His
4. Through man - y— dan - gers, toils, and snares, I
5. When we've been there ten thou - sand years, Bright

1. saved a— wretch like me!*___ I once— was lost, but
2. grace my— fears re - lieved.___ How pre - cious did that
3. word my— hope se - cures.___ He will— my— shield and
4. have al - read - y come.___ 'Tis grace— has— brought me
5. shin - ing— as the sun,___ We've no— less— days to

1. now___ am— found, Was blind, but— now I see!___
2. grace___ ap - pear, The hour I— first be - lieved!___
3. por - tion be As long as— life en - dures.___
4. safe___ thus far, And grace will— lead me home.___
5. sing___ God's praise Than when we'd first be - gun.___

Vss. 1–4: John Newton, 1725–1807, alt.
Vs. 5: Anon.

Traditional American melody

*This phrase has been restored to respect the author's original text.
If the community prefers a different version, they may sing it.

410 God's Holy Mountain We Ascend
WIE SCHÖN LEUCHTET   887 887 48 48

1. God's ho - ly moun - tain we as - cend, Where truth and love to -
2. Up - on God's moun - tain, fair - est heights, The cho - sen peo - ple
3. Christ leads us to his ho - ly hill Where he ful - fills the

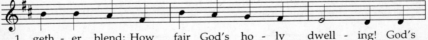

1. geth - er blend; How fair God's ho - ly dwell - ing! God's
2. God in - vites To en - ter here God's dwell - ing; Where
3. Fa - ther's will In per - fect ex - pi - a - tion. Here

1. peo - ple, we as - sem - ble here In ho - ly love and
2. once the loaves were mul - ti - plied, Where heav - en's man - na
3. we re - call that fes - tive meal That Christ his mys - t'ries

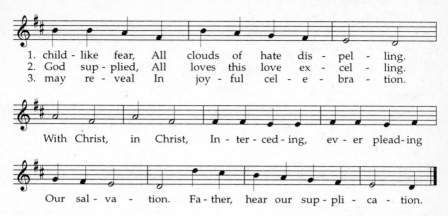

1. child - like fear, All clouds of hate dis - pel - ling.
2. God sup - plied, All loves this love ex - cel - ling.
3. may re - veal In joy - ful cel - e - bra - tion.

With Christ, in Christ, In - ter - ced - ing, ev - er plead-ing

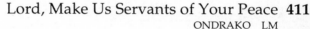

Our sal - va - tion. Fa - ther, hear our sup - pli - ca - tion.

Omer Westendorf
Text © 1964, WLP

Philipp Nicolai, 1556–1608

Lord, Make Us Servants of Your Peace 411
ONDRAKO LM

1. Lord, make us ser - vants of your peace; Where there is
2. Where all is doubt, may we sow faith; Where all is
3. Je - sus, our Lord, may we not seek To be con -
4. May we not look for love's re - turn, But seek to
5. Dy - ing, we live and are re - born Through death's dark

1. hate, may we sow love; Where there is hurt, may
2. gloom, may we sow hope; Where all is night, may
3. soled, but to con - sole, Nor look to un - der -
4. love un - self - ish - ly, For in our giv - ing
5. night to end - less day; Lord, make us ser - vants

1. we for - give; Where there is strife, may we make one.
2. we sow light; Where all is tears, may we sow joy.
3. stand-ing hearts, But look for hearts to un - der-stand.
4. we re - ceive, And in for - giv - ing are for-giv'n.
5. of your peace, To wake at last in heav-en's light.

James Quinn
Text © James Quinn, Selah Publishing Co., Inc., North American agent

Steven R. Janco
Music © 1997, WLP

412 Our Father, We Have Wandered

RECONCILIATION

PASSION CHORALE 76 76 D

1. Our Fa - ther, we have wan - dered And hid - den from your face;
2. And now at length dis - cern - ing The e - vil that we do,
3. O Lord of all the liv - ing, Both ban - ished and re - stored,

1. In fool - ish - ness have squan - dered Your leg - a - cy of grace.
2. Be - hold us Lord, re - turn - ing With hope and trust to you.
3. Com - pas - sion - ate, for - giv - ing And ev - er car - ing Lord,

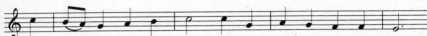

1. But now, in ex - ile dwell - ing, We rise with fear and shame,
2. In haste you come to meet us And home re - joic - ing bring,
3. Grant now that our trans - gress - ing, Our faith - less - ness may cease.

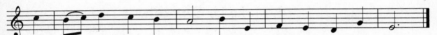

1. As dis - tant but com - pell - ing, We hear you call our name.
2. In glad - ness there to greet us With calf and robe and ring.
3. Stretch out your hand in bless - ing, In par - don and in peace.

Kevin Nichols
Text © 1980, ICEL

Hans Leo Hassler, 1564–1612

413 Hosea (Come Back to Me)

VERSES

1. Come back to me with all your heart.
2. The wil - der - ness will lead you
3. You shall sleep se - cure with peace;

1. Don't let fear keep us a - part.
2. To your heart where I will speak. In -
3. Faith - ful - ness will be your joy. *(To Refrain)*

1. Trees do bend, though straight and tall;
2. teg - ri - ty and jus - tice With

1. So must we____ to oth - ers' call.____
2. ten - der - ness____ — you shall know.____

REFRAIN

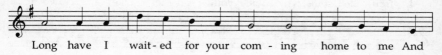

Long have I wait-ed for your com - ing home to me And

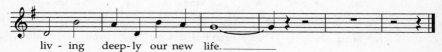

liv - ing deep-ly our new life.____

Hos 6:1, 3:3; 2:16, 21

Gregory Norbet

Text and music © 1972, 1980, The Benedictine Foundation of the State of Vermont, Inc.

For the Healing of the Nations 414

PICARDY 87 87 87

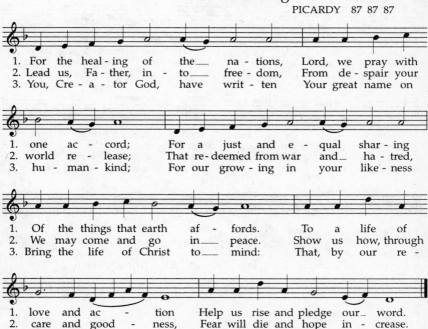

1. For the heal - ing of the__ na - tions, Lord, we pray with
2. Lead us, Fa - ther, in - to__ free - dom, From de - spair your
3. You, Cre - a - tor God, have writ - ten Your great name on

1. one ac - cord; For a just and e - qual shar - ing
2. world re - lease; That re - deemed from war and__ ha - tred,
3. hu - man - kind; For our grow - ing in your like - ness

1. Of the things that earth af - fords. To a life of
2. We may come and go in__ peace. Show us how, through
3. Bring the life of Christ to__ mind: That, by our re -

1. love and ac - tion Help us rise and pledge our__ word.
2. care and good - ness, Fear will die and hope in - crease.
3. sponse and ser - vice, Earth its des - ti - ny may find.

Fred Kaan
Text © 1968, Hope Publishing Co.

Traditional French carol, 17th cent.

415 There's a Wideness in God's Mercy

IN BABILONE 87 87 D

1. There's a___ wide-ness in God's mer-cy Like the_ wide-ness
2. There is___ wel-come for the_ sin-ner, And a___ prom-ised
3. For the_ love of God is___ broad-er Than the_ meas-ures
4. Trou-bled souls, why will you_ scat-ter Like a___ crowd of___

1. of___ the_ sea; There's a___ kind-ness in God's jus-tice,
2. grace made good; There is___ mer-cy with the___ Sav-ior;
3. of___ the_ mind; And the_ heart of the E-ter-nal
4. fright-ened sheep? Fool-ish_ hearts, why will you_ wan-der

1. Which is___ more than lib-er-ty. There is___ plen-ti-
2. There is___ heal-ing_ in___ Christ's blood. There is___ grace e-
3. Is most won-der-ful-ly___ kind. If our love were
4. From a___ love so_ true and_ deep? There is___ wel-come

1. ful re-demp-tion In the_ blood that has been shed;
2. nough for thou-sands Of new worlds as great as___ this;___
3. but more sim-ple, We would know the liv-ing_ Word;
4. for the sin-ner, And more grac-es for the_ good;

1. There is___ joy for all the___ mem-bers
2. There is___ room for fresh cre-a-tions
3. And our___ lives would be thanks-giv-ing
4. There is___ mer-cy with the___ Sav-ior;

1. In the_ sor-rows_ of___ the___ Head.
2. In that_ up-per_ home of___ bliss.
3. In the_ kind-ness_ of___ our___ Lord.
4. There is___ heal-ing_ in___ Christ's blood.

Fredrick W. Faber, 1814–1863, alt.

Traditional Dutch melody
Oude en Nieuwe Hollantse Boerenlities en Contradansen, c. 1710

Grant to Us, O Lord 416

REFRAIN

Cantor/All

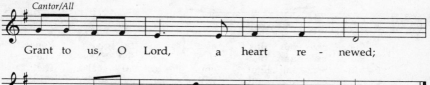

Grant to us, O Lord, a heart re - newed;

Re - cre - ate in us your own Spir - it, Lord!

VERSES

Cantor

1. Be - hold, the days are com - ing, says the Lord our God, When I will

To Refrain

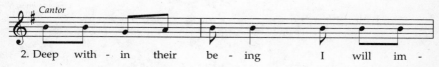

1. make a new cov - e - nant with the house of___ Is - ra - el.

Cantor

2. Deep with - in their be - ing I will im -

To Refrain

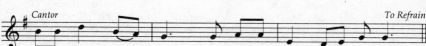

2. plant my___ Law; I will write it in their hearts.

Cantor   *To Refrain*

3. I will be their___ God, and they shall be my___ peo - ple.

Cantor

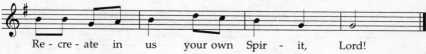

4. And for all their faults I will grant for - give-ness;

To Refrain

4. nev - er - more will I re - mem - ber their sins.

Jer 31:31–34

Lucien Deiss
Text and music © 1965, 1966, 1968, 1973, WLP

417 Forgive Our Sins as We Forgive

WALNUT HILL CM

1. "For - give our sins as___ we for - give," You___
2. How can your par - don___ reach and bless The___
3. In blaz - ing light your___ cross re - veals The___
4. Lord, cleanse the depths with - in our souls And___

1. taught us, Lord, to pray; But___ you a - lone can___
2. un - for - giv - ing heart That___ broods on wrongs and___
3. truth we dim - ly knew: What triv - ial debts are___
4. bid re - sent - ment cease; Then, bound to all in___

1. grant us grace To___ live the words we say.
2. will not let Old___ bit - ter - ness de - part?
3. owed to us; How___ great our debt to you!
4. bonds of love, Our___ lives will spread your peace.

Rosamond E. Herklots, 1905–1987, alt.
Text © 1969, Oxford University Press

Joel Martinson
Music © 1996, WLP

418 O Christ, the Healer, We Have Come

ERHALT UNS, HERR LM

1. O___ Christ, the___ heal - er,___ we have come To
2. From ev - 'ry___ ail - ment flesh en - dures, Our
3. In___ con - flicts that de - stroy our health We
4. Grant that we___ all, made one in faith, In

1. pray for health, to plead for friends. How can we___ fail___ to
2. bod - ies clam - or to be freed: Yet in our___ hearts we
3. rec - og - nize the world's dis - ease: Our com - mon life___ de -
4. your com - mu - ni - ty may find The whole - ness that, en -

1. be___ re - stored When reached by love that nev - er ends?
2. would con - fess That whole - ness is our deep - est need.
3. clares our ills. Is there no cure, O Christ, for these?
4. rich - ing us, Shall reach and pros - per hu - man - kind.

Fred Pratt Green
Text © 1969, Hope Publishing Co.

Geistliche Lieder, Wittenberg, 1543
Joseph Klug, c. 1500–c. 1552

REFRAIN

God full of mer-cy and God of com-pas-sion;

God, rich in kind-ness and faith-ful in your love;

God, who grants par-don to those who seek you,___ and who

treas-ure___ your liv-ing Word.

VERSES

Cantor   *All*

1. God of ten-der-ness and love:
2. Lord, your mer-cy fills the earth:
3. God, the Fa-ther of the poor: You, Lord, are my Sav-ior!
4. God, who calls us all to life:
5. God, the mys-ter-y of light:

Cantor   *All*

1. God, my cour-age and my strength:
2. Lord, you par-don all my sins:
3. God, pro-tec-tor of the weak: You,
4. God, who knows us by our name:
5. God, re-vealed through Christ, your Son:

Lord, are my love; re-veal your name to me; show me___

To Refrain

___ the light___ of your face.

Lucien Deiss
Text and music © 1972, 1975, Lucien Deiss
Pub. by WLP

420 There Is a Balm in Gilead

BALM IN GILEAD 76 76 with Refrain

There is a balm in Gil-e-ad To make the wound-ed whole;___

There is a balm in Gil-e-ad To heal the sin-sick soul.

1. Some - times I feel dis - cour - aged, And___
2. Don't___ ev - er feel dis - cour - aged, For___
3. If you can - not preach like Pe - ter, If you

1. think my work's in vain, But___ then the Ho - ly
2. Je - sus is your friend, And___ if you lack for
3. can - not pray like Paul, You can tell the love of

D.C.

1. Spir - it Re - vives my soul a - gain.___
2. knowl - edge, He'll not re - fuse to lend.___
3. Je - sus And say, "He died for all."___

Jer 8:22

African-American

421 Jesus, Heal Us

REFRAIN

Je - sus, heal us; we rest our cares with you.

VERSES

1. Hear my prayers, Yahweh, answer me, for I am poor and needy. Guard me.

2. Lord, you are forgiving, rich in faithful love for all who call upon you, Yahweh, hear my prayer.

3. All nations will adore you and glorify your name, for you are great and you do marv'lous deeds.

4. Teach me, Lord, your ways, that I may never stray; let my heart's one aim be to love your name.

5. I thank you, Lord, my God; I will glorify your name. Your faithful love is so great, you have rescued me.

Timothy R. Smith
Text and music © 1995, WLP

The Greatest Gift 422

REFRAIN

There are three things that last: faith, hope, and love; And the great - est gift is the gift of ___ love. There are three things that last: faith, hope, and love; And the great - est gift is the gift of ___ love.

To Verses

Final

love. And the great - est gift is the gift of ___ love. ___

VERSES

1. If I speak with the tongue of an an - gel, But I do not
2. And if I have the faith to move moun - tains, But I do not
3. If I give all I have to the low - ly, But I do not

1. love, I am just a voice mak - ing noise. I am
2. love, E - ven faith as might - y as this, It will
3. love, E - ven if I give up my life, It will

To Refrain

1. noth - ing, noth - ing at all. ___
2. pro - fit noth - ing at all. ___
3. gain me noth - ing at all. ___

James V. Marchionda
Text and music © 1982, WLP

423 Hear Us Now, Our God and Father

HYFRYDOL   87 87 D

1. Hear us now, our God and Fa - ther;
2. Give them joy to light - en sor - row;
3. May the grace of Christ our Sav - ior,

1. Send your Spir - it from a - bove
2. Give them hope to bright - en life.
3. And the Fa - ther's bound - less love,

1. On this Chris - tian man and wo - man,
2. Go with them to face the mor - row;
3. With the Ho - ly Spir - it's fa - vor

1. Who here make their vows of love!
2. Stay with them in ev - 'ry strife.
3. Rest up - on them from a - bove.

1. Bind their hearts in true de - vo - tion,
2. As your Word has prom - ised, ev - er
3. Thus may they a - bide in u - nion

1. End - less as the sea - shore's sands,
2. Fill them with your strength and grace,
3. With each oth - er and the Lord,

1. Bound - less as the deep - est o - cean,
2. So that each may serve the oth - er,
3. And pos - sess in sweet com - mun - ion

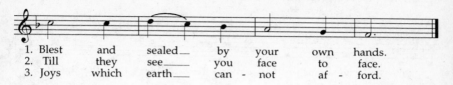

1. Blest and sealed__ by your own hands.
2. Till they see____ you face to face.
3. Joys which earth__ can - not af - ford.

Vss. 1–2: Harry N. Huxhold
Vs. 3: John Newton, 1725–1807, alt.
Vss. 1–2 © 1978, Augsburg Fortress

Rowland H. Prichard, 1811–1887

When Love Is Found 424
O WALY, WALY   LM

1. When love is found and hope comes home,
2. When love has flow'red in trust and care,
3. When love is tried as loved ones change,
4. When love is torn and trust be - trayed,
5. Praise God for love, praise God for life,

1. Sing and be glad that two are__ one.
2. Build both each day, that love may_ dare
3. Still hold to hope though all seems strange,
4. Pray strength to love till tor - ments fade,
5. In age or youth, in hus - band, wife.

1. When love ex - plodes and fills the__ sky,
2. To reach be - yond home's warmth and_ light,
3. Till ease re - turns and love grows wise
4. Till lov - ers__ keep no score of__ wrong,
5. Lift up your hearts; let love be__ fed

1. Praise God and share our Mak - er's_ joy.
2. To serve and strive for truth and_ right.
3. Through lis - t'ning ears and o - pened eyes.
4. But hear through pain love's Eas - ter__ song.
5. Through death and life in bro - ken__ bread.

Brian Wren
Text © 1983, Hope Publishing Co.

Traditional English melody

425 Like Olive Branches

REFRAIN 1

Cantor/All

Like ol - ive branch - es a - round the ta - ble of the Lord, so____ God's chil - dren in the Church.

REFRAIN 2

Cantor/All

May the God of Is - ra - el join____ you in one; In joy and in sor - row, the Lord is your way.

VERSES

Cantor

1. Bless - ed those who fear the Lord, who seek right
2. Bless - ed be the toil of hands: they shall bear
3. With good for - tune in your home shall you be
4. Bless - ed shall your chil - dren be a - round your
5. Blest in - deed shall be the ones who serve the
6. May the Lord who dwells on high give joy to
7. May the sight of man - y chil - dren give you

To Refrain

1. paths, For they shall find fa - vor in God's sight.
2. fruit; In joy and in glad - ness shall you work.
3. blest; Your spouse shall be like a fruit - ful vine.
4. board; Like strong ol - ive branch - es shall they stand.
5. Lord; For they shall pre - vail through-out their lives.
6. you; And may God pro - tect you all your life.
7. joy; May God fa - vor Is - ra - el with peace.

Ps 128

Lucien Deiss
Text and music © 1965, 1966, 1973, WLP

Not for Tongues of Heaven's Angels 426

COMFORT   87 87 with Refrain

VERSES

1. Not for tongues of heav - en's an - gels,
2. Love is hum - ble, love is gen - tle,
3. Nev - er jeal - ous, nev - er self - ish,
4. Soon will fade the word of wis - dom,

1. Not for wis - dom to dis - cern,
2. Love is ten - der, true, and kind;
3. Love will not re - joice in wrong;
4. Faith and hope be one day past:

1. Not for faith that mas - ters moun - tains,
2. Love is gra - cious, ev - er pa - tient,
3. nev - er boast - ful nor re - sent - ful,
4. When we see our Sav - ior clear - ly,

1. For this bet - ter gift we yearn:
2. Gen - er - ous of heart and mind
3. Love be - lieves and suf - fers long
4. Love it is a - lone will last,

REFRAIN

May love be ours, Lord; may love be ours.

May love be ours, O Lord.

Timothy Dudley-Smith
Text © 1985, Hope Publishing Co.

J. Michael Joncas
Music © 1988, GIA

427 How Happy You Who Fear the Lord

LAND OF REST CM

1. How hap - py you__ who fear the Lord__ And
2. Your wife shall be__ a fruit - ful vine__ En -
3. The Lord look down and pros - per you__ From

1. walk a - long__ God's ways;____ Your la - bor's fruit____ you
2. rich - ing your__ a - bode;____ Your chil - dren shall__ be
3. Zi - on's ho - ly place;____ Your chil - dren's chil - dren

1. will en - joy__ With bless - ings all____ your days.____
2. ol - ive plants As heav - en's gifts__ be - stowed.____
3. may you see__ Grow strong in health and grace.____

Omer Westendorf
Text © 1962, WLP

American folk hymn

428 Wherever You Go

Wher- ev- er you go____ I shall go.____

Wher- ev- er you live____ so shall I live.____

Your peo- ple will be my peo - ple, And

your God will be my God too.____

Wher- ev- er you die____ I shall die,____

And there shall I be bur-ied be- side you.___

We will be to- geth-er___ for - ev - er, And

our love___ will be the gift of our life.___

Ru 1:16–17

Gregory R. Norbet
Text and music © 1972, 1981, The Benedictine Foundation of the State of Vermont, Inc.

O Perfect Love **429**

O PERFECT LOVE   11 10 11 10

1. O   per - fect   Love,   all   hu - man thought tran - scend - ing,
2. O   per - fect   Life,   be   now their   full   as - sur - ance
3. Grant   them the   joy   which   bright-ens   earth - ly   sor - row;

1. Hum - bly   we   seek   the   prom - ise   you have   won,
2. Of   ten - der   char - i - ty   and stead-fast   faith,
3. Grant   them the   peace   which   calms all   earth - ly   strife,

1. That   theirs may   be   the   love which knows no   end - ing,
2. Of   pa - tient   hope   and   qui - et,   brave en - dur - ance,
3. And   to   life's   day   the   glo - rious   un-known mor - row

1. And   you   for - ev - er - more will   make   them   one.
2. With   child - like   trust that fears not   pain   nor   death.
3. That   dawns up - on   e - ter - nal   love   and   life.

Dorothy B. Gurney, 1858–1932   Joseph Barnby, 1838–1896

430 Come, My Way, My Truth, My Life

THE CALL   77 77

1. Come, my Way, my Truth, my Life: Such a
2. Come, my Light, my Feast, my Strength: Such a
3. Come, my Joy, my Love, my Heart: Such a

1. way as gives us breath; Such a truth as ends all
2. light as shows a feast; Such a feast as mends in
3. joy as none can move; Such a love as none can

1. strife; Such a life as kill - eth death.
2. length; Such a strength as makes_____ his guest.
3. part; Such a heart as joys_____ in love.

George Herbert, 1593–1633   Ralph Vaughan Williams, 1872–1958

431 Lord, Receive Your Servant

SERVANT   11 9 11 11

1. Lord, re - ceive your ser - vant; Lord, re - ceive your child.
2. Com - fort those re - main - ing; lis - ten to our prayers.
3. Saints of God, come aid him/her; an - gels, meet him/her now;

1. Bring in - to your pres - ence one we love.
2. God of con - so - la - tion, give us peace.
3. Take his/her soul, pre - sent him/her to the Lord.

1. Let your light shine on him/her; give him/her joy and peace.
2. Through the res - ur - rec - tion of your on - ly Son,
3. Christ, who called you, beck - ons; an - gels lead you on,

1. Grant him/her your for - give - ness and e - ter - nal life.
2. We have your as - sur - ance he/she will rise a - gain.
3. With our fa - ther A - bra'm, may you rest in peace.

Vss. 1–2: JoAnn Brown   JoAnn Brown
Vs. 3: *Subvenite*, adapt. by Edward C. Petty   Text and music © 1979, 1997, WLP

Jesus, Remember Me 432

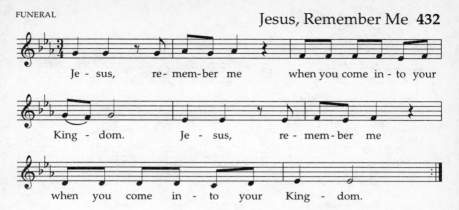

Je - sus, re - mem-ber me when you come in - to your King - dom. Je - sus, re - mem-ber me when you come in - to your King - dom.

Jacques Berthier, 1923–1994
Text and music © 1984, Les Presses de Taizé, pub. by GIA

O Lord, You Died That All Might Live 433
MELITA 88 88 88

1. O Lord, you died that all might live And
2. Lord, bless our friend who died in you, As
3. In your green, pleas - ant pas - tures feed The
4. Di - rect us with your arm of might, That

1. rise to see the per - fect day. The full - ness of your
2. you have giv - en him/her re - lease. En - liv - en him/her since
3. sheep that you have sum - moned hence; And by the still, cool
4. with our friend we may all come To dwell with - in your

1. mer - cy give To this, our friend, for whom we pray.
2. he/she was true, And give him/her ev - er - last - ing peace.
3. wa - ters lead Your flock in lov - ing prov - i - dence.
4. cit - y bright, Je - ru - sa - lem, our heav'n - ly home.

O Lamb of God, Re - deem - er blest,

Grant him/her e - ter - nal light and rest.

Richard F. Littledale, 1833–1890, alt.   John B. Dykes, 1823–1876

434 Litany of Comfort

REFRAIN

Cantor/All

Taste and see how good is the Lord.

VERSES

Cantor

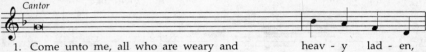

1. Come unto me, all who are weary and heav-y lad-en,
2. God so loved the world we were sent the on-ly Son,
3. Know that the Lord is God, the one who made us, to whom we be-long.

4. I am the resur - rec-tion and life,
5. Blest are those who fear the Lord;
6. The Lord will give you rest forever and fill your soul with splen-dor,

7. You shall eat and drink at my table in the king-dom,
8. My spirit is sweet - er than hon-ey,

To Refrain

1. and I will re-fresh___ you.
2. that whoever believes in him shall have e-ter-nal life.
3. We are God's people the sheep___ of one flock.

4. whoever believes in me shall nev-er die.
5. their homes shall be favored with glo-ry and wealth.
6. and make you like a spring whose wa-ters do not fail.

7. and you shall be seated on thrones to judge the twelve___ tribes.
8. and my reward sweeter than hon-ey and the hon-ey-comb.

Ps 34:9

Francis E. Pellegrini, 1936–1984, alt.
Text and music © 1968, WLP

435 Alleluia! The Strife Is O'er

VICTORY   888 with Alleluias

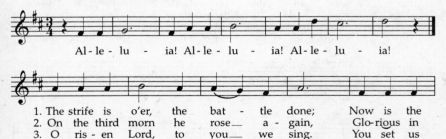

Al-le-lu - ia! Al-le-lu - ia! Al-le-lu - ia!

1. The strife is o'er, the bat - tle done; Now is the
2. On the third morn he rose___ a-gain, Glo-rious in
3. O ris-en Lord, to you___ we sing. You set us

1. Vic - tor's tri - umph won; O let the song of
2. maj - es - ty___ to reign; O let us swell the
3. free from death's cold sting; That all cre - a - tion's

D.C.

1. praise be sung:
2. joy - ful strain: Al - le - lu - ia!
3. song___ may ring:

Symphonia Sirenum Selectarum, Cologne, 1695
Tr. by Francis Pott, 1832–1909, alt.

Giovanni Pierlugi da Palestrina, 1525–1594
Adapt. by William H. Monk, 1823–1889

I Call You to My Father's House 436
NEW BRITAIN CM

1. I call you to my Fa - ther's house, A love - ly___
2. Lay down your sor - row, calm your fear; The Fa - ther
3. Al - though the___ way be hard and long In - to the___
4. I have pre - pared a wed - ding feast Of fin - est___
5. I call you to my Fa - ther's house, A love - ly___

1. dwell - ing place._____ He comes___ to___ meet you
2. bids you come._____ With o - pen___ arms he
3. prom - ised land,_____ Be not_____ a - fraid to
4. food and wine._____ O join_____ us___ at this
5. dwell - ing place._____ Be not_____ a - fraid to

1. on___ the___ road, Arms read - y___ to em - brace._____
2. wel - comes you To your e - ter - nal home._____
3. walk___ with me: I hold you by the hand._____
4. ban - quet where My friends, the saints now dine._____
5. trav - el___ there And meet him face to face._____

Delores Dufner
Text © 1983, The Sisters of St. Benedict

Traditional American melody
James P. Carrell and David S. Clayton's Virginia Harmony, 1831

437 Song of Farewell

OLD HUNDREDTH LM

1. Come to his/her aid, O saints of God;
2. May Christ, who called you, take you home,
3. Give him/her e - ter - nal rest, O Lord.
4. I know that my Re - deem - er lives;

1. Come, meet him/her an - gels____ of the Lord.
2. And an - gels lead you to A - bra - ham.
3. May light un - end - ing____ shine on him/her.
4. The last day I shall____ rise a - gain.

Re - ceive his/her soul, O ho - ly ones;

Pre - sent him/her now to God, Most High.

Based on *Subvenite* and Jb 19:25–27
Dennis C. Smolarski
Text © 1981, Dennis C. Smolarski

Pseaumes octante trois David, 1551, alt.
Louis Bourgeois, c. 1510–c. 1561

438 Jesus, Lord, Have Mercy

ADORO TE DEVOTE 65 65 D

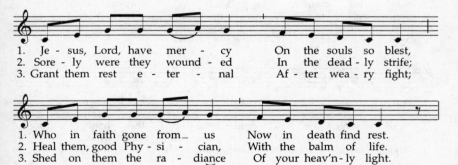

1. Je - sus, Lord, have mer - cy   On the souls so blest,
2. Sore - ly were they wound - ed   In the dead - ly strife,
3. Grant them rest e - ter - nal   Af - ter wea - ry fight;

1. Who in faith gone from__ us   Now in death find rest.
2. Heal them, good Phy - si - cian,   With the balm of life.
3. Shed on them the ra - diance   Of your heav'n - ly light.

1. Here 'mid stress_ and con - flict Toils can nev - er cease;
2. Ev - 'ry taint_ of e - vil, Frail - ty and de - cay,
3. Lead them on - ward, up - ward, To the ho - ly place

1. There the war - fare end - ed, Bid them rest in peace.
2. Good and gra - cious Sav - ior, Cleanse and purge a - way.
3. Where your saints, made per - fect, Gaze up - on your face.

Edmund S. Palmer, 1856–1931, alt.

Chant, Mode V
Processionale, Paris 1697

Precious Lord, Take My Hand 439
PRECIOUS LORD

* 1. Pre - cious Lord, take my hand, Lead me on, let me
  2. When my way grows_ drear, pre-cious Lord, lin - ger
  3. When the dark - ness ap - pears and the night draws_

1. stand, I am tired, I am weak, I am worn;_
2. near, When my life is_ al - most_ gone,_
3. near, And the day is_ past and_ gone,_

1. Through the storm, through the night, Lead me on to the light,
2. Hear my cry, hear my call, Hold my hand lest I fall;_
3. At the riv - er I stand, Guide my feet, hold my hand;_

1. Take my hand, pre-cious Lord, lead me home._
2. Take my hand, pre-cious Lord, lead me home._
3. Take my hand, pre-cious Lord, lead me home._

Thomas A. Dorsey, 1899–1993

George N. Allen, 1812–1877
Arr. by Thomas A. Dorsey, 1899–1993
Text and arr. © 1938, renewed, Unichappell Music

Verse 1 may be sung as a refrain.

440 May the Sending One Sing in You

Cantor

1. May the Send-ing One sing in you, May the Seek-ing One walk
2. May the Gift-ed One re - lieve you, May the Giv-en One re -
3. May the Bind-ing One u - nite you, May the One Be-lov'd in -

1. with you, May the Greet-ing One stand by you, In your
2. trieve you, May the Giv-ing One re - ceive you, In your
3. vite you, May the Lov-ing One de - light you, Three-in -

All

1. glad - ness and in your griev - ing. A - men.
2. fall - ing and your re - stor - ing. A - men.
3. One, joy in life un - end - ing. A - men.

Brian Wren
Text © 1989, Hope Publishing Co.

Michael Bogdan
Music © 1994, WLP

441 Bwana Awabariki/May God Grant You a Blessing

Bwa - na a - wa - ba - ri - ki, Bwa - na a - wa - ba - ri - ki,
May God grant you a bless-ing, may God grant you a bless-ing,

Bwa - na a - wa - ba - ri - ki mi - le - le.
may God grant you a bless-ing ev - er - more.

U - ki-mcha Bwa - na. Bwa - na a - wa - ba - ri - ki.
Re - vere the Lord. May God grant you a bless-ing.

Swahili folk hymn

A Blessing 442

NUMBERS 10 9 10 10

1. May the Lord al - ways bless you and keep you.____
2. May the Lord look up - on you with kind - ness.____

1. May the face of God shine up - on____ you.____
2. May the Lord fill your hearts with ho - ly peace.____

1. May you know true com - pas - sion and mer - cy.____
2. God's____ love be for - ev - er with - in you.____

1. May the Lord walk be - side you for - ev - er.____
2. May the Lord al - ways bless you and

2. keep you.____ May the Lord al - ways bless you and keep you.____

Nm 6:24–26

James V. Marchionda
Text and music © 1982, WLP

443 Blest Are We

REFRAIN

Blest are we who hear the word of God, Who

hear the word of God and keep it.

Let us then re-ceive what we now hear, Be-

lieve what we re-ceive, And be-come what we be-lieve.

VERSES

1. Light of the world, fire of love,
2. Wis-dom of God, Spir-it of truth,

1. Come, make your home in our hearts.
2. Come, breathe your life in our souls.

1. Flame nev-er end-ing, come, burn with a pas-sion,
2. Foun-tain of new-ness, come, burst forth with-in us,

To Refrain

1. Ig-nite us to ac-tion in love.
2. Re-fresh us as food for our hearts.

Vince Ambrosetti
Text and music © 1992, 1993, International Liturgy Publications, dist. by WLP

God Has Spoken by the Prophets 444

IN BABILONE 87 87 D

1. God has spo-ken by the prophets, Spo-ken an un-
2. God has spo-ken by Christ Je-sus, Christ, the ev-er-
3. God is speak-ing by the Spir-it, Speak-ing to the

1. chang-ing word; Each from age to age pro-claim-ing
2. last-ing Son, Bright-ness of the Fa-ther's glo-ry,
3. hearts of all, In the age-less word ex-pound-ing

1. God, the one, the right-eous Lord. In the world's des-
2. With the Fa-ther ev-er one; Spo-ken by the
3. God's own mes-sage for us all. Through the rise and

1. pair and tur-moil, One firm an-chor holds us fast;
2. Word In-car-nate, God of God, be-fore time was;
3. fall of na-tions One sure faith yet stand-ing fast;

1. God is King, en-throned e-ter-nal;
2. Light of light, to earth de-scend-ing,
3. God a-bides in word un-chang-ing;

1. God the first, and God the last.
2. Christ re-veals our God to us.
3. God the first, and God the last.

George W. Briggs, 1875–1959, alt.
Text © 1953, 1981, The Hymn Society

Traditional Dutch melody
Oude en Nieuwe Hollantse Boereulilies en Contradansen, c. 1710

445 Speak Now, O Lord

VERSES

1. Speak now, O Je-sus,— speak now, O Lord!
2. Speak now, O Sav-ior— of all the earth!
3. Speak now, O prom-ise!— God's word re-vealed!
4. Speak now, O lov-er— of all the world!

1. We come to lis-ten,— to hear your word.
2. We come to praise you;— to bless your name.
3. We bow be-fore you,— we call you Lord!
4. We stand be-fore you,— to live your word!

1. We come as ser-vants, to do your will.
2. We are the cap-tives, we are the lame.
3. We are the suf-f'ring, for-got-ten ones.
4. We are the hun-gry,— we are the cold.

REFRAIN

We are your hands and feet! Speak now, speak now!

To Verses | Final

Speak now, O Lord._____ Lord. We are your

hands and feet! Speak now, speak now! Speak now, O Lord.

Joe Mattingly
Text and music © 1994, WLP

446 Song of Good News

YSRAEL V'ORAITA   98 95 with Refrain

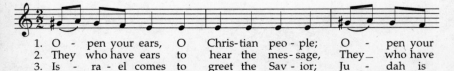

1. O - pen your ears, O Chris-tian peo - ple; O - pen your
2. They who have ears to hear the mes - sage, They— who have
3. Is - ra - el comes to greet the Sav - ior; Ju - dah is

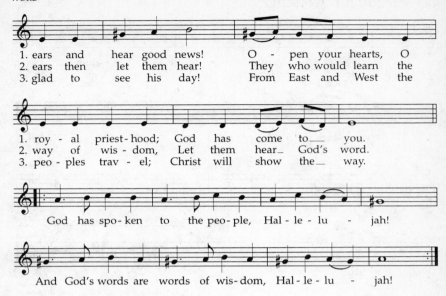

1. ears and hear good news! O - pen your hearts, O
2. ears then let them hear! They who would learn the
3. glad to see his day! From East and West the

1. roy - al priest - hood; God has come to___ you.
2. way of wis - dom, Let them hear_ God's word.
3. peo - ples trav - el; Christ will show the_ way.

God has spo - ken to the peo - ple, Hal - le - lu - jah!

And God's words are words of wis - dom, Hal - le - lu - jah!

Willard F. Jabusch
Text © 1966, 1979, Willard F. Jabusch

Jewish folk tune

In Christ There Is No East or West 447

McKEE CM

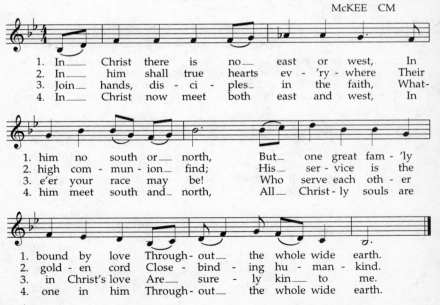

1. In___ Christ there is no___ east or west, In
2. In___ him shall true hearts ev - 'ry - where Their
3. Join___ hands, dis - ci - ples_ in the faith, What-
4. In___ Christ now meet both east and west, In

1. him no south or___ north, But_ one great fam - 'ly
2. high com - mun - ion___ find; His_ ser - vice is the
3. e'er your race may be! Who serve each oth - er
4. him meet south and_ north, All_ Christ - ly souls are

1. bound by love Through - out___ the whole wide earth.
2. gold - en cord Close - bind - ing hu - man - kind.
3. in Christ's love Are_ sure - ly kin___ to me.
4. one in him Through - out___ the whole wide earth.

Gal 3:28
John Oxenham, 1852–1941

African-American
Adapt. by Harry T. Burleigh, 1866–1949

448 Freedom Is Coming

1. O Free - dom,__ O Free - dom,__
2. O Je - sus,__ O Je - sus,__

1. O Free - dom.__ O
2. O Je - sus.__

yes, I__ know.__ O yes, I__ know.__ O

1. 2.

yes, I__ know.__ O

449 They'll Know We Are Christians by Our Love

ST. BRENDAN'S   76 76 86 with Refrain

1. We are one in the Spir - it, we are one in the
2. We will walk with each oth - er, we will walk hand in
3. We will work with each oth - er, we will work side by
4. All__ praise to the Fa - ther, from__ whom all things

1. Lord, We are one in the Spir - it, we are
2. hand, We will walk with each oth - er, we will
3. side, We will work with each oth - er, we will
4. come, And all praise to Christ Je - sus, his__

1. one in the Lord, And we pray that all
2. walk hand in hand, And to - geth - er we'll
3. work side by side, And we'll guard peo - ple's
4. on - ly__ Son, And all praise to the

1. u – ni – ty may one day be re – stored:
2. spread the news that God is in our land:
3. dig – ni – ty and save each per – son's pride:
4. Spir – it, who makes us one:

And they'll know we are Chris-tians by our love, by our love,

Yes, they'll know we are Chris-tians by our love.

Peter Scholtes
Text and music © 1966, FEL Publications
Assigned to Lorenz Corp., 1991

Let Us Be One 450
LET US BE ONE   CM

1. Let us be one in mind and heart
2. Here in our midst true love a – bides,
3. Though we are man – y in his love,

1. With Je – sus Christ our Lord,
2. One Spir – it whom we share,
3. The Fa – ther sees but one,

1. As we pre – pare to break this bread
2. One Lord whose prom – ised gift of peace
3. And hears one voice, the Spir – it's song,

1. And share this cup out – poured.
2. Is ours; his name we bear!
3. In Christ, be – lov – ed Son.

Anon.

Richard E. Dohm
Music © 1982, Richard E. Dohm

451 Lord of All Nations, Grant Me Grace

BEATUS VIR   88 88

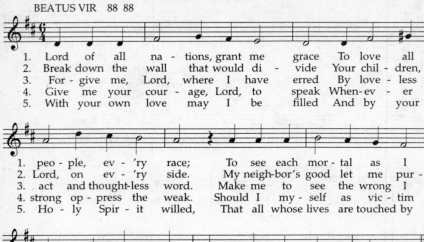

1. Lord of all na - tions, grant me grace To love all
2. Break down the wall that would di - vide Your chil - dren,
3. For - give me, Lord, where I have erred By love - less
4. Give me your cour - age, Lord, to speak When-ev - er
5. With your own love may I be filled And by your

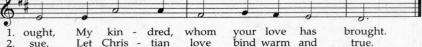

1. peo - ple, ev - 'ry race; To see each mor - tal as I
2. Lord, on ev - 'ry side. My neigh-bor's good let me pur -
3. act and thought-less word. Make me to see the wrong I
4. strong op - press the weak. Should I my - self as vic - tim
5. Ho - ly Spir - it willed, That all whose lives are touched by

1. ought, My kin - dred, whom your love has brought.
2. sue, Let Chris - tian love bind warm and true.
3. do Will cru - ci - fy my Lord a - new.
4. live, Re - mem - b'ring you, may I for - give.
5. mine, May know your heal - ing touch di - vine.

Phil 2:1–18
Olive W. Spannaus; Text © 1969, Concordia Publishing House

Samotulsky Kancional, Slovak, 1561

452 We Are Many Parts

REFRAIN

We are man - y parts,_____ we are all one bod - y_____

_____ and the gifts we have we are giv - en to share._____

_____ May the Spir - it of love make us one in - deed;_____

_____ one, the love that we share,_____ one, our hope in de- spair,_____

To Verses | Final

_____ one, the cross that we bear._____

VERSES

1. God of all, we look to you,___
2. So my pain is pain for you,___
3. All you seek - ers, great and small,___

1. we would be your ser - vants true,___
2. in your joy is my joy, too;___
3. seek the great - est gift of all;___

To Refrain

1. let us be your love to all the world.
2. all is brought to - geth - er in the Lord.
3. if you love, then you will know the Lord.

1 Cor 12, 13

Marty Haugen
Text and music © 1980, 1986, GIA

You Chosen Ones 453

REFRAIN

Cantor

You cho - sen ones, give glo - ry to God!

All

You cho - sen ones, give glo - ry to God!

VERSES

1. Because of your goodness, I owe you my praise. I will keep my pledge to you in front of all your people.

2. The poor will eat their fill; those who seek the Lord will praise the Lord; may their hearts be ever merry!

3. All creation shall remember the care that God has shown: ev'ry race shall gather to praise God. My soul shall live for God, alone.

4. Let all generations learn the love of the Lord; let ev'ry being live out their future proclaiming the Lord who makes them whole!

Ps 22

Carl Johengen
Text and music © 1993, WLP

454 I Want to Walk as a Child of the Light

HOUSTON

VERSES

1. I want to walk as a child of the light. I want to
2. I want to see___ the bright-ness of God. I want to
3. I'm look-ing for___ the com-ing of Christ. I want to

1. fol - low Je - sus. God set the stars to give
2. look at Je - sus. Clear sun of right-eous-ness,
3. be with Je - sus. When we have run___ with

1. light to the world. The star of my life___ is Je - sus.
2. shine on my path, And show me the way to the Fa - ther.
3. pa-tience the race, We shall know the joy___ of Je - sus.

REFRAIN

In him there is no dark-ness at all. The night and the

day___ are both a - like. The Lamb is the light of the

cit - y of God. Shine in my heart, Lord Je - sus.

Kathleen Thomerson
Text and music © 1970, Celebration, admin. by The Copyright Co.

455 The Love of Christ Urges Us On

REFRAIN

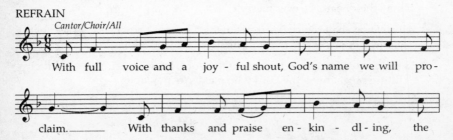

Cantor/Choir/All

With full voice and a joy - ful shout, God's name we will pro-

claim.___ With thanks and praise en - kin - dl - ing, the

Jeffrey Honoré
Text and music © 1993, 1995, WLP

456 Rain Down

FINAL REFRAIN

Cantor/Choir/All

Rain down, rain your love on me, — rain — down.

Rain down, rain your love on me. —

Rain down, rain your love on me, — rain — down.

Rain down, rain your love on me. —

Rain your love — on me. Rain your love — on me.

Rain your love — on me. Rain your love!

Ed Bolduc
Text and music © 1994, WLP

457 Where True Charity and Love Dwell/
Ubi Caritas

UBI CARITAS   12 12 12 12 with Refrain

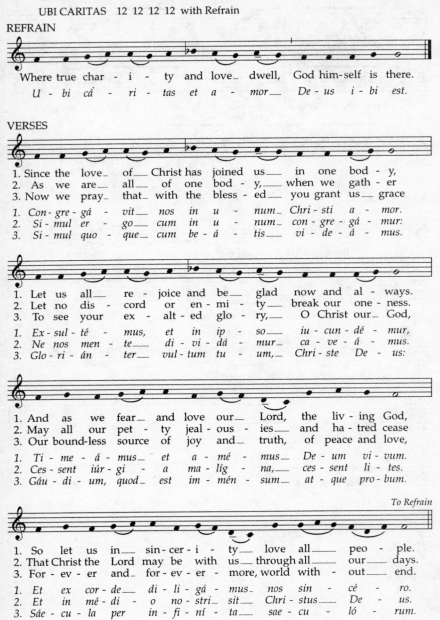

REFRAIN

Where true char - i - ty and love_ dwell, God him-self is there.
U - bi cá - ri - tas et a - mor_ De - us i - bi est.

VERSES

1. Since the love_ of_ Christ has joined us_ in one bod - y,
2. As we are_ all_ of one bod - y,_ when we gath - er
3. Now we pray_ that_ with the bless - ed_ you grant us_ grace

1. *Con - gre - gá - vit_ nos in u - num_ Chri - sti a - mor.*
2. *Si - mul er - go_ cum in u - num_ con - gre - gá - mur:*
3. *Si - mul quo - que_ cum be - á - tis_ vi - de - á - mus.*

1. Let us all_ re - joice and be_ glad now and al - ways.
2. Let no dis - cord or en - mi - ty_ break our one - ness.
3. To see your ex - alt - ed glo - ry,_ O Christ our_ God,

1. *Ex - sul - té - mus, et in ip - so_ iu - cun - dé - mur,*
2. *Ne nos men - te_ di - vi - dá - mur_ ca - ve - á - mus.*
3. *Glo - ri - án - ter_ vul - tum tu - um,_ Chri - ste De - us:*

1. And as we fear_ and love our_ Lord, the liv - ing God,
2. May all our pet - ty jeal - ous - ies_ and ha - tred cease
3. Our bound-less source of joy and_ truth, of peace and love,

1. *Ti - me - á - mus_ et a - mé - mus_ De - um vi - vum.*
2. *Ces - sent iúr - gi - a ma - líg - na,_ ces - sent li - tes.*
3. *Gáu - di - um, quod_ est im - mén - sum_ at - que pro - bum.*

To Refrain

1. So let us in_ sin - cer - i - ty_ love all_ peo - ple.
2. That Christ the Lord may be with us_ through all_ our_ days.
3. For - ev - er and_ for - ev - er - more, world with - out_ end.

1. *Et ex cor - de_ di - li - gá - mus_ nos sin - cé - ro.*
2. *Et in mé - di - o no - stri_ sit_ Chri - stus_ De - us.*
3. *Sáe - cu - la per in - fi - ní - ta_ sae - cu - ló - rum.*

Ubi caritas
Tr. by Joyce M. Glover
Tr. © 1982, Joyce M. Glover

Chant, Mode VI

Go Forth in Peace 458

EDGBASTON 97 97 10 9 97

1. Go forth in peace, for Christ is your peace, and
2. Go forth to love as Christ loved the world, as
3. Go forth to serve as Christ served the world, as

1. God gives you peace in Christ.
2. God has loved us in Christ.
3. God has served us in Christ.

1. Go forth in joy, for Christ goes with you; wher-
2. Love all you meet, for love is of God, and
3. Not to be served but to serve, Christ came to

1. ev - er you go, Christ goes.
2. where love is, there is God.
3. teach us God's way of life.

1. Daugh-ters and sons of God in Christ Je - sus,
2. When on the cross Christ died for all peo - ple,
3. On that last night, with ba - sin and tow - el,

1. share with the world the gift of God's peace.
2. he showed the breadth and depth of God's love.
3. Je - sus knelt down and washed his friends' feet.

1. Go forth in peace, for Christ is your peace, and
2. Go forth to love as Christ loved the world, as
3. Go forth to serve as Christ served the world, as

1. God gives you peace in Christ.
2. God has loved us in Christ.
3. God has served us in Christ.

Delores Dufner
Text © 1997, Sisters of St. Benedict

Christopher Trussell
Music © 1997, WLP

459 We Bring God's Holy Love

1. We bring God's gift of love to the world_____
2. We bring God's gift of truth to the world_____
3. We bring God's gift of joy— to the world_____
4. We bring God's gift of hope to the world_____
5. We bring God's gift of peace to the world_____

1. We bring God's gift of love to the world_____
2. We bring God's gift of truth to the world_____
3. We bring God's gift of joy— to the world_____
4. We bring God's gift of hope to the world_____
5. We bring God's gift of peace to the world_____

1. To ful - fill the com- mand that we walk now hand in
2. Ev - 'ry e - vil to crush, from this world God made for
3. That the king - dom may come, and God's will be— ev - er
4. To be - friend the dis- tressed, and de - liv - er— the op -
5. Our good works to ex - tend, so all wars for - ev - er

1. hand; We— bring God's ho - ly love._____
2. us, We— bring God's ho - ly truth._____
3. done, We— bring God's ho - ly joy._____
4. pressed, We— bring God's ho - ly hope._____
5. end, We— bring God's ho - ly peace._____

Rose Weber
Text © 1971, WLP

African-American

460 We Are Marching in the Light of God

SIYAHAMBA

We are march - ing* in the light of God,___ we are
Si - ya - hamb'___ e - ku - kha- nyen' kwen-khos',___ si - ya -

march-ing in the light of God.___ We are
hamb' e - ku - kha- nyen' kwen - khos.___ Si - ya -

Additional verses: dancing, singing, praying, etc.

marching in the light of God,___ we are
hamb' e - ku - kha- nyen' kwen - khos',___ si - ya -

march - ing___ Oo___ We are
ham - ba___ Oo___ Si - ya

march - ing in the light of God.___
hamb' e - ku - kha - nyen' kwen - khos.___

South African
Text and music © 1984, Utryck, agent: Walton Music Corp.

Lift High the Cross 461

CRUCIFER 10 10 with Refrain

Lift high the cross, the love of Christ pro - claim, Till

all the world___ a - dore___ his sa - cred name.

1. Come, Chris- tians, fol - low where our Sav - ior trod, Our
2. Led on their way by this tri - um - phant sign, The
3. All new - born fol - l'wers of the Cru - ci - fied Bear
4. O Lord, once lift - ed on the glo - rious tree, As
5. So shall our song of tri - umph ev - er be: Praise

D.C.

1. King vic - to - rious, Christ, the Son of God.
2. hosts of___ God in glo - rious ranks com - bine.
3. on their___ brows the seal of him who died.
4. you have___ prom - ised, save and set us free.
5. to the___ Cru - ci - fied for vic - to - ry!

George W. Kitchin, 1827–1912, alt.
Michael R. Newbolt, 1874–1956, alt.

Sydney H. Nicholson, 1875–1947
Text and music © 1974, Hope Publishing Co.

462 Make Your Home in Me

PICARDY 98 98 11 8

1. I am the true vine, you the branch - es.
2. As the Fa - ther loves me, I love you.
3. As I have loved you, love each oth - er.
4. You did not choose me; no, I chose you,
5. E - ven though you grieve for a time now,
6. Je - sus, liv - ing vine, keep your branch - es

1. Ev - 'ry branch in me will bear fruit.
2. Live on in my love; keep my word.
3. I call you not ser - vants but friends.
4. Sent you to go out and bear fruit.
5. Your grief will be turned in - to joy.
6. Flour - ish - ing with life in your love.

1. But with - out me you can do noth - ing,
2. Let my joy be yours, let it fill you.
3. I lay down my life for my loved ones;
4. Ev - 'ry - thing you need, I will give you;
5. When I come a - gain, I will bring you
6. Prune a - way what - ev - er is use - less,

1. Cut off from the source of all life.
2. Be im - mersed in me, in my life.
3. So you are to love in my name.
4. So you shall bear fruit that will last.
5. Last - ing joy that none can de - stroy.
6. That we may bear fruit in your name.

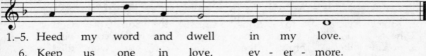

1.–5. Make your home in me as I make mine in you.
6. Make your home in us, and make us one in you.

1.–5. Heed my word and dwell in my love.
6. Keep us one in love, ev - er - more.

Adapt. by Delores Dufner
Text © 1982, WLP

Traditional French carol, 17th. cent.

We Are Called 463

VERSES

1. Come! Live in the light!
2. Come! O-pen your heart!
3. Sing! Sing a new song!

1. Shine with the joy and the love of the Lord! We are
2. Show your mer-cy to all those in fear! We are
3. Sing of that great day when all will be one! God will

1. called to be light for the king-dom, to
2. called to be hope for the hope-less, so all
3. reign, and we'll walk with each oth-er as

1. live in the free-dom of the cit-y of God!
2. ha-tred and blind-ness will be no more!
3. sis-ters and broth-ers, u-ni-ted in love!

REFRAIN

We are called to act with jus-tice,

we are called to love ten-der-ly,

we are called to serve one an-oth-er;

to walk hum-bly with God!

Mi 6:8

David Haas
Text and music © 1988, GIA

464 The Spirit of God

REFRAIN

Cantor/All

The Spir-it of God rests up-on me,_____ The
Spir-it of God con-se-crates me,_____ The Spir-it of God

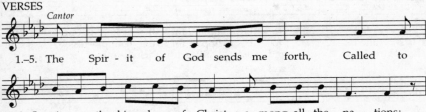

bids me go forth to pro-claim God's peace and joy.

VERSES

Cantor

1.–5. The Spir-it of God sends me forth, Called to

1.–5. wit-ness the king-dom of Christ a-mong all the na-tions;

1. Called to pro-claim__ the good news of Christ to the poor.___
2. Called to con-sole__ the hearts o-ver-come with great sor-row.
3. Called__ to com-fort the poor___ who mourn and who weep.___
4. Called to an-nounce_ the grace of sal-va-tion to all.___
5. Called to re-veal__ God's glo-ry a-mong all the peo-ple.

To Refrain

1.–5. My spir-it re-joic-es in God, my Sav - ior.

Lucien Deiss
Text and music © 1970, 1973, WLP

465 Here I Am, Lord

REFRAIN

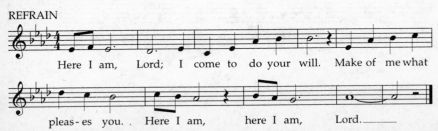

Here I am, Lord; I come to do your will. Make of me what
pleas-es you. . Here I am, here I am, Lord._____

VERSES *Cantor/Choir*

1. You spoke my name and beck-oned me to come.__ Be-
2. You have the words of ev-er-last-ing life.___ If
3. What joy it is to stand a-mid your glo-ry. __
4. Show me the path that you would have me walk,__ And

To Refrain

1. fore you now I stand__ to lis-ten to your word.
2. I should turn from you,__ to whom would I go?
3. Let me al-ways stay in your pres-ence, O God.
4. give me grace to do what is good_ in your sight.

Michael Ward
Text and music © 1979, 1989, WLP

God's Blessing Sends Us Forth 466

ST. ELIZABETH Irregular

1. God's bless-ing sends us forth, Strength-ened for our task on earth,
2. God's news in spo-ken word Joy-ful-ly our hearts have heard;
3. We by one liv-ing bread As one bod-y have been fed;
4. Grant in this age of space Tri-umph of your truth and grace;

1. Re-freshed in soul and re-newed in mind.
2. O may the seed of God's love now grow.
3. So we are one as we share this food.
4. Lord, you a-lone are un-chang-ing truth.

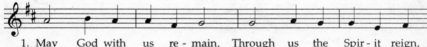

1. May God with us re-main, Through us the Spir-it reign,
2. May we in fruit-ful deeds Glad-ly serve oth-ers' needs,
3. How gra-cious to be-hold All peo-ple of one fold
4. Bring us un-to your side; Pre-serve and ev-er guide;

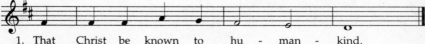

1. That Christ be known to hu-man-kind.
2. That faith in ac-tion we may show.
3. Who ev-er seek each oth-er's good.
4. Your an-cient Church in age-less youth.

Omer Westendorf
Text © 1964, WLP

Schlesische Volkslieder, Leipzig, 1842

467 'Tis the Gift to Be Simple

SIMPLE GIFTS   Irregular

1. 'Tis the gift to be sim-ple, 'tis the gift to be free, 'Tis the
2. 'Tis the gift to be gen-tle, 'tis the gift to be fair, 'Tis the
3. 'Tis the gift to be lov-ing, 'tis the gift best of all, Like a

1. gift to come down where you ought to be, And
2. gift to wake and breathe the morn-ing air; And
3. qui - et rain, it bless - es where it falls; And

1. when we find our-selves in the place just___ right_____ 'Twill
2. ev - 'ry day to walk in the path we___ choose, 'Tis the
3. if we have the gift, we will tru - ly be-lieve_____ 'Tis

1. be in the val - ley of love and de-light.
2. gift that we pray we may ne'er come to lose.
3. bet - ter to give than it is to re - ceive.

When true sim-plic-i-ty is gained, To bow and to bend we

shan't be a-shamed; To turn, turn will be our de-light, Till by

turn - ing, turn - ing we come 'round right._____

Vs. 1: Traditional
Vss. 2–3: Joyce Merman
Vss. 2–3 © 1975, Shawnee Press, Inc.

Shaker song

Go Make of All Disciples 468

ELLACOMBE 76 76 D

1. "Go make of_ all dis - ci - ples." We hear the call, O
2. "Go make of_ all dis - ci - ples." Bap - tiz - ing in the
3. "Go make of_ all dis - ci - ples," We at_ your feet would
4. "Go make of_ all dis - ci - ples." We wel - come your com-

1. Lord, That comes from you, our Fa - ther, In
2. name Of Fa - ther, Son, and Spir - it From
3. stay Un - til each life's vo - ca - tion Shows
4. mand; "Lo, I am_ with you al - ways." We

1. your e - ter - nal Word. In - spire our ways of
2. age_ to age the same. We_ call each new dis-
3. forth your ho - ly way. We_ cul - ti - vate the
4. take your guid - ing hand. The_ task looms large be -

1. learn - ing Through earn - est, fer - vent prayer,
2. ci - ple To_ fol - low you, O Lord,
3. na - ture God_ plants in ev - 'ry heart,
4. fore____ us We_ fol - low with - out fear.

1. And let our_ dai - ly liv - ing
2. Re - deem - ing_ soul and bod - y
3. Re - veal - ing_ in our wit - ness
4. In heav'n and_ earth your pow - er

1. Re - veal_ you ev - 'ry - where.
2. By wa - ter and the word.
3. The Mas - ter Teach - er's art.
4. Shall bring_ God's king - dom here.

Mt 28:19–20
Leon M. Adkins, 1896–1986, alt.
Text © 1955, 1964, Abingdon Press

Mainzer Gesangbuch, Mainz, 1833

469 A Mighty Fortress

EIN FESTE BURG   87 87 66 667

1. A might-y for-tress is___ our God,
2. The wa-ters of___ God's good-ness flow
3. Be-hold! What won-drous deeds of peace

1. A bul-wark nev-er fail - ing,
2. Through-out the ho-ly cit - y,
3. From God, our sole sal-va - tion,

1. Pro-tect-ing us___ with staff___ and rod,
2. And glad-den hearts of those who know
3. Who knows our wars and makes them cease

1. In pow-er all pre-vail - ing.
2. Great ten-der-ness and pi - ty.
3. In ev-'ry land and na - tion.

1. What if___ the na-tions rage   And surg-ing
2. Though na-tions stand un-sure,   God's king-dom
3. The war-rior's spear and___ lance   Are splin-tered

1. seas ram-page;   What though the moun-tains fall,   The Lord is
2. shall en-dure;   In pow-er shall re-main,   In peace shall
3. with one glance;   Our guns and nu-clear might   Stand with-ered

1. God of all;   On earth is found no e - qual.
2. ev-er reign,   Our God, the God of Ja - cob.
3. in God's sight;   The Lord of hosts is with___ us.

Ps 46; Omer Westendorf
Vs. 1, lines 1, 2: Martin Luther, 1483–1546
Tr. by Frederick H. Hedge, 1805–1890; Text © 1964, WLP

Martin Luther, 1483–1546

470 Reason to Live

REFRAIN

Cantor/All

I will love___ the Lord___   al-ways and___ for-ev-

- er.___ He will be___ my strength that
comes from God___ a-bove.___ And I will serve___ the Lord.
___ He will be___ my pas - sion.___
He will be___ my rea - son___ to hope,___ my___
rea - son___ to live.___

VERSES
Cantor

1. No one who be - lieves___ shall ev - er___
2. Je - sus, Liv - ing Bread,___ bring us new

1. thirst.___ No one who be - lieves___
2. life.___ Je - sus, Lamb of God,___

1. ___ shall hun - ger a - gain.___
2. ___ ___ bring us new hope.___

1. All who come to him___ shall live___ for -
2. Je - sus, Bread of Life,___ you make us one

To Refrain

1. ev - er.___
2. bo - dy.___

Ed Bolduc
Text and music © 1993, WLP

471 We Walk by Faith

SHANTI CM

1.,5. We walk by faith and not by sight; No
2. touch the hands and side, Nor
3. Lord, our un - be - lief; And
4. life of faith is done, In

1.,5. gra - cious words we hear_____ From Christ who spoke as
2. fol - low where he trod;_____ Yet in the prom - ise
3. may our faith a - bound,_____ To call on you when
4. realms of clear - er light_____ We may be - hold you

1.,5. none e'er spoke, But we be - lieve him
2. we re - joice, And cry, "My Lord and
3. you are near, and seek where you are
4. as you are, With full and end - less

1.–4.

Final

1.,5. near._____ We may not near._____
2. God!"_____ Help then, O
3. found:_____ That when our
4. sight._____ We walk by

Henry Alford, 1810–1871, alt.

Marty Haugen
Music © 1984, GIA

472 Faith of Our Fathers

ST. CATHERINE   88 88 88

1. Faith of our fa - thers, liv - ing still,
2. Our fa - thers, chained in pris - ons dark,
3. Our moth - ers, too,___ op - pressed and wronged,
4. Faith of our fa - thers, faith___ and prayer
5. Faith of our fa - thers, we___ will love

1. In spite of dun - geon, fire,___ and sword;
2. Were still in heart and con - science free;
3. Still lived their faith with dig - ni - ty;
4. Shall win all na - tions un - to thee;
5. Both friend and foe in all___ our strife,

FAITH

1. O how our hearts_ beat high_ with joy,
2. And tru - ly blest_ would be_ our fate,
3. Their brave ex - am - ple gives_ us strength
4. And through the truth_ that comes from God,
5. And preach thee, too,_ as love_ knows how,

1. When - e'er we hear that glo - rious word:
2. If we, like them, should die_ for thee.
3. To work for jus - tice cease - less - ly.
4. We all shall then in - deed_ be free.
5. By kind - ly deeds and vir - tuous life.

Faith of our fa - thers, ho - ly faith!

We will be true to thee till death.

Frederick W. Faber, 1814–1863, alt.
Vs. 3: Mike Hay
Text (vs. 3) © 1994, WLP

Henri F. Hemy, 1818–1888
Adapt. by James G. Walton, 1821–1905

There Is One Lord 473

REFRAIN

There is one_ Lord, there is one_ faith, there is one_

bap - tism, one God, who is Fa - ther.

VERSES

1. We were called to be one in the Spirit of God, in the bond of peace.
   We sing and we proclaim.

2. We were called to form one body in one spirit.
   We sing and we proclaim.

3. We were called in the same hope in Christ the Lord.
   We sing and we proclaim.

Eph 4:3–6

Lucien Deiss
Text and music © 1965, 1966, 1973, WLP

474 As Jacob with Travel Was Weary

JACOB'S LADDER   Irregular

1. As Jacob with travel was weary one day,___ At___ night on a stone___ for a pil - low he lay; He___ saw in a vi - sion a lad - der so high, That its foot was on earth___ and its top in the sky.

2. The lad - der is long,___ it is strong and well - made,___ Has stood hun - dreds of years___ and is not yet de - cayed; Man - y mil - lions have climbed it and reached Si - on's hill, And___ thou - sands by faith___ are___ climb - ing it still.

3. Come, let us as - cend!___ All may climb it who will;___ For the an - gels of Ja - cob are guard - ing it still: And re - mem - ber, each step that by faith we pass o'er, Some___ proph - et or mar - tyr has walked there be - fore.

4. And when we ar - rive___ at the place of our rest,___ We shall hear the glad words,___ "Come and en - ter, you blest, Here are re - gions of light, here are man - sions of bliss." Oh,___ who would not climb___ such a lad - der as this!

Al - le - lu - ia to Je - sus, who died on the tree___
And has raised up a lad - der of mer - cy for me,
And has raised up a lad - der of mer - cy for me.

English folk song

Shall We Gather at the River **475**

HANSON PLACE 87 87 with Refrain

VERSES

1. Shall we gath-er at the riv-er,
2. On the mar-gin of the riv-er,
3. Ere we reach the shin-ing riv-er,
4. Soon we'll reach the shin-ing riv-er,

1. Where bright an-gel feet have trod,
2. Wash-ing up its sil-ver spray,
3. Lay we ev-'ry bur-den down;
4. Soon our pil-grim-age will cease;

1. With its crys-tal tide for-ev-er
2. We will walk and wor-ship ev-er,
3. Grace our spir-its will de-liv-er,
4. Soon our hap-py hearts will quiv-er

1. Flow-ing by the throne of God?
2. All the hap-py gold-en day.
3. And pro-vide a robe and crown.
4. With the mel-o-dy of peace.

REFRAIN

Yes, we'll gath-er at the riv-er, the

beau-ti-ful, the beau-ti-ful riv-er,

Gath-er with the saints at the riv-er that

flows by the throne of God.

Robert Lowry, 1826–1899

476 I Lift My Heart

DUNEDIN LM

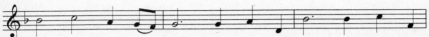

1. I lift my heart to God on high, To God who
2. I need not fear the dark-est night. God shields me
3. I lift my heart to God on high, Who is the

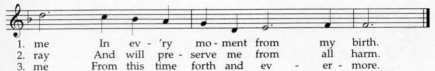

1. made the heav'n and earth. To God who helps and strength-ens
2. with a strong right arm; And shields me from the sun's bright
3. sen - try at my door; For God will guard and com - fort

1. me In ev - 'ry mo - ment from my birth.
2. ray And will pre - serve me from all harm.
3. me From this time forth and ev - er - more.

Mary Williams-Clark
Text © 1977, WLP

Vernon Griffiths, 1894–1985
Music © 1971, Faber Music, Ltd.

477 Lord of All Hopefulness

SLANE 10 11 11 12

1. Lord of all__ hope - ful - ness, Lord of all joy,
2. Lord of all__ ea - ger - ness, Lord of all faith,
3. Lord of all__ kind - li - ness, Lord of all grace,
4. Lord of all__ gen - tle - ness, Lord of all calm,

1. Whose trust, ev - er child - like, no cares could de - stroy:
2. Whose strong hands were skilled at the plane and the lathe:
3. Your hands swift to wel - come, your arms to em - brace:
4. Whose voice is con - tent - ment, whose pres - ence is balm:

1. Be there at__ our__ wak - ing, and give us, we pray,
2. Be there at__ our__ la - bors, and give us, we pray,
3. Be there at__ our__ hom - ing, and give us, we pray,
4. Be there at__ our__ sleep - ing, and give us, we pray,

1. Your bliss in our hearts, Lord, at the break of the day.
2. Your strength in our hearts, Lord, at the noon of the day.
3. Your love in our hearts, Lord, at the eve of the day.
4. Your peace in our hearts, Lord, at the end of the day.

Jan Struther, 1901–1953
Text © 1931, Oxford University Press

Irish folk tune

The King of Love 478
ST. COLUMBA 87 87

1. The King of love my shep - herd is,
2. Where streams of liv - ing wa - ter flow
3. Con - fused and fool - ish oft I strayed,

4. In death's dark vale I fear no ill
5. You spread a ta - ble in my sight,
6. And so through all the length of days

1. Whose good - ness fails me nev - er;
2. My ran - somed soul he's lead - ing,
3. But yet in love he sought me,

4. With you, dear Lord, be - side me;
5. Your sav - ing grace be - stow - ing;
6. Your good - ness fails me nev - er,

1. I noth - ing lack if I am his,
2. And where the ver - dant pas - tures grow
3. And on his shoul - der gent - ly laid,

4. Your rod and staff my com - fort still,
5. And oh, what trans - port of de - light
6. Good Shep - herd, may I sing your praise

1. And he is mine for - ev - er.
2. With food ce - les - tial feed - ing.
3. And home, re - joic - ing, brought me.

4. Your cross be - fore to guide me.
5. From your pure chal - ice flow - ing!
6. With - in your house for - ev - er.

Ps 23:1–6
Henry W. Baker, 1821–1877, alt.

Traditional Irish melody

479 We Have Been Told

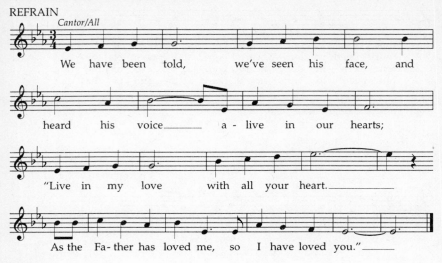

REFRAIN

Cantor/All

We have been told, we've seen his face, and heard his voice_____ a - live in our hearts; "Live in my love with all your heart._____ As the Fa- ther has loved me, so I have loved you."_____

VERSES

1. "I am the vine, you are the branches, And all who live in me will bear great fruit."

2. "You are my friends if you keep my commands; No longer slaves, I call you friends."

3. "No greater love is there than this: To lay down one's life for a friend."

Jn 15

David Haas

Text and music © 1983, GIA

480 Love Divine, All Loves Excelling

HYFRYDOL 87 87 D

1. Love di - vine,__ all loves ex - cel - ling, Joy of
2. Come, Al - might - y, to de - liv - er, Let us
3. Fin - ish then__ your new cre - a - tion, Pure and

1. heav'n to earth__ come down, Fix in us____ your
2. all your life____ re - ceive; Sud - den - ly____ re -
3. spot - less, gra - cious Lord. Let us see____ your

1. hum - ble dwell - ing, All your faith - ful mer - cies crown.
2. turn and nev - er, Nev - er - more your tem - ples leave.
3. great sal - va - tion Per - fect - ly in you__ re - stored,

1. Je - sus, source of all com - pas - sion, Love un -
2. Lord, we would be al - ways bless - ing, Serve you
3. Changed from glo - ry in - to glo - ry, Till in

1. bound - ed, love__ all pure, Vis - it us__ with
2. as__ your hosts__ a - bove, Pray,__ and praise you
3. heav'n we take__ our place, Till__ we sing__ be -

1. your sal - va - tion; Let your love__ in us en - dure.
2. with - out ceas - ing, Glo - ry in__ your pre - cious love.
3. fore th'Al - might - y, Lost in won - der, love, and praise.

Charles Wesley, 1707–1788, alt.   Rowland H. Prichard, 1811–1887

Ubi Caritas/Live in Charity 481

REFRAIN
Cantor/All

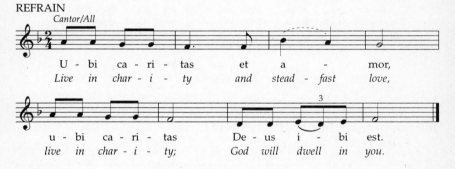

U - bi ca - ri - tas   et   a -   mor,
Live   in   char - i - ty   and   stead - fast   love,

u - bi ca - ri - tas   De - us   i - bi   est.
live   in   char - i - ty;   God   will   dwell   in   you.

VERSES

1. If I have the gift of prophecy, understanding all the mysteries there are,
   knowing ev'rything; if I have faith in all its fullness to move mountains,
   but have not love, I am nothing at all.

2. If I give ev'rything I have to feed the poor, and let them take my body
   to be burned, but have not love, I gain nothing at all.

3. Love is patient, love is not jealous. Love does not rejoice in what is wrong,
   but love rejoices in the truth. Love is always ready to excuse, to hope,
   to trust, and to endure whatever comes.

4. Love never fails. Prophecies will cease, and tongues will be silent,
   knowledge will pass away; but there are only three things in the end
   that last: faith, hope and love, and the greatest of these is love.

1 Cor 13:2–8   Jacques Berthier, 1923–1994
                              Text and music © 1979, Les Presses de Taizé, Pub. by GIA

482 Jesus, the New Covenant

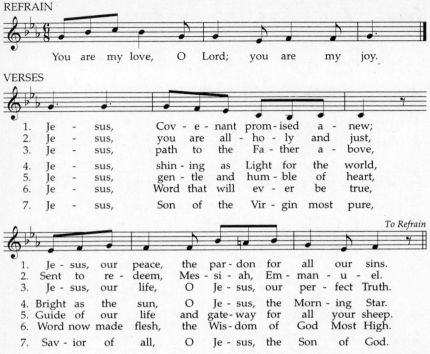

REFRAIN

You are my love, O Lord; you are my joy.

VERSES

1. Je - sus, Cov - e - nant prom - ised a - new;
2. Je - sus, you are all - ho - ly and just,
3. Je - sus, path to the Fa - ther a - bove,
4. Je - sus, shin - ing as Light for the world,
5. Je - sus, gen - tle and hum - ble of heart,
6. Je - sus, Word that will ev - er be true,
7. Je - sus, Son of the Vir - gin most pure,

To Refrain

1. Je - sus, our peace, the par - don for all our sins.
2. Sent to re - deem, Mes - si - ah, Em - man - u - el.
3. Je - sus, our life, O Je - sus, our per - fect Truth.
4. Bright as the sun, O Je - sus, the Morn - ing Star.
5. Guide of our life and gate - way for all your sheep.
6. Word now made flesh, the Wis - dom of God Most High.
7. Sav - ior of all, O Je - sus, the Son of God.

Lucien Deiss
Text and music © 1977, Lucien Deiss, pub. and dist. by WLP

483 Jesu, Jesu, Fill Us with Your Love

CHEREPONI

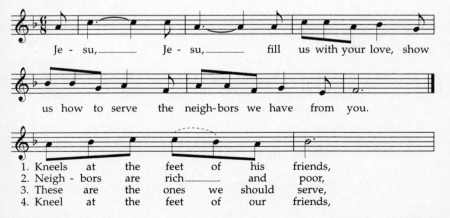

Je - su,_____ Je - su,_____ fill us with your love, show

us how to serve the neigh - bors we have from you.

1. Kneels at the feet of his friends,
2. Neigh - bors are rich_____ and poor,
3. These are the ones we should serve,
4. Kneel at the feet of our friends,

LOVE

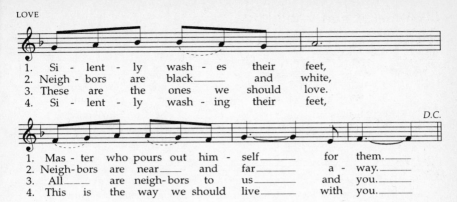

1. Si - lent - ly wash - es their feet,
2. Neigh - bors are black____ and white,
3. These are the ones we should love.
4. Si - lent - ly wash - ing their feet,

D.C.

1. Mas - ter who pours out him - self____ for them.____
2. Neigh-bors are near____ and far____ a - way.____
3. All____ are neigh-bors to us____ and you.____
4. This is the way we should live____ with you.____

Tr. by Tom Colvin

Ghana folk song
Adapt. by Tom Colvin
Tr. and adapt. © 1969, 1982, Hope Publishing Co.

Where Charity and Love Prevail 484
CHRISTIAN LOVE   CM

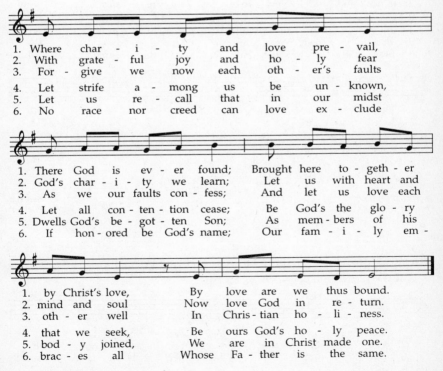

1. Where char - i - ty and love pre - vail,
2. With grate - ful joy and ho - ly fear
3. For - give we now each oth - er's faults
4. Let strife a - mong us be un - known,
5. Let us re - call that in our midst
6. No race nor creed can love ex - clude

1. There God is ev - er found; Brought here to - geth - er
2. God's char - i - ty we learn; Let us with heart and
3. As we our faults con - fess; And let us love each
4. Let all con - ten - tion cease; Be God's the glo - ry
5. Dwells God's be - got - ten Son; As mem - bers of his
6. If hon - ored be God's name; Our fam - i - ly em -

1. by Christ's love, By love are we thus bound.
2. mind and soul Now love God in re - turn.
3. oth - er well In Chris - tian ho - li - ness.
4. that we seek, Be ours God's ho - ly peace.
5. bod - y joined, We are in Christ made one.
6. brac - es all Whose Fa - ther is the same.

Based on *Ubi caritas*, 9th cent.
Omer Westendorf

Paul Benoit, 1893–1979
Text and music © 1960, WLP

485 Where Charity and Love Prevail

1. Where char - i - ty and__ love pre - vail,
2. With grate-ful joy and__ ho - ly fear
3. For - give we now each__ oth - er's faults

4. Let strife a - mong us__ be un-known,
5. Let us re - call that__ in our midst
6. No race nor creed can__ love ex - clude,

1. There God is ev - er found; Brought here to - geth - er__
2. God's char - i - ty we learn; Let us with heart and
3. As we our faults con - fess; And let us love each

4. Let all con - ten - tion cease; Be God's the glo - ry__
5. Dwells God's be - got - ten Son. As mem-bers of his__
6. If hon-ored be God's name; Our fam - i - ly em -

1. by Christ's love, By__ love are__ we thus bound;__ By__
2. mind and soul Now love God in re - turn;____ Now
3. oth - er well In__ Chris-tian ho - li - ness,____ In__

4. that we seek. Be__ ours God's ho - ly__ peace,____ Be__
5. Bod - y joined, We__ are in__ Christ made one,____ We__
6. brac - es all Whose Fath - er__ is the__ same,____ Whose

1. love are we thus bound.
2. love God in re - turn.
3. Chris - tian ho - li - ness.

4. ours God's ho - ly peace.
5. are in Christ made one.
6. Fath - er is the same.

Based on *Ubi caritas*, 9th cent.
Omer Westendorf

Mark Hill
Text and music © 1960, 1993, WLP

486 Shepherd of Souls, in Love, Come, Feed Us

ICH WILL DICH LIEBEN   98 98 88

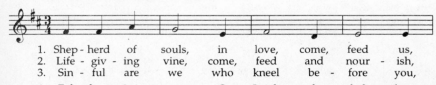

1. Shep - herd of souls, in love, come, feed us,
2. Life - giv - ing vine, come, feed and nour - ish,
3. Sin - ful are we who kneel be - fore you,

4. Fol - low - ing you, O Lord, who led them,
5. Fa - ther, who fed the He - brew na - tion,
6. Help us, dear Lord, pre - pare a dwell - ing

1. Life - giv - ing bread for hun - gry hearts!
2. Strength - en each branch with life di - vine;
3. Wor - thy of you are you a - lone;

4. Mul - ti - tudes thronged the moun - tain - side;
5. Giv - ing them man - na from the sky,
6. Wor - thy of you who made us all;

1. To those re - fresh - ing wa - ters lead us
2. Ev - er in you, O may we flour - ish,
3. Yet in your name do we im - plore you,

4. Filled with com - pas - sion, Lord, you fed them,
5. Give now the bread of our sal - va - tion
6. Cleanse then our hearts, our guilt dis - pel - ling,

1. Where dwells that peace your grace im - parts.
2. Fruit - ful the branch - es on the vine.
3. Rich are the mer - cies you have shown.

4. Fed them with loaves you mul - ti - plied.
5. That we who eat shall ne - ver die.
6. Pu - ri - fy us who heed your call.

1. May we, the way - ward in your fold,
2. Lord, may our souls be pu - ri - fied
3. Say but the word, O Lord di - vine,

4. Come, feed us now, O Lord, we pray;
5. We are your peo - ple, God, in need;
6. "Take this and eat" were words you said;

1. By your for - give - ness rest con - soled.
2. So that in Christ may we a - bide.
3. Then are our hearts made pure like thine.

4. Life - giv - ing bread give us this day.
5. May we on liv - ing bread now feed.
6. So do we gath - er for this bread.

Omer Westendorf
Text © 1964, WLP

Georg Joseph, c. 1630–1668

487 Love Is His Word

DeBLASIO 88 97 with Refrain

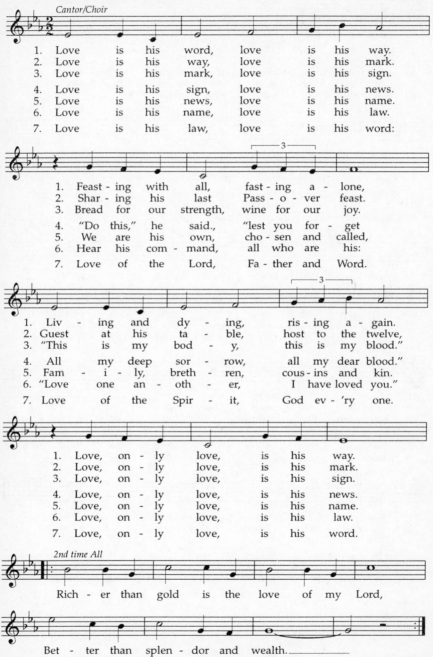

Cantor/Choir

1. Love is his word, love is his way.
2. Love is his way, love is his mark.
3. Love is his mark, love is his sign.
4. Love is his sign, love is his news.
5. Love is his news, love is his name.
6. Love is his name, love is his law.
7. Love is his law, love is his word:

1. Feast - ing with all, fast - ing a - lone,
2. Shar - ing his last Pass - o - ver feast.
3. Bread for our strength, wine for our joy.
4. "Do this," he said., "lest you for - get
5. We are his own, cho - sen and called,
6. Hear his com - mand, all who are his:
7. Love of the Lord, Fa - ther and Word.

1. Liv - ing and dy - ing, ris - ing a - gain.
2. Guest at his ta - ble, host to the twelve,
3. "This is my bod - y, this is my blood."
4. All my deep sor - row, all my dear blood."
5. Fam - i - ly, breth - ren, cous - ins and kin.
6. "Love one an - oth - er, I have loved you."
7. Love of the Spir - it, God ev - 'ry one.

1. Love, on - ly love, is his way.
2. Love, on - ly love, is his mark.
3. Love, on - ly love, is his sign.
4. Love, on - ly love, is his news.
5. Love, on - ly love, is his name.
6. Love, on - ly love, is his law.
7. Love, on - ly love, is his word.

2nd time All

Rich - er than gold is the love of my Lord,

Bet - ter than splen - dor and wealth.

Luke Connaughton, 1917–1979
Text © 1970, McCrimmon Publishing Co., Ltd.

Calvin Hampton, 1938–1984
Music © 1997, WLP

There Is a Love 488

CARTERET 10 10 10 10

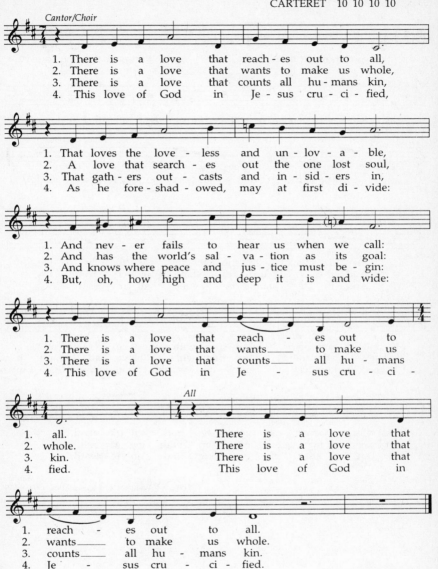

Cantor/Choir

1. There is a love that reach - es out to all,
2. There is a love that wants to make us whole,
3. There is a love that counts all hu - mans kin,
4. This love of God in Je - sus cru - ci - fied,

1. That loves the love - less and un - lov - a - ble,
2. A love that search - es out the one lost soul,
3. That gath - ers out - casts and in - sid - ers in,
4. As he fore - shad - owed, may at first di - vide:

1. And nev - er fails to hear us when we call:
2. And has the world's sal - va - tion as its goal:
3. And knows where peace and jus - tice must be - gin:
4. But, oh, how high and deep it is and wide:

1. There is a love that reach - es out to
2. There is a love that wants to make us
3. There is a love that counts all hu - mans
4. This love of God in Je - sus cru - ci -

All

1. all.   There is a love that
2. whole.   There is a love that
3. kin.   There is a love that
4. fied.   This love of God in

1. reach - es out to all.
2. wants to make us whole.
3. counts all hu - mans kin.
4. Je - sus cru - ci - fied.

Fred Pratt Green
Text © 1989, Hope Publishing Co.

Steven R. Janco
Music © 1997, WLP

489 Set Your Heart on the Higher Gifts

REFRAIN

Cantor/All

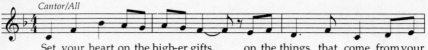

Set your heart on the high-er gifts,— on the things that come from your

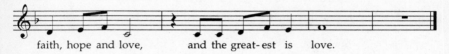

Mak - er in heav - en. These three gifts are all that re-main:

faith, hope and love, and the great-est is love.

VERSES

Cantor

1. If I speak with the tongues of the liv - ing,
2. And if I un - der - stand ev - 'ry mys - t'ry,
3. And if I should re - nounce all my rich - es,

1. and of an - gels, but speak with-out love, I am on - ly
2. hav - ing wis - dom, but think with-out love, had I faith to
3. feed the hun - gry, give o - ver my life; with-out love my

To Refrain

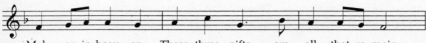

1. brass with-out song, an emp - ty noise on the wind.
2. scat - ter the hills,— I am noth - ing at all.
3. prof - it is loss, my car - ing finds no re - ward.

1 Cor 12:31–13:13

Steven C. Warner
Adapt. text and music © 1992, 1994, WLP

With Eternal Love 490

REFRAIN

Cantor/All

"With e - ter - nal love_____ I have loved you, my

peo - ple, With ev - er - last - ing kind - ness,

I have drawn you to me," says the Lord._____

VERSES

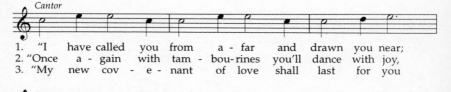

Cantor

1. "I have called you from a - far and drawn you near;
2. "Once a - gain with tam - bou-rines you'll dance with joy,
3. "My new cov - e - nant of love shall last for you

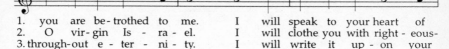

1. you are be - trothed to me. I will speak to your heart of
2. O vir - gin Is - ra - el. I will clothe you with right - eous-
3. through-out e - ter - ni - ty. I will write it up - on your

To Refrain

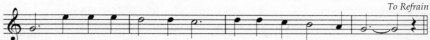

1. love. You shall be filled with peace, with ev - er - last - ing joy."___
2. ness. I shall for - give your sins, re - mem-ber them no more."_
3. heart. You shall be - long to me; know that I am your God."_

Jer 31:3–4, 33

Lucien Deiss
Text and music © 1995, WLP

491 Song of My Love

REFRAIN Cantor/All

Lord, you are the song of my love._____

You are the joy of my life!

VERSES Cantor

1. I_____ am_____ the mill, your love is the
2. I am the spin - ning wheel, your pa - tience is
3. I_____ am_____ the field, your word is the
4. We_____ are_____ the sheep, you are the good

1. brook._____ Help_____ me grind_____ the
2. lin - en._____ Help_____ me weave_____ the
3. seed._____ Rip - en in me_____ the
4. shep - herd._____ Keep_____ us in_____ the

To Refrain

1. grain_____ for the bread_____ of heav - en!_____
2. gar - ment for the feast_____ of heav - en!_____
3. grain_____ for the har - vest in heav - en!_____
4. sheep-fold dwell - ing in_____ your heav - en!_____

Lucien Deiss
Text and music © 1995, WLP

492 Eternal Father, Strong to Save
MELITA 88 88 88

1. E - ter - nal Fa - ther, strong to save, Whose arm has bound the
2. O Christ, the Lord of hill and plain O'er which our traf - fic
3. O Spir - it, whom the Fa - ther sent To spread a - broad the
4. O Trin - i - ty of love and pow'r, Your chil - dren shield in

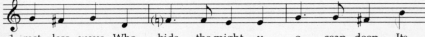

1. rest - less wave, Who bids the might - y o - cean deep Its
2. runs a - main By moun - tain pass or val - ley low; Where -
3. fir - ma - ment; O Wind of heav - en, by your might Save
4. dan - ger's hour; From rock and tem - pest, fire and foe, Pro -

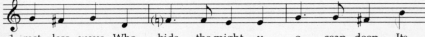

1. own ap - point - ed lim - its keep: O hear us when we
2. ev - er, Lord, your loved ones go, Pro - tect them by your
3. all who dare the ea - gle's flight, And keep them by your
4. tect them where - so - e'er they go; And then shall rise with

1. raise our plea For those in per - il on the sea.
2. guard - ing hand From ev - 'ry per - il on the land.
3. watch - ful care From ev - 'ry per - il in the air.
4. voic - es free Glad praise from air and land and sea.

Vss. 1, 4: William Whiting, 1825–1878, alt.
Vss. 2, 3: Robert N. Spencer, 1877–1961, alt.

John B. Dykes, 1823–1876

Ask and You Shall Receive 493

REFRAIN

Cantor/All

Ask and you shall re - ceive. Seek and you shall

find. Knock and the door will be o - pened,

1.–2. To Verses Final

will be o - pened un - to you. 1. Now you.
2. To —

VERSES

Cantor/Choir

1. hear our pray'r, O Lord, and lis - ten to our sigh - ing.
2. you we pray, O Lord, at dawn you hear our plead - ing.

To Refrain

1. Heed our call for help, our King ___ and our God!
2. Turn your face to us, and lis - ten to our cry.

Ref.: Mt 7:7
Vss.: Ps 5:2–3

Eugene Englert
Text and music © 1991, WLP

494 Hear My Prayer

REFRAIN

Hear my prayer, O Lord my God;
hear the cry I raise to you.
Be with me in my dis-tress: sup-port me, Lord, be
near me, Lord; with-out you, I can do no-thing.

VERSES

1. Be with me, stay with me, do not leave me! I need you to help me:
   you are my only strength. *(to Refrain I)*

2. Speak to me, oh, speak to me words of comfort.
   My eyes and ears are turned to you. O Lord, hear and answer! *(to Refrain I)*

3. In your love relieve my pain: your gentle touch can make me whole again.
   Lay your hand on me. *(to Refrain I)*

4. Here I am, open; here I am, broken: I rely on you alone, you alone,
   you alone, my God! *(to Refrain II)*

REFRAIN II

Hear my prayer, O Lord my God;
hear the cry I raise to you.
Be with me in my dis-tress: sup-port me, Lord, be
near me, Lord; with-out you I can do no-thing.

5. Take me, Lord, in your embrace; bend my heart to do your will. Show me your way; pour out the light of your truth. *(to Final Refrain)*

FINAL REFRAIN

Hear my prayer, O Lord my God; hear the cry I raise to you. Be with me in my dis-tress: sup-port me, Lord, be near me, Lord, pro - tect me, sur-round me, O God, my God!

With - out you I can do no - thing.

Paul Inwood
Text and music © 1992, Paul Inwood
Pub. and dist. by WLP

O Lord, Hear My Prayer 495

OSTINATO

O Lord, hear my prayer, O Lord, hear my prayer: when I call an - swer me. O Lord, hear my prayer, O Lord, hear my prayer. Come and lis - ten to me.

Ps 102

Jacques Berthier, 1923–1994
Text and music © 1984, Les Presses de Taizé, pub. by GIA

496 How Firm a Foundation

FOUNDATION 11 11 11 11

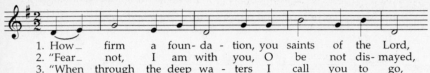

1. How firm a foun-da - tion, you saints of the Lord,
2. "Fear not, I am with you, O be not dis-mayed,
3. "When through the deep wa - ters I call you to go,
4. "When through fier - y tri - als your path - way shall lie,
5. "The soul that on Je - sus still leans for re - pose,

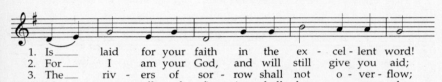

1. Is laid for your faith in the ex - cel - lent word!
2. For I am your God, and will still give you aid;
3. The riv - ers of sor - row shall not o - ver - flow;
4. My grace, all suf - fi - cient, shall be your sup - ply;
5. I will not, I will not de - sert to its foes;

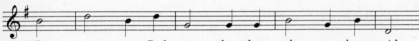

1. What more can God say than has al - ways been said,
2. I'll strength - en you, help you, and cause you to stand,
3. For I will be with you, your trou - bles to bless,
4. The flame shall not hurt you, I on - ly de - sign
5. That soul, though all hell should en - deav - or to shake,

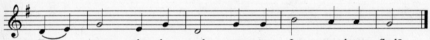

1. To you who for ref - uge to Je - sus have fled?
2. Up - held by my right - eous, om - nip - o - tent hand."
3. And sanc - ti - fy to you your deep - est dis - tress."
4. Your waste to con- sume, and your gold to re - fine."
5. I'll nev - er, no, nev - er, no, nev - er for - sake!"

1 Cor 3:11
Rippon's *Selection of Hymns*, 1787, alt.

Traditional American melody

497 Blessed Assurance, Jesus Is Mine

ASSURANCE 9 10 9 9 with Refrain

1. Bless - ed as - sur - ance, Je - sus is mine! Oh, what a
2. Per - fect sub - mis - sion, per- fect de - light, Vi - sions of
3. Per - fect sub - mis - sion, all is at rest, I, in my

1. fore - taste of glo - ry di - vine! Heirs of sal - va - tion, chil- dren of
2. rap - ture now burst on my sight; An- gels de- scend-ing, bring from a-
3. Sav - ior, am hap- py and blest; Watch-ing and wait- ing, look - ing a-

1. God, Born of one Spir - it, washed in his blood.
2. bove Ech - oes of mer - cy, whis-pers of love.
3. bove, Filled with his good - ness, lost in his love.

This is my sto - ry, this is my song, Prais-ing my

Sav - ior all the day long; This is my sto - ry, this is my

song, Prais-ing my Sav - ior all the day long.

Fanny J. Crosby, 1820–1915, alt.   Phoebe P. Knapp, 1839–1908

Give Me Jesus 498

GIVE ME JESUS 7 7 7 4 with Refrain

1. In the morn-ing when I rise, in the morn-ing when I
2. Dark___ mid-night was my cry, dark___ mid-night was my
3. Just a-bout the break of day, just a-bout the break of
4. Oh,___ when I come to die, Oh,___ when I come to

1. rise, in the morn-ing when I rise, give me Je - sus.
2. cry, dark___ mid-night was my cry, give me Je - sus.
3. day, just a-bout the break of day, give me Je - sus.
4. die, Oh,___ when I come to die, give me Je - sus.

Give me Je - sus, give me Je - sus, you may

have all this world, give me Je - sus.

African-American

499 O God, Our Help in Ages Past

ST. ANNE CM

1. O God, our help in a - ges past, Our
2. Be - neath the shad - ow of your throne Your
3. Be - fore the hills in or - der stood, Or
4. A thou - sand a - ges in your sight Are
5. Time, like an ev - er - roll - ing stream, Bears
6. O God, our help in a - ges past, Our

1. hope for years to come, Our shel - ter from the
2. saints have dwelt se - cure; Suf - fi - cient is your
3. earth re - ceived her frame, From ev - er - last - ing
4. like an eve - ning gone, Short as the watch that
5. all our lives a - way; They fly, for - got - ten,
6. hope for years to come, Be now our guide while

1. storm - y blast, And our e - ter - nal home.
2. arm a - lone, And our de - fense is sure.
3. you are God, To end - less years the same.
4. ends the night Be - fore the ris - ing sun.
5. as a dream Dies at the o - p'ning day.
6. life shall last, And our e - ter - nal home.

Ps 90:1-2, 4-6, 12
Isaac Watts, 1674-1748, alt.

William Croft, 1678-1727

500 How Can I Keep from Singing

QUAKER HYMN

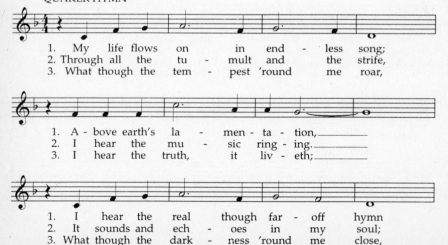

1. My life flows on in end - less song;
2. Through all the tu - mult and the strife,
3. What though the tem - pest 'round me roar,

1. A - bove earth's la - men - ta - tion,_____
2. I hear the mu - sic ring - ing._____
3. I hear the truth, it liv - eth;_____

1. I hear the real though far - off hymn
2. It sounds and ech - oes in my soul;
3. What though the dark - ness 'round me close,

1. That hails a new cre - a - tion._____
2. How can I keep from sing - ing?_____
3. Songs in the night it giv - eth._____

No storm can shake my___ in-most calm While to that

rock I'm cling-ing._____ Since love is Lord of___

heav-en and earth, How can I keep from sing-ing?_____

Anon.

Robert Lowry, 1826–1899

My Soul Is Longing 501

REFRAIN

Cantor/All

My soul is long-ing for your peace, near to you, my God!

VERSES

Cantor

1. Lord, you know that my heart is not proud,
2. Loft - y thoughts have nev - er filled my mind;
3. In your peace I have main - tained my soul;
4. As a child rests on its moth - er's knee,
5. Is - ra - el, put all your hope in God;

To Refrain

1. And my eyes are not lift - ed from the earth.
2. Far be - yond my sight all am - bi - tious deeds.
3. I have kept my heart in your qui - et peace.
4. So I place my soul in your lov - ing care.
5. Place your trust in God, now and ev - er - more.

Lucien Deiss
Text and music © 1965, WLP

1. O Lord, my God, when I in awe-some won-der
2. When through the woods and for-est glades I wan-der,
3. And when I think that God, his Son not spar-ing,
4. When Christ shall come, with shout of ac-cla-ma-tion,

1. Con-sid-er all the worlds thy hand hath made,
2. And hear the birds sing sweet-ly in the trees;
3. Sent him to die, I scarce can take it in,
4. And take me home, what joy shall fill my heart!

1. I see the stars, I hear the roll-ing thun-der,
2. When I look down from loft-y moun-tain gran-deur
3. That on the cross my burd-en glad-ly bear-ing,
4. Then I shall bow in hum-ble ad-o-ra-tion

1. Thy pow'r through-out the u-ni-verse dis-played;
2. And hear the brook and feel the gen-tle breeze;
3. He bled and died to take a-way my sin;
4. And there pro-claim, "My God, how great thou art!"

Then sings my soul, my Sav-ior God, to thee;

How great thou art! How great thou art!

Then sings my soul, my Sav-ior God, to thee;

How great thou art! How great thou art!

Stuart K. Hine, 1899–1989, alt.
Text and music © 1953, 1981, Manna Music, Inc.

Lead Me, Guide Me 503

REFRAIN

Lead__ me, guide__ me, a - long the way,
For_____ if you lead me, I can - not stray.
Lord,_____ let me walk each day with thee.
Lead me, oh Lord, lead me._____

VERSES

1. I am weak_____ and I need your strength and power
2. Help me tread_____ in the paths of right - eous - ness,
3. I am lost_____ if you take your hand from me,

1. To_____ help me o - ver my weak - est hour.
2. Be my aid when e - vil and sin op - press.
3. I am blind with - out_____ your light to see,

1. Help me through the dark - ness your face to see,
2. I am put - ting all_____ my trust in thee.
3. Lord, just al - ways let me your ser - vant be.

To Refrain

1. Lead me, oh Lord,__ lead me._____
2. Lead me, oh Lord,__ lead me._____
3. Lead me, oh Lord,__ lead me._____

Doris M. Akers
Text and music © 1953, Doris M. Akers

504 Seek Ye First

SEEK YE FIRST Irregular

1. Seek ye___ first the___ king - dom of God
2. Ask and it shall be___ giv - en un - to you;
3. You do not live by___ bread___ a - lone,
4. Where two or three are___ gath - ered in my name,
5. Come to___ me when bur - dened and op - pressed,
6. Take up my yoke and___ learn___ from___ me;

1. and his___ right - eous - ness,___
2. seek and___ ye shall___ find;___
3. But by___ ev - 'ry___ word,___
4. There am___ I in their midst;___
5. And find___ rest for your soul.
6. I am___ gen - tle and mild.___

1. and all these things shall be add - ed un - to you.
2. knock and it shall be___ o - pened un - to you.
3. that comes___ forth from the mouth___ of___ God.
4. and what - so - ev - er you ask___ I will do.
5. I will re - fresh you with strength on your way.
6. My yoke is eas - y, my bur - den is light.

Al - le - lu, al - le - lu - ia.

Vs. 1: Karen Lafferty; Vs. 2–4: Anon.; Vss. 5, 6: James E. Wilbur
Text (vss. 5, 6) © 1994, WLP

Karen Lafferty

Text (vs. 1) and music © 1972, Maranatha! Music, admin. by The Copyright Co.

505 My Shepherd Will Supply My Need

RESIGNATION CMD

1. My shep - herd will sup - ply my need, The
2. When I walk through the shades of death, Your
3. The sure pro - vi - sions of my God At -

1. God of love su - preme. In pas - tures green I
2. pres - ence is my stay; One word of your sup-
3. tend me all my days; O may your house be

1. come to feed, Be - side the liv - ing stream. My
2. port - ing breath Drives all my fears a - way. Your
3. my a - bode, And all my work be praise! There

1. wan - d'ring spir - it is brought back When - e'er I
2. hand, in sight of all my foes, Does still my
3. would I find a set - tled rest, While oth - ers

1. go a - stray; For mer - cy's sake my
2. ta - ble spread; My cup with bless - ings
3. go and come, No more a stran - ger

1. heart is led In paths of truth and grace.
2. o - ver - flows, Your oil a - noints my head.
3. nor a guest, But like a child at home.

Ps 23
Isaac Watts, 1674–1748, alt.

William Walker's *Southern Harmony*, 1835

506 Eye Has Not Seen

REFRAIN

Eye has not seen, ear has not heard what God has read - y for

CONSOLATION

those who love him. Spir-it of love, come, give us the mind of

Last time to Final
To Verses

Je - sus;_____ teach us the wis-dom of God._____

Final

Eye has not seen, ear has not heard what God has

read-y_____ for those_____ who love him._____

VERSES

1. When pain and sor-row weigh us down, be near to us, O
2. Our lives are but a sin - gle breath, we flow - er and we
3. To those who see with eyes of faith, the Lord is ev - er
4. We sing a mys-t'ry from the past in halls where saints have

1. Lord; For - give the weak - ness of our faith, and
2. fade; Yet all our days are in your hands, so
3. near, Re - flect - ed in the fac - es of
4. trod; Yet ev - er new the mu - sic rings to

1.–3. *To Refrain*

1. bear us up with- in your peace-ful word._____
2. we re- turn in love what love has made._____
3. all the poor and low - ly of the world._____

4. *To Refrain*

4. Je- sus, liv - ing Song of God._____

1 Cor 2:9–10

Marty Haugen
Text and music © 1982, GIA

507 By the Waters of Babylon

CONSOLATION

REFRAIN

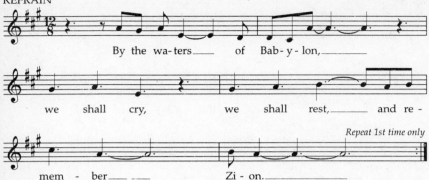

By the wa-ters___ of Bab-y-lon,___

we shall cry, we shall rest,___ and re-

Repeat 1st time only

mem - ber___ ___ Zi - on.___

VERSES

1. We long to play our harps and raise a song to you.
   But how can we sing our song in a foreign land?

2. May we not forget beloved Jerusalem!
   Lord, help up to sing our song in this foreign land!

3. Lord, we need your strength! Fill us with your spirit!
   Inspire us to bring your song to this foreign land!

Paul A Tate
Text and music © 1996, WLP

508 I Heard the Voice of Jesus Say

KINGSFOLD CMD

1. I___ heard the voice of Je - sus say, "Come un - to me___ and
2. I___ heard the voice of Je - sus say, "Be - hold, I free - ly
3. I___ heard the voice of Je - sus say, "I___ am this dark world's

1. rest; Lay___ down, O wea - ry one, lay down Your
2. give The___ liv - ing wa - ter; thirst - y one, Stoop
3. light; Look un - to me, your morn shall rise, And___

1. head up - on___ my breast." I___ came to Je - sus
2. down, and drink, and live." I___ came to Je - sus,
3. all your day___ be bright." I___ looked to Je - sus,

CONSOLATION

1. as I was, So_ wea - ry,_ worn, and sad;
2. and I drank Of_ that life - giv - ing stream;
3. and I found In_ him my_ star, my sun;

1. I_ found in him_ a_ rest - ing place,
2. My_ thirst was quenched, my_ soul re - vived,
3. And_ in that light_ of_ life I'll walk

1. And_ he has made_ me glad.
2. And_ now I live_ in him.
3. Till_ trav - 'ling days_ are done.

Horatius Bonar, 1808–1889   Traditional English folk song

Jerusalem, My Happy Home 509
LAND OF REST   CM

1. Je - ru - sa - lem,_ my hap - py home,_ When
2. O hap - py har - bor of the saints,_ O
3. Your gar - dens and_ your gal - lant walks_ Con -
4. There, trees for - ev - er - more bear fruit_ And
5. Je - ru - sa - lem,_ Je - ru - sa - lem,_ God

1. shall I with_ you be?_ When shall my sor - rows
2. sweet and pleas - ant soil!_ In you no sor - row
3. tin - ual - ly_ are green;_ There grow such sweet_ and
4. ev - er - more do spring,_ There, ev - er - more_ the
5. grant that I_ may see_ Your end - less joy,_ and

1. have an end?_ Your joys, when shall_ I see?_
2. may be found, No grief, no care,_ no toil._
3. pleas - ant flow'rs As no - where else_ are seen._
4. an - gels sit_ And ev - er - more_ do sing._
5. of the same_ Par - tak - er ev - er be!_

F.B.P. in *Song of Mary,* 1601   American folk melody
Adapt. by Annabel Morris Buchanan, 1889–1983; Adapt. © 1938, J. Fischer & Bro.

510 Yahweh

REFRAIN

Yah - weh, the God of our sal - va - tion:_____ we trust in
you,_____ and have no fear._____ We sing of the
joy which your love gives to us,_____ and we draw
deep - ly from the springs of your great kind - ness._____

VERSES

1. O - pen our eyes to the won - der of this
2. Be with us, God, as we break through with each
3. When eve - ning comes and our day of toil is
4. Take us be - yond_____ the vi - sion of this

1. mo - ment the be - gin - ning of_____ an -
2. oth - er _____ to find_____ the truth_____ and
3. o - ver give us rest,_____ O God, in the
4. day to _____ the deep and wide ways of your

To Refrain

1. oth - er day._____
2. beau - ty of each friend._____
3. joy_____ of man - y friends._____
4. in - fi - nite love and life._____

Is 12:2, 3

Gregory R. Norbet

511 Come to Me

REFRAIN

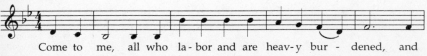

Come to me, all who la - bor and are heav - y bur - dened, and

CONSOLATION

I shall give you rest. Take up my yoke and
learn from me, for I am meek and hum-ble of
heart, and you'll find rest for your souls.
Yes, my yoke is eas-y and my
bur - den is light.

VERSES

1. You, God, are my shep-herd. I shall
2. Be - side peace-ful wa - ters you re -
3. Should I be sur-round-ed by the
4. Be - fore my deep hun - ger you spread
5. Pur - sue me, O God, with your

1. nev - er be in need. Fresh and green are the
2. store my true self; There you lead me to
3. shad - ows of death, I will not fear, for
4. out your feast. My skin you a -
5. fath - om - less love. In your tent let me

To Refrain

1. mead - ows where you give me rest.
2. walk in the path of new life.
3. you are stead - fast in your love.
4. noint with the rich - est of oil.
5. dwell all the days of my life.

Ps 23:1–6; Mt 11:28–30

Gregory R. Norbet
Text and music © 1971, 1994 (inclusive language text and added vss.)
The Benedictine Foundation of the State of Vermont Inc.

512 Just a Closer Walk with Thee

CONSOLATION

CLOSER WALK   Irregular

Refrain:	Just	a	clos - er	walk	with	thee,
1.	I	am	weak, but	thou	art	strong;
2.	Through	this	world of	toil	and	snares,
3.	When	my	fee - ble	life	is	o'er,

Ref.	Grant	it,	Je - sus,	is	my	plea;
1.	Je -	sus,	keep me from	all	wrong;
2.	If	I	fal - ter,	Lord, who	cares?
3.	Time	for	me will be	no	more;

Ref.	Dai - ly	walk - ing	close	to	thee,		Let	it
1.	I'll	be	sat - is - fied	as	long		As	I
2.	Who	with	me my	bur - den	shares?		None but
3.	Guide	me	gent - ly,	safe - ly	o'er		To	thy

Ref.	be,	dear	Lord,	let	it	be.
1.	walk;	let me	walk	close	to	thee.
2.	thee,	dear	Lord,	none	but	thee.
3.	king - dom	shore,	to	thy	shore.

Traditional

American folk song

513 O, Lord, You Are My Shepherd

WOOLLEN   76 76 D

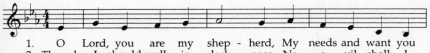

1.	O Lord, you	are	my	shep - herd,	My	needs and	want you
2.	Though I should	walk	in	dark - ness	No	e - vil	shall I
3.	Your good-ness	and your	kind - ness	Shall	ev - er	fol - low

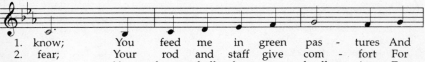

1.	know;	You	feed	me	in	green	pas - tures	And
2.	fear;	Your	rod	and	staff	give	com - fort	For
3.	me;	Your	house	shall	be	my	dwell - ing	For

1. there give me re - pose. You lead me to cool
2. you are ev - er near. You spread a sump-tuous
3. all e - ter - ni - ty. Give praise to God the
   *O, Lord, you are my

1. streams where Re - fresh - ment shall not cease; A -
2. ban - quet In sight of all my foes; With
3. Fa - ther, To Christ, his on - ly Son, And
   shep - herd, My needs and wants you know; You

1. long safe paths you guide me, True to your name of peace.
2. oil you do a - noint me, My cup now o - ver - flows.
3. to the Ho - ly Spir - it, True God in es - sence One.
   feed me in green pas - tures And there give me re - pose.

Omer Westendorf

Russell Woollen, 1923–1994
Text and music © 1962, WLP

*The first part of the psalm may be repeated at the end of the third verse, rather than "Give Praise..."

All Will Be Well 514

REFRAIN

All will be well, and all will be well, all

1.–5. / To Verses

man - ner of things will be well.

Final

well. will be well, will be well.

The Revelations of Divine Love, Chapter 32
Julian of Norwich
Adapt. by S.C.W.

Steven C. Warner
Text and music © 1993, WLP

515 God of Love

BEACH SPRING   87 87 D

1. God of love, whose mer-cies dai - ly Like the
2. Christ, who lived through earth-ly suf - f'ring, Loss, be -
3. Ho - ly Spir - it, whose in - dwell - ing Makes a
4. God of mer - cy, love and mem - 'ry, Give us

1. morn - ing are re - born, Look on us, your gath - ered
2. tray - al, fear and death, Ev - er - faith - ful to your
3. tem - ple of each heart, Par - a - clete of strength-'ning
4. strength to fol - low you; Let us trust that our de -

1. peo - ple: Heart-sick, trou - bled, wea - ry, worn,
2. call - ing, Serv - ing till your fi - nal breath:
3. pow - er, Be with us and ne'er de - part;
4. part - ed, Now at rest, their strug - gle through,

1. Who be - fore you raise our voic - es, Nam - ing
2. In your name we make me - mo - rial Of those
3. As we name each name be - fore you, For - ti -
4. All are known and loved and count - ed; As we

1. those called from our sight, Con - fi - dent that each is
2. gath - ered at your hand; Freed from pain, de - spair and
3. fy us with your grace That we strive to live in
4. name them, so may we, Joined with them in one com -

1. pre - cious And is pres - ent in your light.
2. sor - row, Ris - en Lord, with you they stand.
3. whole - ness Till in heav'n we see your face.
4. mun - ion, Lov - ing, serv - ing, ev - er be.

J. Michael Thompson
Text © 1994, WLP

The Sacred Harp, Philadelphia, 1844
Setting © 1978, Augsburg Fortress

You Are Mine 516

VERSES

1. I will come to you   in the si - lence,
2. I am hope for all   who are hope - less,—
3. I am strength for all   the des - pair - ing,—
4. am the Word that leads   all to free - dom,   I

1. I will lift you from___   all your fear.
2. I am eyes for all   who long to see.   In the
3. heal - ing for the ones   who dwell in shame.
4. am the peace the world___   can - not give.

1. You will hear my voice   I claim you as my choice,   be
2. shad - ows of the night,___   I will be your light,___
3. All the blind will see,   the lame will all run free,   and
4. I will call your name,   em - brac - ing all your pain,   stand

1. still and__ know I am here._____   *To Verse 2*
2. come and__ rest in me._____   *To Refrain*
3. all will__ know my name._____   *To Refrain*
4. up, now__ walk, and live!_____   *To Refrain*

REFRAIN

Do not be a - fraid, I am with you. I have called you each by

name. Come and fol - low me, I will bring you home;___

To Verses

I love you and you are mine.___

4. I

David Haas
Text and music © 1991, GIA

517 Keep in Mind

REFRAIN

Cantor/All

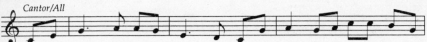

Keep in mind that Je-sus Christ has died for us and is ris-en from the

dead. He is our sav-ing Lord, he is joy for all a - ges.

VERSES

Cantor *To Refrain*

1. _ If we die with the Lord, we shall live with the Lord.
   If we en - dure with the Lord, we shall reign with the Lord.

Cantor *To Refrain*

2. In Christ all our sor - row, in Christ all our joy.
   In him hope of glo - ry, in him all our love.
3. In Christ our re - demp - tion, in Christ all our grace.
   In him our sal - va - tion, in him all our peace.

2 Tm 2:8–12

Lucien Deiss
Text and music © 1965, WLP

518 Come to Me

HOLY MANNA 87 87 D

1. Come to__ me, all pil - grims thirst - y,__
2. Come to__ me, all trav - 'lers__ wea - ry,__
3. Come to__ me, be - liev - ers__ bur - dened,

1. Drink the__ wa - ter I will give.
2. Come that__ I may give you rest.
3. Find re - fresh - ment in this place.

1. If you__ knew what gift I__ of - fer,__
2. Drink the__ cup of life I__ of - fer;__
3. If you__ knew the gift I__ of - fer,__

1. You would come to me and live.
2. At this ta - ble be my guest.
3. You would turn and seek my face.

Je - sus, ev - er - flow - ing__ foun - tain, Give us wa - ter__

from your__ well. In the__ gra - cious gift you__ of - fer__

There is__ joy no tongue can tell.

Delores Dufner
Text © 1992, Sisters of St. Benedict

William Walker's *Southern Harmony*, 1835

O God of Love 519
QUEBEC LM

1. O God of love, O King of peace,
2. Re - mem - ber, Lord, your works of old,
3. Whom shall we trust but you, O Lord?
4. Where saints and an - gels dwell a - bove,

1. Make wars through - out the world to cease;
2. The won - ders that to us were told;
3. Where rest but on your faith - ful word?
4. All hearts are knit in ho - ly love;

1. Vi - o - lent acts, O God, re - strain;
2. Re - mem - ber not our sin's dark stain;
3. None ev - er called on you in vain;
4. O bind us in that heav'n - ly chain;

Give peace, O God,__ give peace a - gain!

Henry Williams Baker, 1821–1877

Henry Baker, 1835–1910

520 On That Holy Mountain

VERSES

Cantor

1. The wolf___ is the guest___ of the lamb,___
2. The poor___ shall re-ceive___ from the rich,___
3. ___ Jus-tice shall flow'r for all time,

All   *Cantor*

1. on that ho-ly moun-tain. And the calf and the lion___
2. on that ho-ly moun-tain.___ And the sick and the lame
3. on that ho-ly moun-tain.___ As long as the sun___

All

1. ___ shall lie down, on that ho-ly moun-tain.
2. ___ shall be healed, on that ho-ly moun-tain.
3. ___ still can shine, on that ho-ly moun-tain.

Cantor

1. To-geth-er___ they shall rest with the___ child,
2. The wick-ed___ shall be slain by God's___ breath,
3. ___ Peace___ till the moon be no___ more,

All

1. on that ho-ly moun-tain, on that ho-ly moun-tain,
2. on that ho-ly moun-tain, on that ho-ly moun-tain,
3. on that ho-ly moun-tain, on that ho-ly moun-tain,

To Refrain

1. on that ho-ly moun-tain of the Lord.___
2. on that ho-ly moun-tain of the Lord.___
3. on that ho-ly moun-tain of the Lord.___

REFRAIN

Cantor/All

No harm or ruin___ on that ho-ly moun-tain.___

That sa-cred day___ shall be filled with knowl-edge.

There shall be peace,___ led by all the chil-dren,

on that ho - ly moun - tain, __ on that ho - ly moun-

Last time to Coda

- tain, __ on that ho - ly moun - tain __ of the Lord.

To Verses

CODA

2

Ho - ly and

peace - ful the day of __ the moun - tain.

Joe Mattingly
Text and music © 1990, WLP

Peace for Our Times 521

O WALY, WALY LM

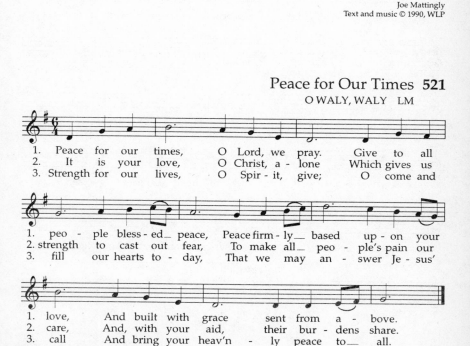

1. Peace for our times, O Lord, we pray. Give to all
2. It is your love, O Christ, a - lone Which gives us
3. Strength for our lives, O Spir - it, give; O come and

1. peo - ple bless - ed __ peace, Peace firm - ly __ based up - on your
2. strength to cast out fear, To make all __ peo - ple's pain our
3. fill our hearts to - day, That we may an - swer Je - sus'

1. love, And built with grace sent from a - bove.
2. care, And, with your aid, their bur - dens share.
3. call And bring your heav'n - ly peace to __ all.

Susan G. Wente
Text © 1979, WLP

English melody

522 Let There Be Peace on Earth

Let there be peace on earth And let it be - gin with

me.___ Let there be peace on earth, The

peace that was meant to be.___ With God as our

Fa - ther,___ *Broth - ers all are we.___

Let me walk with my broth- er___ In per - fect har - mo-

ny.___ Let peace be - gin with me; Let

this be the mo - ment now.___ With ev - 'ry

step I take, Let this be my sol - emn vow:___ To

take each mo-ment and live each mo-ment In peace e - ter - nal-

1.
ly.___ Let there be peace on earth And let it be -

Final
gin with me. let it be - gin with me.___

Sy Miller, 1908–1971 and Jill Jackson
Text and music © 1955, 1983, Jan-Lee Music

*May be sung: "Neighbors all are we. Let us walk with each other..." if desired.

Gather Us In 523

1. Here in this place new light is stream - ing;
2. We are the young, our lives are a mys - t'ry;
3. Here we will take the wine and the wa - ter;
4. Not in the dark of build - ings con - fin - ing,

1. Now is the dark - ness van - ished a - way.
2. We are the old who yearn for your face.
3. Here we will take the bread of new birth.
4. Not in some heav - en, light - years a - way, But

1. See, in this space, our fears and our dream - ings,
2. We have been sung through - out all of his - t'ry,
3. Here you shall call your sons and your daugh - ters,
4. here in this place, the new light is shin - ing;

1. Brought here to you in the light of this day.
2. Called to be light to the whole hu - man race.
3. Call us a - new to be salt for the earth.
4. Now is the king - dom, now is the day.

1. Ga - ther us in, the lost and for - sak - en; Ga - ther us in, the
2. Ga - ther us in, the rich and the haugh - ty; Ga - ther us in, the
3. Give us to drink the wine of com - pas - sion; Give us to eat the
4. Ga - ther us in and hold us for - ev - er; Ga - ther us in and

1. blind and the lame. Call to us now and we shall a - wak - en;
2. proud and the strong. Give us a heart so meek and so low - ly;
3. bread that is you. Nour - ish us well and teach us to fash - ion
4. make us your own. Ga - ther us in, all peo - ples to - geth - er,

1. We shall a - rise at the sound of our name.
2. Give us the cour - age to en - ter the song.
3. Lives that are ho - ly and hearts that are true.
4. Fire of love in our flesh and our bone.

Marty Haugen
Text and music © 1982, GIA

524 We Gather Together

KREMSER 12 11 12 11

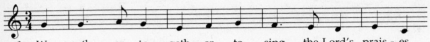

1. We gath - er to - geth - er to sing the Lord's prais - es,
2. We greet our Lord pres - ent with - in our as - sem - bly;
3. Since Christ is the vine and his peo - ple the branch - es,

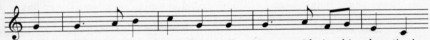

1. To wor - ship the Fa - ther through Je - sus, his Son.
2. We hear the good news an - nounced clear - ly to all.
3. In him we give praise to the Fa - ther a - bove.

1. In this cel - e - bra - tion, all sing with ju - bi - la - tion!
2. With songs of re - joic - ing our prais - es we are voic - ing,
3. Christ brings ev - 'ry na - tion the won - ders of sal - va - tion,

1. We are his ho - ly peo - ple whose free - dom he won.
2. As we in - voke God's bless - ing and an - swer the call.
3. That all may grow in knowl - edge, in faith, hope, and love.

Omer Westendorf
Text © 1970, WLP

Traditional Dutch melody
Adrianus Valerius, 1575–1620, *Nederlandtsch Gedencklanck*, 1626

525 God Is Here! As We His People

ABBOT'S LEIGH 87 87 D

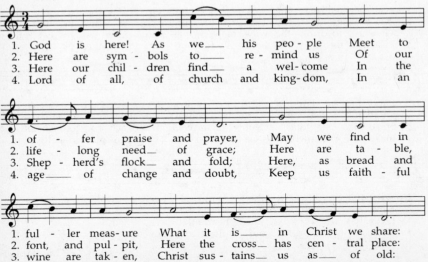

1. God is here! As we___ his peo - ple Meet to
2. Here are sym - bols to___ re - mind us Of our
3. Here our chil - dren find___ a wel - come In the
4. Lord of all, of church and king - dom, In an

1. of - fer praise and prayer, May we find in
2. life - long need___ of grace; Here are ta - ble,
3. Shep - herd's flock___ and fold; Here, as bread and
4. age___ of change and doubt, Keep us faith - ful

1. ful - ler meas - ure What it is___ in Christ we share:
2. font, and pul - pit, Here the cross___ has cen - tral place:
3. wine are tak - en, Christ sus - tains___ us as___ of old:
4. to the gos - pel, Help us work___ your pur - pose out:

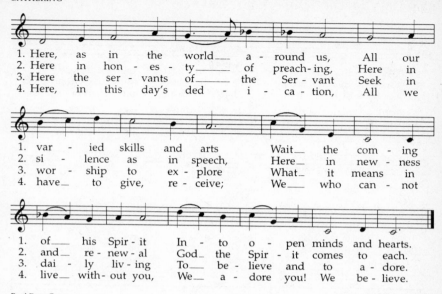

1. Here, as in the world_ a - round us, All our
2. Here in hon - es - ty____ of preach-ing, Here in
3. Here the ser - vants of_____ the Ser - vant Seek in
4. Here, in this day's ded - i - ca - tion, All we

1. var - ied skills and arts Wait__ the com - ing
2. si - lence as in speech, Here__ in new - ness
3. wor - ship to ex - plore What__ it means in
4. have__ to give, re - ceive; We__ who can - not

1. of___ his Spir - it In - to o - pen minds and hearts.
2. and__ re - new - al God_ the Spir - it comes to each.
3. dai - ly liv - ing To__ be - lieve and to a - dore.
4. live__ with- out you, We__ a - dore you! We be - lieve.

Fred Pratt Green

Cyril V. Taylor, 1907–1991
Text and music © 1942, 1970, 1979, Hope Publishing Co.

Come, Christians, Join to Sing 526
SPANISH CHANT 66 66 D

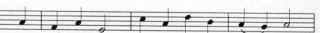

1. Come, Chris-tians, join to sing:
2. Come, lift your hearts on high: Al - le - lu - ia! A - men!
3. Praise yet the Lord a - gain:

1. Loud, praise to Christ our King:
2. Let prais-es fill the sky: Al - le - lu - ia! A - men!
3. Raise up the joy - ful strain:

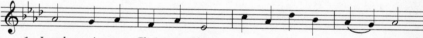

1. Let all, with heart and voice, Be - fore the throne re - joice,
2. Christ is our guide and friend; Let prayer to him as - cend;
3. Hymns to the heav - ens soar As all God's Son a - dore,

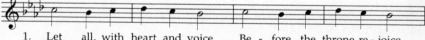

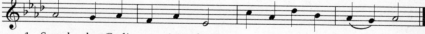

1. Saved by God's gra - cious choice.
2. Christ's love shall nev - er end: Al - le - lu - ia! A - men!
3. Sing - ing for - ev - er - more:

Christian H. Bateman, 1813–1889, alt.

Anon.

527 On This Day, the First of Days

LÜBECK 77 77

1. On this day, the first of days,
2. On this day, th'e - ter - nal Son
3. Fa - ther, who did fash - ion all
4. Word - made - flesh, our praise we bring;
5. Ho - ly Spir - it, you im - part
6. God, the bless - ed Three - in - One,

1. God the Fa - ther's name we praise;
2. O - ver death his tri - umph won;
3. God - like by your lov - ing call,
4. Now the grave has lost its sting;
5. Gifts of love to ev - 'ry heart;
6. May your ho - ly will be done;

1. Who, cre - a - tion's Lord and spring,
2. On this day the Spir - it came
3. Fill us with that love di - vine,
4. Made like you, we die and rise
5. Give us light and grace, we pray,
6. In your word our souls are free,

1. Did the world from dark - ness bring.
2. Bring - ing gifts of liv - ing flame.
3. And our wills to yours in - cline.
4. Un - to God in sac - ri - fice.
5. Fill our hearts this ho - ly day.
6. Liv - ing, lov - ing Trin - i - ty.

Carcasonne Breviary, 1745
Tr. by Henry W. Baker, 1821–1877, alt.
Text (rev.) © 1955, 1994, WLP

Johann A. Freylinghausen's *Geistreiches Gesangbuch,* 1704

528 Come, Christians, Unite

REFRAIN
Cantor/All

Come, Chris - tians, u - nite._____ Let us sing_____ for our

God!_____ Come, peo - ple, re - joice!_____

Let us sing_____ for our God!_____

VERSES

1. The One who makes all things wor - thy,_____ the
2. The Lord of all_____ cre - a - tion,_____ the
3. Come, fill our hearts with your good - ness;_____ come,

1. One who makes all things bright!_____
2. Lord, the giv - er of life!_____
3. fill our lives with new life!_____

1. Let us sing!
2. Let us sing!
3. Let us sing!

Ed Bolduc
Text and music © 1993, WLP

Sing Joyfully unto the Lord 529
CAHILL 88 11 with Alleluias

1. Sing joy - ful - ly un - to the Lord, Al - le - lu -
2. Sing praise to Christ, Re - deem - er, King, Al - le - lu -
3. Come, Ho - ly Spir - it, we im - plore, Al - le - lu -

1. ia! And praise the Lord with one ac - cord,
2. ia! As we our glad ho - san - nas sing, Al -
3. ia! Re - new the earth with love once more,

le - lu - ia! In the praise of God, O fill the earth with song,

Final

Al - le - lu - ia! Al - le - lu - ia!

Helen M. Cahill
Text and music © 1979, WLP

530 Joyful, Joyful, We Adore You

HYMN TO JOY   87 87 D

1. Joy - ful, joy - ful, we a - dore you, God of glo - ry,
2. All your works with joy sur - round you, Earth and heav'n re -
3. Al - ways giv - ing and for - giv - ing, Ev - er bless - ing,
4. Mor - tals, join the might - y cho - rus Which the morn - ing

1. Lord of love; Hearts un - fold like flow'rs be - fore you,
2. flect your rays, Stars and an - gels sing a - round you,
3. ev - er blest, Well - spring of the joy of liv - ing,
4. stars be - gan; God's own love is reign - ing o'er us,

1. Op'n - ing to the sun a - bove. Melt the clouds of
2. Cen - ter of un - bro - ken praise! Field and for - est,
3. O - cean - depth of hap - py rest! Lov - ing Fa - ther,
4. Join - ing peo - ple hand in hand. Ev - er sing - ing,

1. sin and sad - ness; Drive the dark of doubt a - way;
2. vale and moun - tain, Flow - 'ry mead - ow, flash - ing sea,
3. Christ our broth - er, Let your light up - on us shine;
4. march we on - ward, Vic - tors in the midst of strife;

1. Giv - er of im - mor - tal glad - ness, Fill us with the light of day!
2. Chant - ing bird and flow - ing foun - tain, Prais - ing you e - ter - nal - ly!
3. Teach us how to love each oth - er, Lift us to the joy di - vine.
4. Joy - ful mu - sic lifts us sun - ward In the tri - umph song of life.

Henry van Dyke, 1852–1933, alt.   Ludwig van Beethoven, 1770–1827

REFRAIN

All you na - tions, sing out your joy to the

Lord: Al - le - lu - ia, al - le - lu - ia!

VERSES

Cantor

1. Joy - ful - ly shout, all you on earth, give
2. Lift up your hearts, sing to our God: "Tre -
3. Let all the earth kneel in God's sight, ex -

4. Come forth and see all the great works that
5. Part - ing the seas with might and power, God
6. Test - ed are we by God the Lord, as

1. praise to the glo - ry of God;
2. men - dous your deeds on the earth!
3. tol - ling God's mar - vel - ous fame;

4. God has brought forth in great might;
5. res - cued the cho - sen from shame;
6. sil - ver is test - ed by fire:

1. And with a hymn, sing out___ with glo - ri - ous praise:
2. Van-quished your foes, struck down by pow - er and might:"
3. Hon - or God's name, in high - est heav - en give praise:

4. Fall on your knees be - fore___ the glo - ri - ous throne:
5. Let us give thanks for all___ these mer - ci - ful deeds:
6. Bur - dened with pain, we fall___ en - snared in our sins;

To Refrain

Al - le - lu - ia!

Ps 66

Lucien Deiss
Text and music © 1965, WLP

532 All Creatures of Our God and King

LASST UNS ERFREUEN   88 8 88 with Refrain

1. All crea-tures of our God and King, Lift
2. O rush-ing wind and breez-es soft, O
3. O flow-ing wa-ters, pure and clear, Make
4. Dear moth-er earth, who day by day Un -
5. O ev-'ry-one of ten-der heart, For -
6. And you, most kind and gen-tle death, Wait -
7. Let all things their Cre-a-tor bless And

1. up your voice and with us sing: Al - le - lu - ia!
2. clouds that ride the winds a - loft: Oh,___ praise him!
3. mu - sic for your Lord to hear. Oh,___ praise him!
4. folds rich bless-ings on our way, Oh,___ praise him!
5. giv - ing oth - ers, take your part, Oh,___ praise him!
6. ing to hush our fi - nal breath, Oh,___ praise him!
7. wor - ship God in hum - ble - ness. Oh,___ praise him!

1. Al - le - lu - ia! O burn-ing sun with gold-en beam
2. Al - le - lu - ia! O ris-ing morn, in praise re-joice,
3. Al - le - lu - ia! O fire so mas-ter-ful and bright,
4. Al - le - lu - ia! The fruits and flow'rs that ver-dant grow,
5. Al - le - lu - ia! All you who pain and sor-row bear,
6. Al - le - lu - ia! You lead to heav'n the child of God,
7. Al - le - lu - ia! Oh, praise the Fa-ther, praise the Son,

1. And sil - ver moon with soft - er gleam:
2. O lights of eve - ning, find a voice.
3. Pro - vid - ing us with warmth and light,
4. Let them his praise a - bun - dant show.
5. Praise God and lay on him your care.
6. Where Christ our Lord the way has trod.
7. And praise the Spir - it, Three - in - One,

Oh,___ praise him! Oh,___ praise him! Al - le - lu - ia,

al - le - lu - ia, al - le - lu - ia!

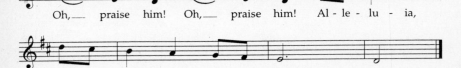

Based on Francis of Assisi, 1182–1226
Tr. by William H. Draper, 1855–1933, alt.
Text © 1925, J. Curwen & Sons, Ltd.

Geistliche Kirchengesänge, Cologne, 1623

Lift Every Voice and Sing 533

ANTHEM Irregular

1. Lift ev-'ry voice and sing, Till earth and heav - en ring,
2. Ston-y the road we trod, Bit - ter the chas - t'ning rod,
3. God of our wea - ry years, God of our si - lent tears,

1. Ring with the har - mo - nies of lib - er - ty;
2. Felt in the days when hope un - born had died;
3. You who have brought us thus far on the way;

1. Let our re - joic - ing rise High as the lis - t'ning skies,
2. Yet with a stead - y beat, Have not our wea - ry feet
3. You who have by your might Led us in - to the light,

1. Let it re - sound loud as the roll - ing sea.
2. Come to the place for which our peo - ple sighed?
3. Keep us for - ev - er in the path, we pray.

1. Sing a song full of the faith that the dark past has taught us;
2. We have come o - ver a way that with tears has been wa - tered;
3. Lest our feet stray from the plac - es, our God, where we met you;

1. Sing a song full of the hope that the pres - ent has brought
2. We have come, tread - ing our path through the blood of the slaugh -
3. Lest, our hearts drunk with the wine of the world, we for - get

1. us; Fac - ing the ris - ing sun Of our new day be -
2. tered; Out from the gloom - y past, Till now we stand at
3. you; Shad-owed be - neath your hand, May we for - ev - er

1. gun, Let us march on till vic - to - ry is won.
2. last Where the bright gleam of our bright star is cast.
3. stand, True to our God, true to our na - tive land.

James W. Johnson, 1871–1938

J. Rosamund Johnson, 1873–1954
Text and music © 1921, renewed, Edward B. Marks Music Co.

534 Sing Praise to God

MIT FREUDEN ZART 87 87 887

1. Sing praise to God who reigns a-bove, The___
2. The an-gel host, O King of kings, Your___
3. What God's al-might-y pow'r has made With___
4. Then all my glad-some way a-long I___

1. God of all cre-a-tion, The God of pow'r, the
2. praise for-ev-er___ tell-ing, In earth and sky all
3. gra-cious mer-cy___ keep-ing, By morn-ing glow or
4. sing a-loud your prais-es, That all may hear the

1. God of love, The___ God of our sal-va-tion; With
2. liv-ing things Be-neath your shad-ow___ dwell-ing, A-
3. eve-ning shade God's___ watch-ful eye ne'er sleep-ing: With-
4. grate-ful song My___ voice un-wea-ried___ rais-es: Be

1. heal-ing balm my soul is filled, And ev-'ry faith-less
2. dore the wis-dom which could span, And pow'r which formed cre-
3. in the reign of end-less might, Lo, all is just and
4. joy-ful in the Lord, my heart: Both soul and bod-y,

1. mur-mur stilled: To God all praise and___ glo-ry!
2. a-tion's plan: To God all praise and___ glo-ry!
3. all is right: To God all praise and___ glo-ry!
4. bear your part: To God all praise and___ glo-ry!

Ps 95:1–7
Johann J. Schütz, 1640–1690, alt.
Tr. by Frances E. Cox, 1812–1897, alt.

Une pastourelle gentille, 1529
Pseaumes octante trois de David, 1551, of Louis Bourgeois, c. 1510–c. 1561
Bohemian Bethren's *Kirchengeseng,* 1566

535 Praise the Lord, His Glories Show

LLANFAIR 77 77 with Alleluias

1. Praise the Lord, his glo-ries show,
2. Earth to heav'n and heav'n to___ earth, Al - le - lu - ia!
3. Praise the Lord, his mer-cies trace,
4. Strings and voic-es, hands and hearts,

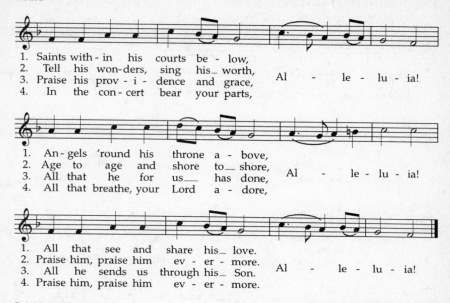

1. Saints with-in his courts be - low,
2. Tell his won-ders, sing his— worth,
3. Praise his prov - i - dence and grace,
4. In the con-cert bear your parts,

Al - le - lu - ia!

1. An-gels 'round his throne a - bove,
2. Age to age and shore to— shore,
3. All that he for us— has done,
4. All that breathe, your Lord a - dore,

Al - le - lu - ia!

1. All that see and share his— love.
2. Praise him, praise him ev - er - more.
3. All he sends us through his— Son.
4. Praise him, praise him ev - er - more.

Al - le - lu - ia!

Ps 148:1–6; 150:3–6
Henry F. Lyte, 1793–1847

Attr. to Robert Williams, 1781–1821
Joseph Parry's *Peroriaeth Hyfryd*, 1837

Praise the Lord, Lift Up Your Voice 536
LLANFAIR 77 77 with Alleluias

1. Praise the Lord, lift up your voice, Alleluia!
   Saints in heav'n and earth, rejoice, Alleluia!
   Angels, 'round the throne of love, Alleluia!
   All that see and share God's love. Alleluia!

2. Earth to heav'n and heav'n to earth, Alleluia!
   Tell God's wonders, might and worth, Alleluia!
   Age to age and shore to shore, Alleluia!
   Sing in praise forevermore. Alleluia!

3. Praise the Lord in ev'ry place, Alleluia!
   Praise God's providence and grace, Alleluia!
   Life and light, salvation won, Alleluia!
   Through the Spirit and the Son. Alleluia!

4. Strings and voices, hands and hearts, Alleluia!
   In the concert bear your parts, Alleluia!
   All that breathe, your Lord adore, Alleluia!
   Blessing, praising evermore. Alleluia!

Henry F. Lyte, 1793–1847, alt.
Alt. by Alan J. Hommerding
Text (alt.) © 1994, WLP

537 Praise the Lord of Heaven

UNE VAINE CRAINTE   65 65 D

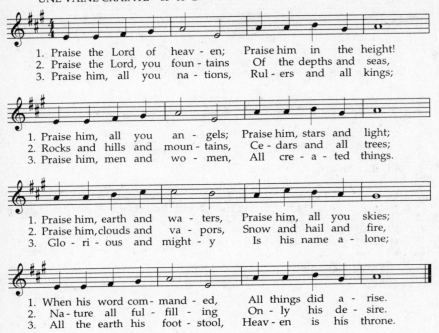

1. Praise the Lord of heav - en; Praise him in the height!
2. Praise the Lord, you foun - tains Of the depths and seas,
3. Praise him, all you na - tions, Rul - ers and all kings;

1. Praise him, all you an - gels; Praise him, stars and light;
2. Rocks and hills and moun - tains, Ce - dars and all trees;
3. Praise him, men and wo - men, All cre - a - ted things.

1. Praise him, earth and wa - ters, Praise him, all you skies;
2. Praise him, clouds and va - pors, Snow and hail and fire,
3. Glo - ri - ous and might - y Is his name a - lone;

1. When his word com - mand - ed, All things did a - rise.
2. Na - ture all ful - fill - ing On - ly his de - sire.
3. All the earth his foot - stool, Heav - en is his throne.

Ps 148
Thomas B. Browne, 1805–1874, alt.

French noël

538 Praise the Lord of Heaven *(alt.)*

UNE VAINE CRAINTE   65 65 D

1. Praise the Lord of heaven From the heav'nly heights;
   Praise the Lord, you angels; Stars and moon and lights;
   Sing in praise, creation, Waters, earth, and skies;
   At the word commanding All things to arise.

2. Praise the Lord, you fountains Of the depths and seas,
   Rocks and hills and mountains, Cedars and all trees;
   Lofty clouds above us, Snow and hail and fire;
   Nature all around us, Serving God's desires.

3. From each man and woman, From all nations bring
   Praise to God the maker Of all earthly things.
   Glorious and mighty Is God's name alone;
   Reigning now and ever From the heav'nly throne.

Thomas B. Browne, 1805–1874, alt.
Alt. by Alan J. Hommerding
Text (alt.) © 1994, WLP

From All That Dwell below the Skies 539
Praise God, from Whom All Blessings Flow
OLD HUNDREDTH LM

1. From all that dwell be - low the skies Let the Cre - a - tor's praise a - rise; Let the Re - deem - er's name be sung Through ev - 'ry land, by ev - 'ry tongue.

2. E - ter - nal are your mer - cies, Lord, E - ter - nal truth at - tends your word; Your praise shall sound from shore to shore, Till suns shall rise and set no more.

Dox. Praise God, from whom all bless - ings flow; Sing praise, all crea - tures here be - low; Joined with the praise of heav'n - ly host; Praise Fa - ther, Son, and Ho - ly Ghost.

Ps 72:17–19; Ps 117:1–2
Vss. 1–2: Isaac Watts, 1674–1748
Doxology: Thomas Ken, 1637–1711, alt.

Genevan Psalter
Pseaumes octante trois de David, 1551, alt.
Louis Bourgeois, c.1510–c. 1561

All People That on Earth Do Dwell 540
OLD HUNDREDTH LM

1. All people that on earth do dwell,
   Sing to the Lord with cheerful voice;
   Him serve with mirth, his praise forth tell,
   Come ye before him and rejoice.

2. Know that the Lord is God indeed;
   Without our aid he did us make;
   We are his folk, he doth us feed,
   And for his sheep he doth us take.

3. O enter then his gates with praise;
   Approach with joy his courts unto;
   Praise, laud, and bless his name always,
   For it is seemly so to do.

4. For why? The Lord our God is good:
   His mercy is forever sure;
   His truth at all times firmly stood,
   And shall from age to age endure.

Ps 100:1–4
William Kethe, c. 1530–c.1608
Alt. as in *Scottish Psalter,* 1650

541 Resound with Your Praises

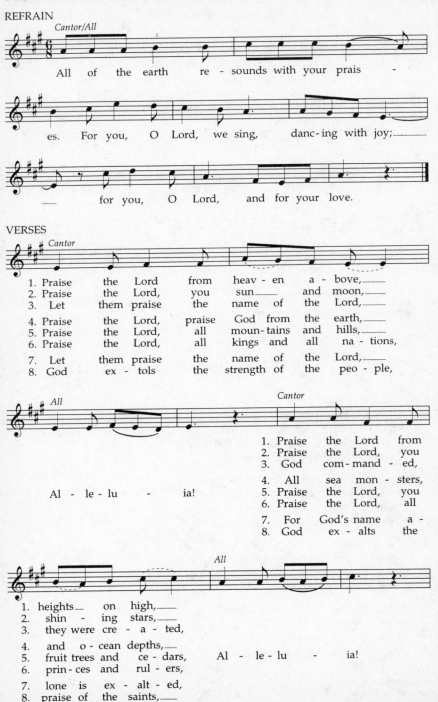

REFRAIN

Cantor/All

All of the earth re - sounds with your prais - es. For you, O Lord, we sing, danc-ing with joy;____ ____ for you, O Lord, and for your love.

VERSES

Cantor

1. Praise the Lord from heav - en a - bove,____
2. Praise the Lord, you sun____ and moon,____
3. Let them praise the name of the Lord,____

4. Praise the Lord, praise God from the earth,____
5. Praise the Lord, all moun-tains and hills,____
6. Praise the Lord, all kings and all na - tions,

7. Let them praise the name of the Lord,____
8. God ex - tols the strength of the peo - ple,

All

Al - le - lu - ia!

Cantor

1. Praise the Lord from
2. Praise the Lord, you
3. God com - mand - ed,

4. All sea mon - sters,
5. Praise the Lord, you
6. Praise the Lord, all

7. For God's name a -
8. God ex - alts the

All

1. heights__ on high,____
2. shin - ing stars,____
3. they were cre - a - ted,

4. and o - cean depths,____
5. fruit trees and ce - dars,
6. prin - ces and rul - ers,

7. lone is ex - alt - ed,
8. praise of the saints,____

Al - le - lu - ia!

1. Praise the Lord, all an - gels in heav - en,
2. Praise the Lord in high - est heav - en,
3. God has fixed their plac - es for - ev - er,
4. Hail and light - ning, snow, ice and clouds,___
5. Praise the Lord, all wild beasts and cat - tle,
6. Praise the Lord, young men and young maid - ens,
7. High a - bove the earth and the heav - ens,
8. Of the chil - dren of Is - ra - el,___

Al - le - lu - ia!

1. Praise the Lord, all
2. And the wa - ters
3. By a rule which
4. Storm - y winds, ful -
5. All small crea - tures
6. Young and old must
7. Mag - ni - fy the
8. Of the peo - ple

1. heav - en - ly hosts,
2. in the dark clouds,
3. nev - er shall fail,

4. fill - ing God's word,
5. and fly - ing birds, Al - le - lu - ia!
6. all praise the Lord,

7. name of the Lord,
8. close to God's heart,

Ps 148

Lucien Deiss
Text and music © 1995, WLP

542 All the Earth

REFRAIN
Cantor/All

All the earth, pro-claim the Lord; sing your praise to God.

VERSES
Cantor

1. Serve you the Lord, heart filled with glad - ness.
2. Know that the Lord is our cre - a - tor.
3. We are the sheep of the green pas - ture;
4. Come to the gates bring - ing thanks - giv - ing;
5. Our Lord is good, with love en - dur - ing;
6. Hon - or and praise be to the Fa - ther,

To Refrain

1. Come in - to God's pres - ence sing - ing for joy!
2. Yes, God is our Fa - ther; we are his own.
3. For we are God's peo - ple; cho - sen by God.
4. O en - ter the court - yards sing - ing in praise.
5. God's word is a - bid - ing now with us all.
6. The Son, and the Spir - it, world with - out end.

Ps 100

Lucien Deiss
Text and music © 1965, WLP

543 Canticle of the Sun

REFRAIN

The heav-ens are tell-ing the glo-ry of God, and

all cre - a - tion is shout-ing for joy. Come,

dance in the for-est, come, play in the field, and

To Verses

sing, sing to the glo - ry of the Lord.

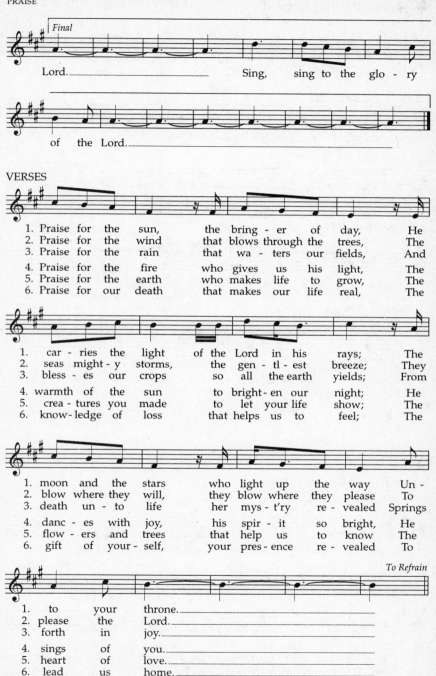

Final

Lord. _____ Sing, sing to the glo - ry

of the Lord. _____

VERSES

1. Praise for the sun, the bring - er of day, He
2. Praise for the wind that blows through the trees, The
3. Praise for the rain that wa - ters our fields, And

4. Praise for the fire who gives us his light, The
5. Praise for the earth who makes life to grow, The
6. Praise for our death that makes our life real, The

1. car - ries the light of the Lord in his rays; The
2. seas might - y storms, the gen - tl - est breeze; They
3. bless - es our crops so all the earth yields; From

4. warmth of the sun to bright - en our night; He
5. crea - tures you made to let your life show; The
6. know - ledge of loss that helps us to feel; The

1. moon and the stars who light up the way Un -
2. blow where they will, they blow where they please To
3. death un - to life her mys - t'ry re - vealed Springs

4. danc - es with joy, his spir - it so bright, He
5. flow - ers and trees that help us to know The
6. gift of your - self, your pres - ence re - vealed To

To Refrain

1. to your throne. _____
2. please the Lord. _____
3. forth in joy. _____

4. sings of you. _____
5. heart of love. _____
6. lead us home. _____

Marty Haugen
Text and music © 1980, GIA

544 Sing, People of God

BOWMAN Irregular

Sing, peo-ple of God; re-joice! Let hymns of praise be sung;___ For

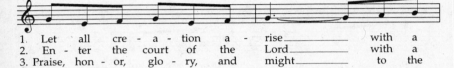

great and might - y is the Lord, our King and Ho - ly One!

1. Let all cre - a - tion a - rise_____ with a
2. En - ter the court of the Lord_____ with a
3. Praise, hon - or, glo - ry, and might_____ to the

1. hymn to our God,___ A hymn that is full of
2. heart full of love,___ A heart that speaks out the
3. blest Trin - i - ty;___ U - nit - ed in faith we

D.C.

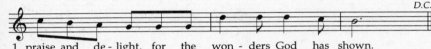

1. praise and de - light, for the won - ders God has shown.
2. great-ness of God who has saved us from all harm.
3. sing and pro - claim our be - lief in Christ the Lord.

Michael L. Markson
Text and music © 1983, WLP

545 Holy, Holy, Holy

NICAEA 11 12 12 10

1. Ho - ly, ho - ly, ho - ly! Lord___ God Al - might - y!
2. Ho - ly, ho - ly, ho - ly! All the saints a - dore thee,
3. Ho - ly, ho - ly, ho - ly! Though the dark-ness hide thee,
4. Ho - ly, ho - ly, ho - ly! Lord___ God Al - might - y!

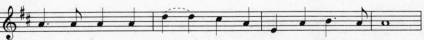

1. Ear - ly in the morn - ing our song shall rise to thee.
2. Cast - ing down their gold - en crowns a- round the glass - y sea;
3. Though the eye made blind by sin thy glo - ry may not see,
4. All thy works shall praise thy name in earth and sky and sea.

1. Ho - ly, ho - ly, ho - ly, mer - ci - ful and might - y!
2. Cher - u - bim and ser - a - phim fall - ing down be - fore thee,
3. On - ly thou art ho - ly; there is none be - side thee,
4. Ho - ly, ho - ly, ho - ly, mer - ci - ful and might - y!

1. God in three Per - sons, bless - ed Trin - i - ty!
2. Which wert and art and ev - er - more shall be.
3. Per - fect in pow'r, in love and pu - ri - ty.
4. God in three Per - sons, bless - ed Trin - i - ty!

Reginald Heber, 1783–1826, alt.

John B. Dykes, 1823–1876

Tell Out, My Soul, the Greatness of the Lord 546

WOODLANDS 10 10 10 10

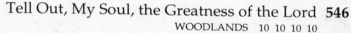

1. Tell out, my soul, the great - ness of the Lord!
2. Tell out, my soul, the great - ness of his name!
3. Tell out, my soul, the great - ness of his might!
4. Tell out, my soul, the glo - ries of his word!

1. Un - num - bered bless - ings give my spir - it voice;
2. Make known his might, the deeds his arm has done;
3. Pow'rs and do - min - ions lay their glo - ry by.
4. Firm is his prom - ise, and his mer - cy sure.

1. Ten - der to me the prom - ise of his word;
2. His mer - cy sure, from age to age the same;
3. Proud hearts and stub - born wills are put on flight,
4. Tell out, my soul, the great - ness of the Lord

1. In God my Sav - ior shall my heart re - joice.
2. His ho - ly name— the Lord, the Might - y One.
3. The hun - gry fed, the hum - ble lift - ed high.
4. To chil - dren's chil - dren and for - ev - er - more!

Timothy Dudley-Smith
Text © 1962, 1990, Hope Publishing Co.

Walter Greatorex, 1877–1949, alt.

547 Sing Out, Earth and Skies

SING OUT   77 77 with Refrain

VERSES

1. Come, O God of all the earth: Come to us, O
2. Come, O God of wind and flame: Fill the earth with
3. Come, O God of flash-ing light: Twin-kling star and
4. Come, O God of snow and rain: Show-er down up -
5. Come, O Jus-tice, come, O Peace: Come and shape our

1. Right-eous One; Come and bring our love to birth:
2. right-eous-ness; Teach us all to sing your name:
3. burn-ing sun; God of day and God of night:
4. on the earth; Come, O God of joy and pain:
5. hearts a-new; Come and make op-pres-sion cease:

1. In the glo - ry of your Son.
2. May our lives your love con - fess.
3. In your light we all are one.
4. God of sor - row, God of mirth.
5. Bring us all to life in you.

REFRAIN

Sing out, earth and skies! Sing of the God who loves you!

Raise your joy-ful cries! Dance to the life a - round you!

Marty Haugen
Text and music © 1985, GIA

548 Praise, My Soul, the King of Heaven

LAUDA ANIMA   87 87 87

1. Praise, my soul, the King of heav - en; To his
2. Praise him for his grace and fa - vor; To his
3. Fa - ther - like he tends and spares us; Well our
4. An - gels, help us to a - dore him; You be -

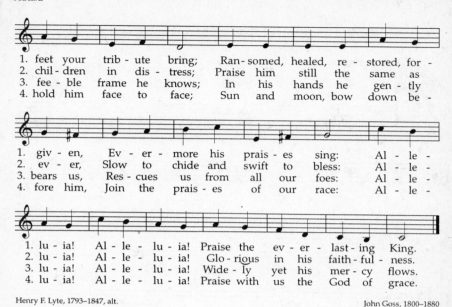

1. feet your trib - ute bring; Ran- somed, healed, re - stored, for -
2. chil - dren in dis - tress; Praise him still the same as
3. fee - ble frame he knows; In his hands he gen - tly
4. hold him face to face; Sun and moon, bow down be -

1. giv - en, Ev - er - more his prais - es sing: Al - le -
2. ev - er, Slow to chide and swift to bless: Al - le -
3. bears us, Res - cues us from all our foes: Al - le -
4. fore him, Join the prais - es of our race: Al - le -

1. lu - ia! Al - le - lu - ia! Praise the ev - er - last - ing King.
2. lu - ia! Al - le - lu - ia! Glo - rious in his faith - ful - ness.
3. lu - ia! Al - le - lu - ia! Wide - ly yet his mer - cy flows.
4. lu - ia! Al - le - lu - ia! Praise with us the God of grace.

Henry F. Lyte, 1793–1847, alt.

John Goss, 1800–1880

Praise, My Soul, the King of Heaven *(alt.)* 549

LAUDA ANIMA 87 87 87

1. Praise, my soul, the King of heaven; Come, your adoration bring,
Ransomed, healed, restored, forgiven, Evermore in praise we sing:
Alleluia! Alleluia! Praise the everlasting King.

2. Praise eternal grace and favor, To all people in distress;
Praising still, the same forever, Slow to chide and swift to bless.
Alleluia! Alleluia! Glorious in his faithfulness.

3. Fatherlike, we know God spares us, And our feeble frame well knows,
Tender hands will gently lead us, Rescue us from all our foes:
Alleluia! Alleluia! Widely endless mercy flows.

4. Motherlike, with boundless caring, God will hear us when we call,
Sick and helpless gently bearing, Raising up the weak and small.
Alleluia! Alleluia! Wondrous might reigns over all.

5. Angels, join our acclamation, You, who see the holy face;
Sun and moon, with ev'ry nation, Dwelling in each sacred place:
Alleluia! Alleluia! Praise with us the God of grace.

Henry F. Lyte, 1793–1847, alt.
Vs. 4: Alan J. Hommerding
Text (vs. 4) © 1994, WLP

550 Our God

1. Praise him all you nations. Oh, praise him with your dancing.
   Praise him with the angels, Oh, praise him with singing.
   Come, eat the bread come and drink the wine.

2. Glory to the Father, Oh, glory to the Spirit,
   Holy God is with us, sing glory, he is Jesus.
   Come, eat the bread come and drink the wine.

Ed Bolduc
Text and music © 1992, WLP

Vine Para Que Tengan/I Have Come to Give You 551

Lorenzo Florián
Text and music © 1994, WLP

552 Wonderful and Great

REFRAIN

Al - le - lu - ia! Al - le - lu - ia!

VERSE 1 *To Refrain*

1. Won-der-ful and great are your works, O Lord God al-might-y.

VERSE 2 *To Refrain*

2. Just and true are your ways, O King of all na - tions.

VERSE 3

3. Who shall not re - vere you, O Lord! Who shall not give

To Refrain

3. glo - ry to your name! You a - lone are___ ho - ly.

VERSE 4

4. All na - tions shall come to wor-ship you in your

To Refrain

4. pres - ence, for your jus - tice has been made___ known.

Rv 15:3–4

Lucien Deiss
Text and music © 1965, WLP

553 Song of Judith

REFRAIN

Cantor/Choir/Assembly

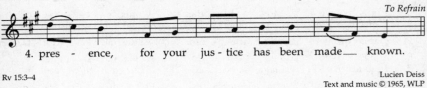

Sing to God with the tam - bour - ine, Sing with

cym - bals in praise of the Lord! Raise a can - ti - cle!

Last time to Coda ⊕   *To Verses*

Ring out the name of God!_____

⊕ CODA

God!_____ Raise a can - ti - cle! Ring out the

name_____ of God!_____

VERSES
Cantor

1. Sing to God with the tam - bour and drum, with
2. I will sing a new song to my God:
3. For you spoke and it all came to be, the
4. Should the moun-tains be tossed from their base, to

1. cym - bals in hon - or of God._____
2. Lord, you are glo - rious and great._____
3. force of your breath built it up._____ Your
4. mix with the waves of the sea,_____ if the

1. Sing to the Lord! Raise up a psalm! Re-
2. Source of our strength! Marv - 'lous in might, may
3. Spi - rit pre - vailed! Called us as one, to
4. stones were to melt like wax in your sight, your

                                                       2 *To Refrain*

1. joice____ in the name of the Lord!_____
2. all____ cre - a - tion serve you!
3. serve____ the voice of the Lord!_____
4. kind-ness to us would en - dure!_____

Jdt 16:1–2, 13–15
Adapt. by S.C.W.

Steven C. Warner
Text and music © 1993, WLP

554 Praise to the Lord

LOBE DEN HERREN   14 14 4 7 8

1. Praise to the Lord, the Al - might - y, the King of cre -
2. Praise to the Lord, who doth pros - per thy work and de -
3. Praise to the Lord! O let all that is in me a -

1. a - tion; O my soul, praise him, for
2. fend thee; Sure - ly his good - ness and
3. dore him! All that has life and breath

1. he is thy health and sal - va - tion.
2. mer - cy shall dai - ly at - tend thee.
3. come now in prais - es be - fore him!

1. All you who hear, Now to his al - tar draw
2. Pon - der a - new What the Al - might - y can
3. Let the A - men Sound from his peo - ple a -

1. near, Join - ing in glad ad - o - ra - tion.
2. do, Who with his love doth be - friend thee.
3. gain: Now as we wor - ship be - fore him.

Joachim Neander, 1650–1680
Tr. by Catherine Winkworth, 1827–1878, alt.

Erneuerten Gesangbuch, Stralsund, 1665

555 Sing a New Song to the Lord

CANTATE DOMINO   Irregular

1. Sing a new song to the Lord,
2. Now to the ends of the earth,
3. Sing a new song and re - joice;
4. Join with the hills and the sea,

1. He, to whom won - ders be - long!___ Re - joice___ in his
2. See, his sal - va - tion is shown;___ And still___ he re -
3. Pub - lish his prais - es a - broad!___ Let voic - es___ in___
4. Thun - ders of praise to pro - long!___ In judg - ment___ and___

1. tri - umph___ and tell___ of his pow'r;___ O
2. mem - bers___ his mer - cy___ and___ truth,___ Un -
3. cho - rus,___ with trum-pet___ and___ horn,___ Re -
4. jus - tice___ he comes___ to the earth;___ O

1. sing___ to the Lord___ a new song!
2. chang - ing in love___ to his own.
3. sound___ for the joy___ of the Lord!
4. sing___ to the Lord___ a new song!

Timothy Dudley-Smith
Text © 1973, Hope Publishing Co.

David G. Wilson
Music © 1973, Church Pastoral Aid Society

We Sing the Mighty Power of God 556

MOZART   CMD

1. We sing the might - y pow'r of God That made the moun-tains
2. We sing the good-ness of the Lord That filled the earth with
3. There's not a plant or flow'r be - low But makes your glo - ries

1. rise,___ That spread the flow - ing seas a - broad, And
2. food;___ God formed the crea - tures with the word, And
3. known;___ And clouds a - rise and tem - pests blow, By

1. built the__ loft - y skies.___ We sing the wis - dom
2. then pro - nounced them good.___ Lord, how your won - ders
3. or - der__ from your throne;___ While all that bor - rows

1. that or - dained The sun to rule the day; The
2. are dis - played Where - e'er we turn our eye, If
3. life from you Is ev - er in your care. And

1. moon shines full at God's com - mand And all the stars o - bey!__
2. we sur - vey the ground we tread, Or gaze up - on the sky!__
3. ev - 'ry-where that we can be, You, Lord, are pres-ent there.

Ps 103:5–6, 19–20, 14–15, 24, 27–28
Isaac Watts, 1674–1748

Wolfgang Amadeus Mozart, 1756–1791

557 Festival Canticle

FESTIVAL CANTICLE   Irregular with Refrain

REFRAIN

This is the feast_____ of vic-to-ry for our God.

Al-le-lu-ia, al-le-lu-ia, al-le-lu - ia!

VERSES

1. Wor - thy is Christ, the_ Lamb who was slain, Whose
2. Pow_____ er, rich - es,_ wis - dom, and strength, And
3. Sing_____ with all the_ peo - ple of God, And
4. Bless - ing, hon - or,_ glo - ry, and might Be to
5. For_____ the Lamb_____ who was slain Has be -

To Refrain

1. blood set us free_____ to be peo - ple of God.
2. hon - or,_____ bless - ing, and glo - ry are his.
3. join in the hymn of all cre - a - tion.
4. God and the Lamb for - ev - er. A - men.
5. gun his_ reign._ Al - le - lu - ia!

FINAL REFRAIN

This is the feast_____ of vic-to-ry for our God.

Al-le-lu-ia, al-le-lu-ia, al-le-lu - ia!

Adapt. by John W. Arthur, 1922–1980
Text © 1978, Augsburg Fortress

Richard Hillert
Music © 1975, 1988, Richard Hillert

O God beyond All Praising 558

THAXTED   13 13 13 13 13 13

1. O__ God   be-yond all   prais-ing, We   wor-ship you to - day
2. Then hear,   O gra-cious Sav - ior, Ac - cept the love we bring,

1. And sing   the love a - maz-ing That songs can-not   re - pay;
2. That we   who know your fa - vor May serve you as   our King;

1. For   we   can on-ly won - der At__ ev - 'ry gift you send,
2. And wheth - er our to- mor-rows Be__ filled with good or   ill,

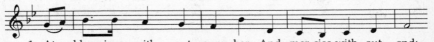

1. At__ bless-ings with - out num - ber And mer-cies with-out   end:
2. We'll tri-umph through our   sor - rows And rise to bless you   still:

1. We   lift   our hearts be - fore you And   wait up-on your word,
2. To__ mar - vel at your beau - ty And   glo-ry in   your ways,

1. We   hon - or and a - dore you, Our great and might - y   Lord.
2. And make   a joy-ful du - ty Our sac - ri - fice   of   praise.

Michael Perry
Text © 1982, Hope Publishing Co.

Gustav Holst, 1874–1934

559 Our God Reigns

VERSES

1. How love-ly on the moun-tains are the feet of him
2. He had no state - ly form. He had no maj - es - ty
3. It was our sin and guilt that bruised and wound-ed him,
4. Meek as a lamb that's led out to the slaugh-ter-house,
5. Out of the tomb he came with grace and maj - es - ty,

1. who brings good news,_____ good___ news;_____
2. that we should be_____ drawn to him._____
3. it was our sin_____ brought him down.
4. still as a sheep_____ be-fore its shearer,_____
5. he is a - live,_____ he is a - live!_____

1. An-nounc-ing peace, pro claim-ing news of hap - pi - ness:_____
2. He was de-spised and we took no ac-count of him;_____
3. When we like sheep had gone a - stray, our shep-herd came___
4. His life ran down up-on the ground like pour-ing rain___
5. God loves us so; see here his hands, his feet, his side:___

1. our God reigns,_____ our God reigns!_____
2. Yet now he reigns_____ with the Most High!_____
3. and on his shoul - ders bore our shame!_____
4. that we might be_____ born a - gain!_____
5. yes, we know_____ he is a - live!_____

Our God reigns,_____ our God reigns,_____

our God reigns,_____ our God reigns!

Is 52:7; Lk 24:5, 6, 39

Leonard E. Smith, Jr.
Text and music © 1974, 1978, New Jerusalem Music

God, We Praise You 560

NETTLETON 87 87 D

1. God, we praise you! God, we bless you! God, we
2. True a - pos - tles, faith - ful proph - ets, Saints who
3. Je - sus Christ, the King of glo - ry, Ev - er -
4. Christ, at God's right hand vic - to - rious, You will

1. name you sov-'reign Lord! Might - y King whom an - gels
2. set their world a - blaze, Mar - tyrs, once un - known, un -
3. last - ing Son of God, Hum - ble was your vir - gin
4. judge the world you made; Lord, in mer - cy help your

1. wor - ship, Fa - ther, by your Church a - dored:
2. heed - ed, Join one grow - ing song of praise,
3. moth - er, Hard the lone - ly path you trod:
4. ser - vants For whose free - dom you have paid:

1. All cre - a - tion shows your glo - ry, Heav'n and
2. While your Church on earth con - fess - es One ma -
3. By your cross is sin de - feat - ed, Hell con -
4. Raise us up from dust to glo - ry, Guard us

1. earth draw near your throne, Sing - ing "Ho - ly, ho - ly,
2. jes - tic Trin - i - ty: Fa - ther, Son, and Ho - ly
3. front - ed face to face, Heav - en o - pened to be -
4. from all sin to - day; King en - throned a - bove all

1. ho - ly Lord of hosts and God a - lone!"
2. Spir - it, God, our hope e - ter - nal - ly.
3. liev - ers, Sin - ners jus - ti - fied by grace.
4. prais - es, Save your peo - ple, God, we pray.

Te Deum laudamus
Tr. by Christopher Idle
Text © 1982, Hope Publishing Co.

John Wyeth's *Repository of Sacred Music*, Part Second, 1813

561 When in Our Music God Is Glorified

ENGELBERG 10 10 10 with Alleluia

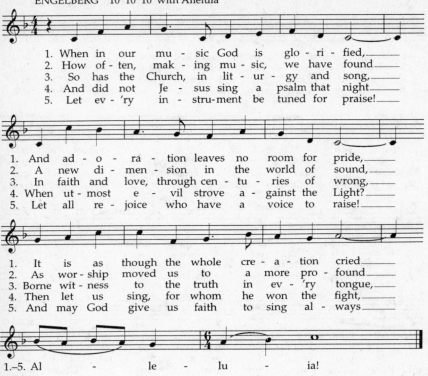

1. When in our mu - sic God is glo - ri - fied,____
2. How of - ten, mak - ing mu - sic, we have found____
3. So has the Church, in lit - ur - gy and song,____
4. And did not Je - sus sing a psalm that night____
5. Let ev - 'ry in - stru-ment be tuned for praise!____

1. And ad - o - ra - tion leaves no room for pride,____
2. A new di - men - sion in the world of sound,____
3. In faith and love, through cen - tu - ries of wrong,____
4. When ut - most e - vil strove a - gainst the Light?____
5. Let all re - joice who have a voice to raise!____

1. It is as though the whole cre - a - tion cried____
2. As wor - ship moved us to a more pro - found____
3. Borne wit - ness to the truth in ev - 'ry tongue,____
4. Then let us sing, for whom he won the fight,____
5. And may God give us faith to sing al - ways____

1.–5. Al - le - lu - ia!

Fred Pratt Green
Text © 1972, Hope Publishing Co.

Charles V. Stanford, 1852–1924

562 Praise the Lord in Heaven

FAUX SONG

Leader/Cantor   Choir/All

1. Praise the Lord in Heav'n, Praise the Lord in Heav'n,
2. With a joy - ful song, With a joy - ful song,
3. With the trum - pet blast, With the trum-pet blast,
4. With a cym - bal crash, With a cym - bal crash,
5. With the flute and harp, With the flute and harp,
6. In this ho - ly place, In this ho - ly place,
7. On the might-y throne, On the might-y throne,
8. At the break of day,_ At the break of day,_
9. When the sun goes down, When the sun goes down,
10. Ev - 'ry liv - ing thing, Ev - 'ry liv - ing thing,
11. Praise the Fa - ther,_ Praise the Fa - ther,
12. Praise the Son,____ Praise the Son,____
13. Praise the Spir - it,____ Praise the Spir - it,____
14. Al - le - lu - ia,____ Al - le - lu - ia,____

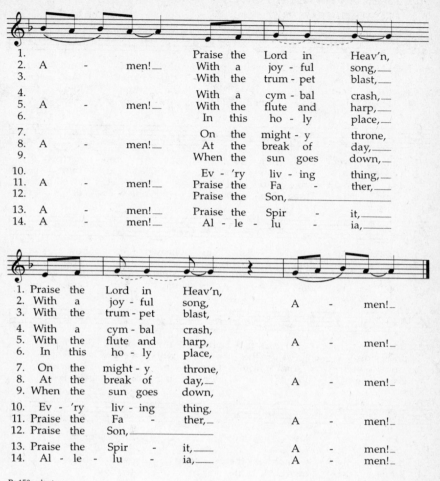

1. Praise the Lord in Heav'n,
2. With a joy - ful song, __
3. With the trum - pet blast, __

4. With a cym - bal crash, __
5. With the flute and harp, __
6. In this ho - ly place, __

7. On the might - y throne,
8. At the break of day, __
9. When the sun goes down, __

10. Ev - 'ry liv - ing thing, __
11. Praise the Fa - ther, __
12. Praise the Son, _____

13. Praise the Spir - it, __
14. Al - le - lu - ia, __

1. Praise the Lord in Heav'n,
2. With a joy - ful song,
3. With the trum - pet blast,

4. With a cym - bal crash,
5. With the flute and harp,
6. In this ho - ly place,

7. On the might - y throne,
8. At the break of day, __
9. When the sun goes down,

10. Ev - 'ry liv - ing thing,
11. Praise the Fa - ther, __
12. Praise the Son, _____

13. Praise the Spir - it, __
14. Al - le - lu - ia, __

A - men! __
A - men! __
A - men! __
A - men! __
A - men! __

Ps 150, adapt.
Alan J. Hommerding

Anonymous
Text and music © 1995, WLP

563 Holy God, We Praise Thy Name

GROSSER GOTT 78 78 77

1. Ho - ly God,__ we praise thy name; Lord of
2. Hark! The loud__ ce - les - tial hymn An - gel
3. Lo! The ap - os - tol - ic train Join, the
4. Ho - ly Fa - ther, Ho - ly Son, Ho - ly

1. all,__ we bow__ be - fore thee! All on earth thy
2. choirs a - bove are rais - ing, Cher - u - bim__ and
3. sa - cred name to hal - low; Proph - ets swell the
4. Spir - it, Three we name thee; While in es - sence

1. rule__ ac - claim, All in heav'n a - bove__ a -
2. ser - a - phim, In un - ceas - ing cho - rus
3. loud__ re - frain, And the white - robed mar - tyrs
4. on - ly One, Un - di - vid - ed God__ we

1. dore thee; In - fi - nite__ thy vast do - main,
2. prais - ing; Fill the heav'ns with sweet ac - cord:
3. fol - low; And from morn__ to set of sun,
4. 'claim thee; And a - dor - ing bend the knee,

1. Ev - er - last - ing is__ thy reign.
2. "Ho - ly, ho - ly, ho - ly. Lord."
3. Through the Church the song__ goes on.
4. While we own__ the mys - ter - y.

Te Deum
Attr. to Ignaz Franz, 1719–1790
Tr. by Clarence A. Walworth, 1820–1900

Allgemeines Katholisches Gesangbuch, Vienna, 1774

Whatsoever You Do 564

REFRAIN

What - so - ev - er   you   do   to the least   of   my
peo - ple,   that   you   do   un - to   me.

VERSES

1. When   I   was   hun - gry,   you   gave   me   to   eat;
2. When   I   was   home - less,   you   o - pened your   door;
3. When   I   was   wea - ry,   you   helped me   find   rest;

4. When   I   was   lit - tle,   you   taught me   to   read;
5. When   in   a   pris - on,   you   came   to   my   cell;
6. In   a   strange coun - try,   you   made   me   at   home;

7. Hurt   in   a   bat - tle,   you   bound   up   my   wounds;
8. When   I   was   a - ged,   you   both - ered   to   smile;
9. You   saw   me   cov - ered with   spit - tle   and   blood;

10. When   I   was   laughed at,   you   stood   by   my   side;

1. When   I   was   thirst - y,   you   gave   me   to   drink.
2. When   I   was   nak - ed,   you   gave   me   your   coat.
3. When   I   was   anx - ious, you   calmed   all   my   fears.

4. When   I   was   lone - ly,   you   gave   me   your   love.
5. When   on   a   sick - bed,   you   cared   for   my   needs.
6. Seek - ing   em - ploy - ment, you   found   me   a   job.

7. Search - ing   for   kind - ness, you   held   out   your   hand.
8. When   I   was   rest - less,   you   lis - tened and   cared.
9. You   knew   my   fea - tures, though grim - y   with   sweat.

10. When   I   was   hap - py,   you   shared   in   my   joy.

To Refrain

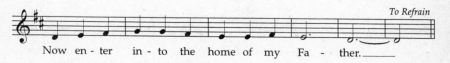

Now   en - ter   in - to   the   home   of   my   Fa - ther.____

565 The Church of Christ in Every Age

WINCHESTER NEW   LM

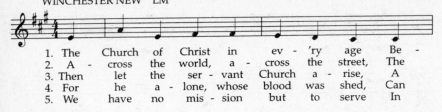

1. The Church of Christ in ev - 'ry age Be -
2. A - cross the world, a - cross the street, The
3. Then let the ser - vant Church a - rise, A
4. For he a - lone, whose blood was shed, Can
5. We have no mis - sion but to serve In

1. set by change but Spir - it - led, Must claim and test its
2. vic - tims of in - jus - tice cry For shel - ter and for
3. car - ing Church that longs to be A part - ner in Christ's
4. cure the fe - ver in our blood, And teach us how to
5. full o - be - dience to our Lord: To care for all, with -

1. her - it - age And keep on ris - ing from the dead.
2. bread to eat, And nev - er live un - til they die.
3. sac - ri - fice, And clothed in Christ's hu - man - i - ty.
4. share our bread And feed the starv - ing mul - ti - tude.
5. out re - serve, And spread his lib - er - at - ing ward.

Fred Pratt Green
Text © 1971, Hope Publishing Co.

Musicalisches Hand-Buch, Hamburg, 1690
Melody adapt. by William H. Havergal, 1793–1870

566 Lord, Whose Love in Humble Service

BEACH SPRING   87 87 D

1. Lord, whose love in hum - ble ser - vice Bore the
2. Still your chil - dren wan - der home - less; Still the
3. As we wor - ship, grant us vi - sion, Till your
4. Called from wor - ship in - to ser - vice, Forth in

1. weight of hu - man need, Who up - on the cross, for -
2. hun - gry cry for bread; Still the cap - tives long for
3. love's re - veal - ing light, In its height and depth and
4. your great name we go To the child, the youth, the

1. sak - en, Worked your mer - cy's per - fect deed:
2. free - dom; Still in grief we mourn our dead.
3. great - ness, Dawns up - on our quick-ened sight,
4. a - ged, Love in liv - ing deeds to show,

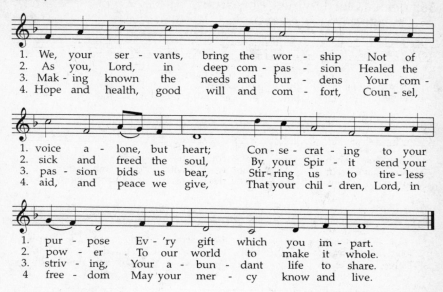

1. We, your ser-vants, bring the wor-ship Not of
2. As you, Lord, in deep com-pas-sion Healed the
3. Mak-ing known the needs and bur-dens Your com-
4. Hope and health, good will and com-fort, Coun-sel,

1. voice a-lone, but heart; Con-se-crat-ing to your
2. sick and freed the soul, By your Spir-it send your
3. pas-sion bids us bear, Stir-ring us to tire-less
4. aid, and peace we give, That your chil-dren, Lord, in

1. pur-pose Ev-'ry gift which you im-part.
2. pow-er To our world to make it whole.
3. striv-ing, Your a-bun-dant life to share.
4. free-dom May your mer-cy know and live.

Albert F. Bayly, 1901–1984, alt.
Text © 1988, Oxford University Press

The Sacred Harp, Philadelphia, 1844

Whom Shall I Send 567
DUNEDIN LM

1. "Whom shall I send?" our Mak-er cries; And man-y,
2. For who can serve a God so pure, Or claim to
3. And yet, be-liev-ing God who calls Knows what we
4. Those who are called God pur-i-fies, And dai-ly

1. when they hear God's voice, Are sure where their vo-ca-tion
2. speak in such a—name, While doubt makes ev-'ry step un-
3. are and still may be Our past de-feats, our fu-ture
4. gives us strength to—bend Our thoughts, our skills, our en-er-

1. lies; But man-y shrink from such a choice.
2. sure, And self con-fus-es ev-'ry aim?
3. falls, We dare to an-swer: "Lord, send me!"
4. gies, And life it-self to this one end.

Fred Pratt Green
Text © 1971, Hope Publishing Co.

Vernon Griffiths, 1894–1985
Music © 1971, Faber Music Ltd.

568 Jesus, Our Divine Companion

PLEADING SAVIOR 87 87 D

1. Je - sus, our di - vine com - pan - ion, By your low - ly
2. All who tread the path of la - bor Fol - low where your
3. Ev - 'ry task, how - ev - er hum - ble, Fills the soul with

1. hu - man birth You have come to join all work - ers,
2. feet have trod; All who work with - out com - plain - ing
3. grace a - new; Ev - 'ry deed of love and kind - ness

1. Bur - den - bear - ers of the earth. Son of Jo - seph,
2. Do the ho - ly will of God. Christ, the peace sur -
3. Done in faith is done for you. Je - sus, our di -

1. gift - ed work - er, Toil - ing for your dai - ly food,
2. pass - ing know-ledge, Dwell with us in dai - ly strife;
3. vine com - pan - ion, Help us all to work our best;

1. By your pa - tience and your cour - age,
2. Christ, the bread of heav - en, bro - ken
3. Bless us in our dai - ly la - bor,

1. You have taught us toil is good.
2. In the sac - ra - ment of life.
3. Lead us to our heav'n - ly rest.

Henry van Dyke, 1852–1933, alt.   Joshua Leavitt's *Christian Lyre*, 1831

569 Now Let Us from This Table Rise

DUKE STREET LM

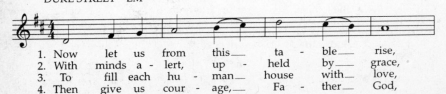

1. Now let us from this ta - ble rise,
2. With minds a - lert, up - held by grace,
3. To fill each hu - man house with love,
4. Then give us cour - age, Fa - ther God,

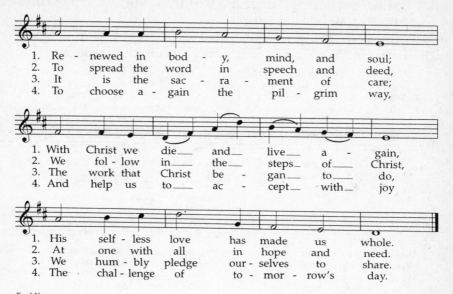

1. Re - newed in bod - y, mind, and soul;
2. To spread the word in speech and deed,
3. It is the sac - ra - ment of care;
4. To choose a - gain the pil - grim way,

1. With Christ we die___ and___ live___ a - gain,
2. We fol - low in___ the___ steps_ of___ Christ,
3. The work that Christ be - gan___ to___ do,
4. And help us to___ ac - cept___ with_ joy

1. His self - less love has made us whole.
2. At one with all in hope and need.
3. We hum - bly pledge our - selves to share.
4. The chal - lenge of to - mor - row's day.

Fred Kaan
Text © 1968, Hope Publishing Co.

Attr. to John Hatton, c. 1710–1793

This Little Light of Mine 570

1. This lit - tle light of mine,
2. Ev - 'ry - where I go,___
3. Je - sus gave it to me,___

I'm gon - na let it shine.___

1. This lit - tle light of mine,
2. Ev - 'ry - where I go,___
3. Je - sus gave it to me,___

I'm gon - na let it shine.___

1. This lit - tle light of mine,
2. Ev - 'ry - where I go,___
3. Je - sus gave it to me,___

I'm gon - na let it shine,___

let it shine,___ let it shine,___ let it shine.___

African-American

571 Where Armies Scourge the Countryside

PACE MIO DIO   CM with Refrain

1. Where ar - mies scourge the coun - try - side,
2. Where an - ger fes - ters in the heart,
3. Where homes are torn by bit - ter strife,
4. O God, whose heart com - pas - sion - ate

1. And peo - ple flee in fear;
2. And strikes with cru - el hand;
3. And love dis - solves in blame;
4. Bears ev - 'ry hu - man pain,

1. Where si - rens scream through flam - ing nights,
2. Where vio - lence stalks the trou - bled streets,
3. Where walls you meant for shel - t'ring care
4. Re - deem this vio - lent, wound - ing world

1. And death is ev - er near:
2. And ter - ror haunts the land:
3. Hide deeds of hurt and shame:
4. Till gen - tle - ness shall reign.

O God of mer - cy, hear our prayer: Bring peace to earth a - gain!

Herman G. Stuempfle, Jr.

Perry Nelson
Text and music © 1996, WLP

572 Make Us True Servants

SLANE   10 10 10 10

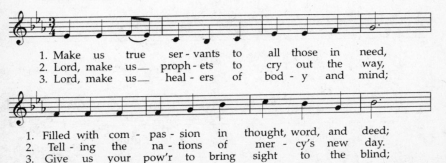

1. Make us true ser - vants to all those in need,
2. Lord, make us— proph - ets to cry out the way,
3. Lord, make us— heal - ers of bod - y and mind;

1. Filled with com - pas - sion in thought, word, and deed;
2. Tell - ing the na - tions of mer - cy's new day.
3. Give us your pow'r to bring sight to the blind;

1. Lov - ing_ our_ neigh - bor, what - ev - er the cost,_
2. Let us_ break bar - riers of ha - tred and scorn,
3. Love to_ the_ love - less and glad - ness for pain,_

1. Feed - ing the hun - gry and_ find - ing the lost.
2. Speak - ing of hope to all_ peo - ple for - lorn.
3. Fill - ing all hearts with the_ joy of your name.

Susan G. Wente
Text © 1978, WLP

Irish folk song

Stewards of Earth 573

FINLANDIA 11 10 11 10 11 10

1. All praise to you, O Lord of all cre - a - tion;_____
2. With won - drous grace you clothed the earth in splen - dor;_____
3. To tend the earth is our en - trust - ed du - ty,_____

1. You made the world, and it is yours a - lone.
2. With teem - ing life you filled the sea and land.
3. For earth is ours to use and not a - buse.

1. The plan - et earth you spun in its lo - ca - tion_____
2. In - still in us a sense of awe and won - der_____
3. O gra - cious Lord, true source of all re - sourc - es,_____

1. A - mid the stars a - dorn - ing heav - en's dome._____
2. When we be - hold the boun - ty of your hand._____
3. For - give our greed that wields de - struc - tion's sword._____

1. We lease the earth but for a life's du - ra - tion,_____
2. Then, when we hear the voice of bird or thun - der,_____
3. Then let us serve as wise and faith - ful stew - ards_____

1. Yet for this life it is our cher - ished home._____
2. We hear the voice our faith can un - der - stand._____
3. While earth gives glo - ry to cre - a - tion's Lord._____

Omer Westendorf
Text © 1984, WLP

Jean Sibelius, 1865–1957

574 We Are the Light of the World

1. Bless - ed are they who are poor in spir - it,
2. Bless - ed are they who are meek and hum - ble,
3. Bless - ed are they who will mourn in sor - row,

4. Bless those who hun - ger and thirst for jus - tice,
5. Bless - ed are they who show oth - ers mer - cy,
6. Bless - ed are hearts that are clean and ho - ly,

7. Bless - ed are they who bring peace a - mong us,
8. Bless those who suf - fer from per - se - cu - tion,

1. Theirs is the King-dom of God. Bless us, O Lord, make us
2. They will in - her - it the earth. Bless us, O Lord, make us
3. They will be com - fort - ed. Bless us, O Lord, when we

4. They will be sat - is - fied. Bless us, O Lord, hear our
5. They will know mer - cy too. Bless us, O Lord, hear our
6. They will be - hold___ the Lord. Bless us, O Lord, make us

7. They are the chil - dren of God. Bless us, O Lord, may your
8. Theirs is the King-dom of God. Bless us, O Lord, when they

1. poor in spir - it; Bless us, O Lord, our God.
2. meek and hum - ble; Bless us, O Lord, our God.
3. share their sor - row; Bless us, O Lord, our God.

4. cry for jus - tice; Bless us, O Lord, our God.
5. cry for mer - cy; Bless us, O Lord, our God.
6. pure and ho - ly; Bless us, O Lord, our God.

7. peace be with us; Bless us, O Lord, our God.
8. per - se - cute us; Bless us, O Lord, our God.

We are the light of the world, may our light shine be - fore all,

That they may see the good that we do, and give glo - ry to God.

Jean Anthony Greif
Text and music © 1966, Vernacular Hymns Publishing Co.

Blessed Are the Poor 575
SALVADOR

REFRAIN

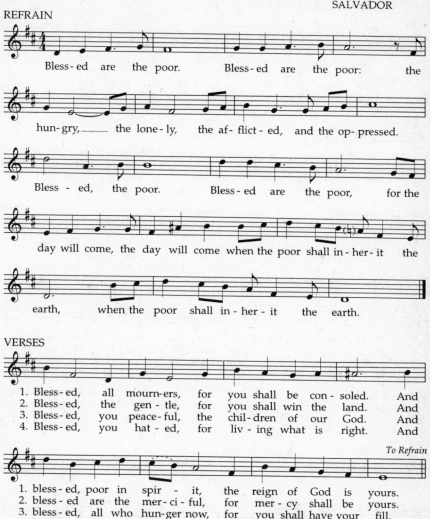

Bless-ed are the poor. Bless-ed are the poor: the

hun-gry,____ the lone-ly, the af-flict-ed, and the op-pressed.

Bless-ed, the poor. Bless-ed are the poor, for the

day will come, the day will come when the poor shall in-her-it the

earth, when the poor shall in-her-it the earth.

VERSES

1. Bless-ed, all mourn-ers, for you shall be con-soled. And
2. Bless-ed, the gen-tle, for you shall win the land. And
3. Bless-ed, you peace-ful, the chil-dren of our God. And
4. Bless-ed, you hat-ed, for liv-ing what is right. And

To Refrain

1. bless-ed, poor in spir-it, the reign of God is yours.
2. bless-ed are the mer-ci-ful, for mer-cy shall be yours.
3. bless-ed, all who hun-ger now, for you shall have your fill.
4. bless-ed, per-se-cut-ed ones, the king-dom will be yours.

Mt 5:3–12; Lk 6:20–22

James V. Marchionda
Text and music © 1988, 1989, WLP

576 The Kingdom of God

LAUDATE DOMINUM 10 10 11 11

1. The king-dom of God is jus-tice and joy;
2. The king-dom of God is mer-cy and grace;
3. The king-dom of God is chal-lenge and choice:
4. God's king-dom is come, the gift and the goal;

1. For Je-sus re-stores what sin would de-stroy.
2. The cap-tives are freed, the sin-ners find place,
3. Be-lieve the good news, re-pent and re-joice!
4. In Je-sus be-gun, in heav-en made whole.

1. God's pow-er and glo-ry___ in___ Je-sus we know;
2. The out-cast are wel-comed God's ban-quet to share;
3. God's love for us sin-ners brought Christ to his cross:
4. The heirs of the king-dom shall an-swer his call;

1. And here and here-af-ter the king-dom shall grow.
2. And hope is a-wak-ened in place of de-spair.
3. Our cri-sis of judg-ment for gain or for loss,
4. And all things cry "Glo-ry!" to God all in all.

Bryn A. Rees, 1911–1983
Text © Mrs. Olwen Scott

Charles H. H. Parry, 1848–1918

577 Blest Are They

VERSE 1

1. Blest are they, the poor in spir-it, theirs is the

1. king-dom of God.____ Blest are they,

To Refrain

1. full of sor-row, they shall be con-soled.____

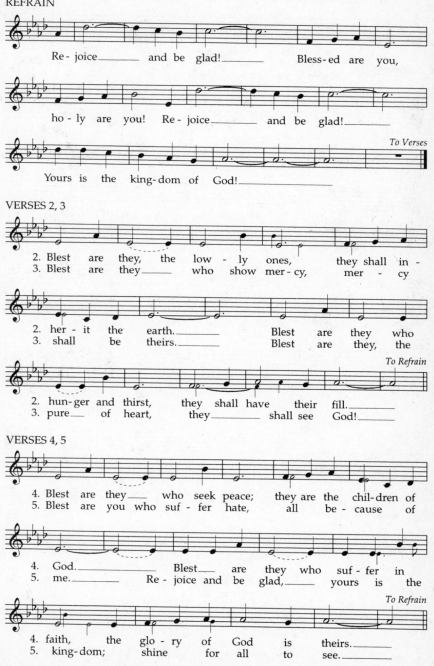

REFRAIN

Re - joice___ and be glad!___ Bless- ed are you,

ho - ly are you! Re - joice___ and be glad!___

To Verses

Yours is the king-dom of God!___

VERSES 2, 3

2. Blest are they, the low - ly ones, they shall in -
3. Blest are they___ who show mer - cy, mer - cy

2. her - it the earth.___ Blest are they who
3. shall be theirs.___ Blest are they, the

To Refrain

2. hun- ger and thirst, they shall have their fill.___
3. pure___ of heart, they___ shall see God!___

VERSES 4, 5

4. Blest are they___ who seek peace; they are the chil-dren of
5. Blest are you who suf - fer hate, all be - cause of

4. God.___ Blest___ are they who suf - fer in
5. me.___ Re - joice and be glad,___ yours is the

To Refrain

4. faith, the glo - ry of God is theirs.___
5. king-dom; shine for all to see.___

Mt 5:3–12

David Haas
Text and music © 1985, GIA

578 I Know Not Where the Road Will Lead

KING'S HIGHWAY CMD

1. I know not where the road will lead I
2. And some I love have reached the end, But
3. The count-less hosts lead on be-fore, I

1. fol - low day by day, Or where it ends; I
2. some with me may stay, Their faith and hope still
3. must not fear nor stray; With them, the pil - grims

1. on - ly know I walk the King's high - way.
2. guid-ing me; I walk the King's high - way.
3. of the faith I walk the King's high - way.

1. I know not if the way is long, And
2. The way is truth, the way is love, For
3. Through light and dark the road leads on Till

1. no - one else can say; But rough or smooth, up -
2. light and strength I pray, And through the years of
3. dawns the end - less day, When I shall know why

1. hill or down, I walk the King's high - way.
2. life, to God I walk the King's high - way.
3. in this life I walk the King's high - way.

Evelyn Atwater Cummins, 1891–1971

V. Earle Copes
Music © 1997, WLP

On the Wings of Change 579

REFRAIN

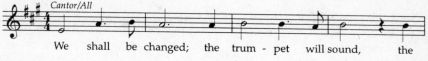

We shall be changed; the trum - pet will sound, the

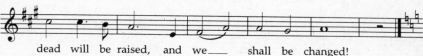

dead will be raised, and we___ shall be changed!

VERSES

Cantor/Choir

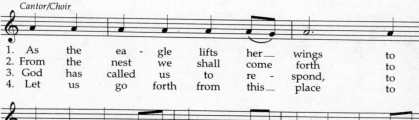

1. As the ea - gle lifts her___ wings to
2. From the nest we shall come forth to
3. God has called us to re - spond, to
4. Let us go forth from this___ place to

1. bring her young from the nest, so the wings of God hov - er
2. bring God's peace to the poor; and to lead all peo - ple to
3. bring good news to the poor, let us lift our hearts and our
4. bring God's light to the world, for in Christ we die and are

To Refrain

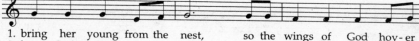

1. o - ver us and we shall be changed!
2. jus - tice, and we shall be changed!
3. voic - es, and we shall be changed!
4. ris - en, and we have been changed!

Ref.: 1 Cor 15:51, 52
Vs. 1: Dt 32:11

Jerry Galipeau
Text (vss.) and music © 1994, WLP

Look to the One 580

REFRAIN

Look to the One, look to the One,

look to the One who comes in glo - ry!

Ed Bolduc
Text and music © 1993, WLP

581 Wake the Song of Jubilee

ST. GEORGE'S WINDSOR   77 77 D

1. Wake the song of ju - bi - lee, Let it ech - o
2. Now the des - ert lands re - joice, And the is - lands
3. Bless - ing, hon - or, glo - ry, might Are the Pas - chal

1. o'er the sea! Now is come the prom - ised hour,
2. join their voice; Yes, the whole cre - a - tion sings,
3. Vic - tim's right; Thrones and pow'rs in hom - age fall,

1. Je - sus reigns with sov - 'reign pow'r. Come, you na - tions,
2. "Je - sus is the King of kings." See the ran - somed
3. To the Lamb and Lord of all, Time has near - ly

1. join and sing, To the throne your prais - es bring;
2. mil - lions stand, Palms of con - quest in their hands;
3. reached its sum; Spir - it and the bride say "Come!"

1. Let it sound from shore to shore:
2. This be - fore the throne their strain:
3. Je - sus, whom all worlds a - dore,

1. "Je - sus reigns for - ev - er - more."
2. "Hell is van - quished, death is slain."
3. Come, and reign for - ev - er - more.

Leonard Bacon, 1802–1881, alt.   George J. Elvey, 1816–1893

Lift Up Your Heads 582

TRURO   LM

1. Lift up your heads, O might - y gates;
2. O blest the land, the cit - y blest,
3. Fling wide the por - tals of your heart;
4. Re - deem - er come! I o - pen wide
5. So come, my Sov - 'reign; en - ter in!

1. Be - hold the King__ of glo - ry waits!
2. Where Christ the ru - ler__ is con - fessed!
3. Make it a tem - ple,__ set a - part
4. My heart to you:__ here,__ Lord, a - bide!
5. Let new and no - bler__ life be - gin;

1. The King of kings is draw - ing__ near;
2. O hap - py hearts and hap - py__ homes
3. From earth - ly use for heaven's em - ploy,
4. Let me your in - ner pres - ence__ feel:
5. Your Ho - ly Spir - it guide us__ on,

1. The Sav - ior of__ the__ world is here.
2. To whom this King__ of__ tri - umph comes!
3. a - dorned with prayer and__ love and joy.
4. Your grace and love__ in__ me re - veal.
5. Un - til the glo - rious__ crown be won.

Georg Weissel, 1590–1635
Tr. by Catherine Winkworth, 1827–1878

Psalmodia Evangelica, Part II, 1789

583 For the Fruits of All Creation

AR HYD Y NOS   84 84 88 84

1. For the fruits of all cre - a - tion, Thanks be to God.
2. In the just re - ward of la - bor, God's will is done.
3. For the har - vests of the Spir - it, Thanks be to God.

1. For the gifts to ev - 'ry na - tion, Thanks be to God.
2. In the help we give our neigh - bor, God's will is done.
3. For the good we all in - her - it, Thanks be to God.

1. For the plow - ing, sow - ing, reap - ing, Si - lent
2. In our world - wide task of car - ing For the
3. For the won - ders that as - tound us, For the

1. growth while we are sleep - ing, Fu - ture needs in
2. hun - gry and de - spair - ing, In the har - vests
3. truths that still con - found us, Most of all, that

1. earth's safe - keep - ing, Thanks be to God.
2. we are shar - ing, God's will is done.
3. love has found us, Thanks be to God.

Fred Pratt Green, alt.
Text © 1970, Hope Publishing Co.

Traditional Welsh melody

All Beautiful the March of Days 584

FOREST GREEN   CMD

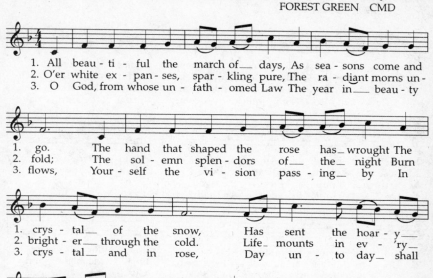

1. All beau - ti - ful the march of__ days, As sea - sons come and
2. O'er white ex - pan - ses, spar - kling pure, The ra - diant morns un -
3. O God, from whose un - fath - omed Law The year in__ beau - ty

1. go. The hand that shaped the rose has__ wrought The
2. fold; The sol - emn splen - dors of__ the__ night Burn
3. flows, Your - self the vi - sion pass - ing__ by In

1. crys - tal__ of the snow, Has sent the hoar - y__
2. bright - er__ through the cold. Life__ mounts in ev - 'ry__
3. crys - tal__ and in rose, Day un - to day__ shall

1. frost of__ heav'n, The flow - ing wa - ters sealed, And
2. throb - bing vein, Love deep - ens 'round the hearth, And
3. ut - ter__ speech, And night to night pro - claim, In

1. laid a si - lent love - li - ness On hill and wood and field.
2. clear - er sounds the an - gel__ hymn, "Good will to__ all on earth."
3. ev - er - chang - ing words of__ light, The won - der of your name.

Ps 19:3
Frances W. Wile, 1878–1939, alt.

Surrey folk melody

585 Come, Ye Thankful People, Come

ST. GEORGE'S WINDSOR   77 77 D

1. Come, ye thank - ful peo - ple, come, Raise the song of
2. All the world is God's own field, Fruit un - to God's
3. For the Lord our God shall come, And shall take the
4. Ev - en so, Lord, quick - ly come, Bring the fi - nal

1. har - vest home; All is safe - ly gath - ered in
2. praise to yield; Wheat and weed to - geth - er sown,
3. har - vest home, From the field shall in that day
4. har - vest home; Gath - er all your peo - ple in,

1. Ere the win - ter storms be - gin; God, our Mak - er,
2. Un - to joy or sor - row grown; First the blade and
3. All of - fen - ses purge a - way; Giv - ing an - gels
4. Free from sor - row, free from sin; There, for - ev - er

1. does pro - vide For our wants to be sup - plied:
2. then the ear, Then the ri - pened stalk ap - pears:
3. charge at last In the fire the weeds to cast:
4. pu - ri - fied, In your pres - ence to a - bide:

1. Come, to God's own tem - ple come;
2. Lord of har - vest, grant that we
3. But the fruit - ful ears to store;
4. Come, with all your an - gels, come;

1. Raise the song of har - vest home.
2. Whole - some grain and pure may be.
3. Boun - teous har - vest ev - er - more.
4. Raise the glo - rious har - vest home.

Henry Alford, 1810–1871, alt.

George J. Elvey, 1816–1893

For the Beauty of the Earth 586

DIX   77 77 77

1. For the beau-ty of the earth, For the beau-ty
2. For the won-der of each hour, Of the day and
3. For the joy of ear and eye, For the heart and
4. For the joy of hu-man love, Broth-er, sis-ter,
5. For your Church that ev-er-more Lifts its ho-ly
6. For your-self, best Gift Di-vine! To this world so

1. of the skies, For the love which from our birth
2. of the night, Hill and vale and tree and flower,
3. mind's de-light, For the mys-tic har-mo-ny
4. par-ent, child, Friends on earth and friends a-bove,
5. hands a-bove, Of-f'ring up on ev-'ry shore
6. free-ly giv'n; Word In-car-nate, God's de-sign,

1. O-ver and a-round us lies,
2. Sun and moon and stars of light,
3. Link-ing sense to sound and sight,
4. For all gen-tle thoughts and mild,
5. Its pure sac-ri-fice of love:
6. Peace on earth and joy in heav'n:

Christ, our Lord, to

you we raise This our sac-ri-fice of praise.

Folliot S. Pierpoint, 1835–1917, alt.

Conrad Kocher, 1786–1872

587 Sent Forth by God's Blessing

THE ASH GROVE   12 11 12 11 D

1. Sent forth by God's bless-ing, Our true faith con-fess-ing,
2. With praise and thanks-giv-ing To God who is_ liv-ing,

1. The peo-ple_ of_ God from this dwell-ing take leave.
2. The tasks of_ our_ ev-'ry-day life we em-brace.

1. God's sac-ri-fice_ end-ed, O now be ex-tend-ed
2. Our faith ev-er_ shar-ing, In love ev-er_ car-ing,

1. The fruits of_ this_ Mass in all hearts who be-lieve.
2. We claim as_ our_ fam-'ly all those of each race.

1. The_ seed of_ Christ's teach-ing, Our in-ner_ souls reach-ing,
2. One bread that has_ fed us, One light that has_ led us

1. Shall blos-som in_ ac-tion for God and for all.
2. U-nite us as_ one in the life that we share.

1. God's grace shall in-cite us, In love shall u-nite us
2. Then may all the_ liv-ing With praise and_ thanks-giv-ing

1. To fur-ther_ God's king-dom and an-swer the call.
2. Give hon-or_ to_ Christ and his name that we bear.

Omer Westendorf
Text © 1964, WLP

Traditional Welsh folk melody

Sent Forth by God's Blessing *(alt.*)* 588
THE ASH GROVE   12 11 12 11 D

1. Sent forth by God's blessing, Our true faith confessing,
   The people of God from this dwelling take leave.
   Our prayer here has ended, O now be extended
   The fruits of our worship in all who believe.
   The seed of Christ's teaching, Our inner souls reaching,
   Shall blossom in action for God and for all.
   God's grace shall incite us, In love shall unite us
   To further God's kingdom and answer the call.

2. With praise and thanksgiving To God who is living,
   The tasks of our ev'ryday life we embrace.
   Our faith ever sharing, In love ever caring,
   We claim as our fam'ly all those of each race.
   With grace God has fed us, One true light has led us,
   Uniting us all in the life that we share.
   Then may all the living With praise and thanksgiving
   Give honor to Christ and his name that we bear.

Omer Westendorf, alt.
Alt. by Alan J. Hommerding
Text © 1964, 1994, WLP

Alternative text for non-Eucharistic liturgies

Let All Things Now Living 589
THE ASH GROVE   12 11 12 11 D

1. Let all things now living A song of thanksgiving
   To God our Creator triumphantly raise;
   Who fashioned and made us, Protected and stayed us,
   By guiding us on to the end of our days.
   God's banners are o'er us, Pure light goes before us,
   A pillar of fire shining forth in the night;
   Till shadows have vanished And darkness is banished,
   As forward we travel from light into light.

2. The law God enforces, The stars in their courses,
   The sun in its orbit obediently shine.
   The hills and the mountains, The rivers and fountains,
   The depths of the ocean proclaim God divine.
   We, too, should be voicing Our love and rejoicing,
   With glad adoration a song let us raise,
   Till all things now living Unite in thanksgiving
   To God in the highest, hosanna and praise.

Katherine K. Davis, 1892–1980
Text © 1939, 1966, E. C. Schirmer Music Co.

590 Now Thank We All Our God

NUN DANKET   67 67 66 66

1. Now thank we all our God With
2. O may this boun - teous God Through
3. All praise and thanks to God The

1. heart and hands and voic - es, Who won-drous things has
2. all our life be near us, With ev - er - joy - ful
3. Fa - ther now be giv - en, The Son and Spir - it

1. done, In whom this world re - joic - es; Who
2. hearts And bless - ed peace to cheer us; Pre -
3. blessed Who reign in high - est heav - en; E -

1. from our moth-ers' arms Has blessed us on our way
2. serve us in his grace, And guide us when per-plexed,
3. ter - nal, tri - une God, Whom earth and heav'n a - dore;

1. With count-less gifts of love, And still is ours to - day.
2. And free us from all ills In this world and the next.
3. For thus it was, is now, And shall be ev - er - more.

Martin Rinckart, 1586–1649
Tr. by Catherine Winkworth, 1827–1878, alt.

Johann Crüger, 1598–1662

Sing to the Lord of Harvest 591

WIE LIEBLICH IST DER MAIEN   76 76 D

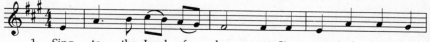

1. Sing   to   the Lord   of__   har - vest, Sing songs   of   love and
2. The clouds   all   drop   God's boun - ty, The   des - erts bloom and
3. Place   on   the sa - cred   al - tar   The   gifts which good-ness

1. praise;   With   joy - ful   hearts   and__   voic - es   Your
2. spring;   The   hills   leap   up__   in__   glad - ness,   The
3. gave,   The   gold - en   sheaves of__   har - vest,   The

1. al - le - lu - ias   raise!   By   God   the roll - ing__
2. val - leys laugh and   sing.   God   gifts   the earth   in__
3. souls Christ came   to   save;   Your   hearts   lay down   in__

1. sea - sons   In   fruit - ful   or - der__   move;   Sing
2. full - ness,   All   things with   large   in - crease,   And
3. hom - age,   At   ho - ly   feet   now_   fall,   Through

1. to   the Lord   of__   har - vest   A   joy - ful song of   love.
2. crowns   the   year   with   good - ness, With   plen - ty   and with   peace.
3. all   your life_   a - dor - ing   The   One who died for   all.

John S. B. Monsell, 1811–1875, alt.   Johann Steuerlein, 1546–1613

592 By All Your Saints Still Striving

ST. THEODULPH   76 76 D

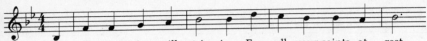

1. By all your saints still striv - ing, For all your saints at rest,
*2. A - pos - tles, proph-ets, mar - tyrs, And all the no - ble throng
3. Then let us praise the Fa - ther And wor-ship God the Son

1. Your ho - ly Name, O Je - sus, For - ev - er - more be blessed.
2. Who wear the spot-less gar - ment And raise the cease-less song:
3. And sing to God the Spir - it, E - ter - nal Three - in - One,

1. You rose, our King vic - to - rious, That they might wear the crown
2. For them and those whose wit - ness Is on - ly known to you
3. Till all the ran-somed num - ber Who stand be - fore the throne,

1. And ev - er shine in splen - dor Re - flect - ed from your throne.
2. By walk-ing in their foot - steps We give you praise a - new.
3. A - scribe all pow'r and glo - ry And praise to God a - lone.

Horatio Nelson, 1823–1913, alt.
Text © 1985, The Church Pension Fund

Melchior Teschner, 1584–1635

This stanza may be replaced by one of the following.

January 25: Conversion of Paul
Praise for the light from heaven
    And for the voice of awe:
Praise for the glorious vision
    The prosecutor saw.
O Lord, for Paul's conversion,
    We bless your name today.
Come, shine within our darkness
    And guide us in the way.

February 22: Chair of Peter
We praise you, Lord, for Peter,
    So eager and so bold:
Thrice falling, yet repentant,
    Thrice charged to feed your fold.
Lord, make your pastors faithful
    To guard your flock from harm
And hold them when they waver
    With your almighty arm.

March 19: Joseph, Husband of Mary
All praise, O God, for Joseph,
    The guardian of your Son,
Who saved him from King Herod,
    When safety there was none.
He taught the trade of builder,
    When they to Naz'reth came,
And Joseph's love made "Father"
    To be, for Christ, God's name.

March 25: Annunciation of Our Lord
We sing with joy of Mary
    Whose heart with awe was stirred
When, youthful and unready,
    She heard the angel's word;
Yet she her voice upraises
    God's glory to proclaim,
As once for our salvation
    Your mother she became.

April 25: Mark

For Mark, O Lord, we praise you,
  The weak by grace made strong:
His witness in his gospel
  Becomes victorious song.
May we, in all our weakness,
  Receive your pow'r divine,
And all, as faithful branches,
  Grow strong in you, the vine.

July 3: Thomas

All praise, O Lord, for Thomas
  Whose short-lived doubtings prove
Your perfect twofold nature,
  The depth of your true love.
To all who live with questions
  A steadfast faith afford;
And grant us grace to know you,
  Made flesh, yet God and Lord.

July 22: Mary Magdalene

All praise for Mary Magdalene,
  Whose wholeness was restored
By you, her faithful Master,
  Her Savior and her Lord.
On Easter morning early,
  A word from you sufficed:
Her faith was first to see you,
  Her Lord, the risen Christ.

July 25: James

O Lord, for James, we praise you,
  Who fell to Herod's sword.
He drank the cup of suff'ring
  And thus fulfilled your word.
Lord, curb our vain impatience
  For glory and for fame,
Equip us for such suff'rings
  As glorify your name.

August 24: Bartholomew

Praised for your blest apostle
  Surnamed Bartholomew,
We know not his achievements
  But know that he was true,
For he at the Ascension
  Was an apostle still.
May we discern your presence
  And seek, like him, your will.

September 21: Matthew

We praise you, Lord, for Matthew,
  Whose gospel words declare
That, worldly gain forsaking,
  Your path of life we share.
From all unrighteous mammon,
  O raise our eyes anew,
That we, whate'er our station
  May rise and follow you.

October 18: Luke

For Luke, belov'd physician,
  All praise; whose gospel shows
The healer of the nations,
  The one who shares our woes.
Your wine and oil, O Savior,
  Upon our spirits pour,
And with true balm of Gilead
  Anoint us evermore.

October 28: Simon and Jude

Praise, Lord, for your apostles,
  Saint Simon and Saint Jude.
One love, one hope impelled them
  To tread the way, renewed.
May we with zeal as earnest
  The faith of Christ maintain,
Be bound in love together,
  And life eternal gain.

November 30: Andrew

All praise, O Lord, for Andrew,
  The first to follow you;
He witnessed to his brother,
  "This is Messiah true."
You called him from his fishing
  Upon Lake Galilee;
He rose to meet your challenge,
  "Leave all and follow me."

December 26: Stephen

All praise, O Lord, for Stephen
  Who, martyred, saw you stand
To help in time of torment,
  To plead at God's right hand.
Like you, our suff'ring Savior,
  His enemies he blessed,
With "Lord, receive my spirit,"
  His faith, in death, confessed.

December 27: John

For John, your loved disciple,
  Exiled to Patmos' shore,
And for his faithful record,
  We praise you evermore;
Praise for the mystic vision
  His words to us unfold.
Instill in us his longing,
  Your glory to behold.

December 28: Holy Innocents

Praise for your infant martyrs,
  Whom your mysterious love
Called early from life's conflicts
  To share your peace above.
O Rachel, cease your weeping;
  They're free from pain and cares.
Lord, grant us crowns as brilliant
  And lives as pure as theirs.

593 For All the Saints

SINE NOMINE 10 10 10 with Alleluias

1. For all the saints, who from their la - bors
2. You were their rock, their for - tress, and their
3. O may your sol - diers, faith - ful, true, and

4. O blest com - mun - ion, fam - i - ly di -
5. And when the strife is fierce, the war - fare
6. The gold - en eve - ning bright - ens in the

7. But then there breaks a yet more glo - rious
8. From earth's wide bounds, from o - cean's far - thest

1. rest, All who by faith be -
2. might; You, Lord, their cap - tain
3. bold, Fight as the saints who

4. vine! We fee - bly strug - gle,
5. long, Steals on the ear the
6. west; Soon, soon to faith - ful

7. day; The saints tri - um - phant
8. coast, Through gates of pearl streams

1. fore the world con - fessed, Your name, O
2. in the well - fought fight; You, in the
3. no - bly fought of old, And win, with

4. they in glo - ry shine; Yet all are
5. dis - tant tri - umph song, And hearts are
6. war - riors comes their rest; Sweet is the

7. rise in bright ar - ray; The King of
8. in the count - less host, Sing - ing to

1. Je - sus, be for - ev - er blest.
2. dark - ness drear, their one true light.
3. them, the vic - tor's crown of gold.

4. one with - in your great de - sign.
5. brave a - gain, and arms are strong.
6. calm of par - a - dise the blest.

7. glo - ry pas - ses on his way.
8. Fa - ther, Son, and Ho - ly Ghost.

Al - le - lu - ia! Al - le - lu - ia!

William Walsham How, 1823–1897, alt.   Ralph Vaughan Williams, 1872–1958

Ye Watchers and Ye Holy Ones 594

LASST UNS ERFREUEN 88 8 88 with Alleluias

1. Ye watch-ers and ye ho-ly ones, Bright
2. O high-er than the cher-u-bim, More
3. Re-spond, ye souls in end-less rest, Ye
4. O friends, in glad-ness let us sing, All

1. ser-aphs, cher-u-bim, and thrones, Raise the glad strain,
2. glo-rious than the ser-a-phim, Lead their prais-es,
3. pa-tri-archs and proph-ets blest, Al-le-lu-ia,
4. heav-en's an-thems ech-o-ing, Al-le-lu-ia,

1. Al-le-lu-ia! Cry out, do-min-ions, prince-doms, powr's
2. Al-le-lu-ia! Thou bear-er of th'e-ter-nal Word,
3. al-le-lu-ia! Ye ho-ly twelve, ye mar-tyrs strong,
4. al-le-lu-ia! To God the Fa-ther, God the Son,

1. Vir-tues, arch-an-gels, an-gel choirs,
2. Most gra-cious, mag-ni-fy the Lord,
3. All saints tri-um-phant, raise the song:
4. And God the Spir-it, Three-in-One,

Al-le-lu-ia, Al-le-lu-ia, Al-le-lu-ia,

Al-le-lu-ia, Al-le-lu-ia!

J. Athelstan Riley, 1858–1947, alt.

Geistliche Kirchengesänge, Cologne, 1623

595 Rise Up, O Saints of God

FESTAL SONG SM

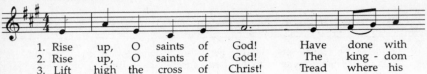

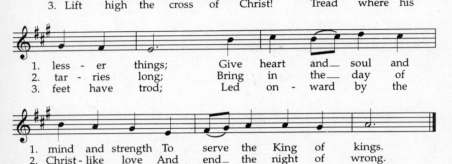

1. Rise up, O saints of God! Have done with
2. Rise up, O saints of God! The king - dom
3. Lift high the cross of Christ! Tread where his

1. less - er things; Give heart and soul and
2. tar - ries long; Bring in the day of
3. feet have trod; Led on - ward by the

1. mind and strength To serve the King of kings.
2. Christ - like love And end the night of wrong.
3. Son of Man, Rise up, O saints of God!

William Pierson Merrill, 1867–1954, alt.
Text © The Presbyterian Outlook Foundation

William H. Walter, 1825–1893

596 All Honor to Saint Patrick

ST. PATRICK'S HARVEST 75 75 D

1. All hon - or to Saint Pat - rick, the ser - vant of God,
2. To Slane Hill Pat - rick came in the dark - ness of night,
3. Now health to all who hear us, and joy on this day

1. Who plant - ed heav - en's seed in the green I - rish sod.
2. And kin - dled there a flame that set Ire - land a - light.
3. When God sent bless - ed Pat - rick to light - en our way.

1. He sowed the Word of Christ in that wel - com - ing soil,
2. His faith made kings em - brace it, his words made all see
3. May he and all the ho - ly ones ev - er be near,

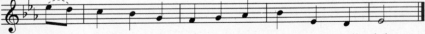

1. And brought forth a har - vest that nev - er shall fail.
2. In a sham - rock the glo - ry of God One - in - Three.
3. Giv - ing help for sal - va - tion and hope through the year.

Dan Tucker
Text and music © 1987, WLP

O Joseph, Mighty Patron 597
AURELIA 76 76 D

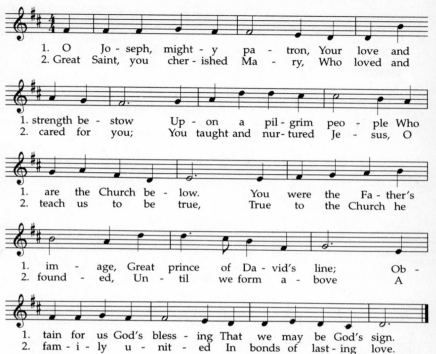

1. O Jo - seph, might - y pa - tron, Your love and
2. Great Saint, you cher - ished Ma - ry, Who loved and

1. strength be - stow Up - on a pil - grim peo - ple Who
2. cared for you; You taught and nur- tured Je - sus, O

1. are the Church be - low. You were the Fa - ther's
2. teach us to be true, True to the Church he

1. im - age, Great prince of Da - vid's line; Ob -
2. found - ed, Un - til we form a - bove A

1. tain for us God's bless - ing That we may be God's sign.
2. fam - i - ly u - nit - ed In bonds of last - ing love.

Marie M. Keane
Text © 1970, WLP

Samuel S. Wesley, 1810–1876

598 Saint Joseph Was a Just Man

MUNICH 76 76 D

1. Saint Jo-seph was a just man, A
2. As— head of God's own fam-'ly, Saint

1. man of— up-right life; Our Lord's kind fos-ter
2. Jo-seph is re-nowned; He— searched the an-cient

1. fa - ther Took Ma - ry— as his wife.
2. ci - ty, Un - til his— Child was found.

1. He knew the pain of ex - ile In
2. All hon - or to Saint Jo - seph, Whose

1. far E - gyp - tian land. O - be - dient, kind and
2. mer - its we ac - claim! God bless each home and

1. faith - ful, He fol - lowed God's com - mand.
2. fam - 'ly In good Saint Jo - seph's name.

Omer Westendorf
Text © 1970, WLP

Neuvermehrtes Meiningisches Gesangbuch, Meiningen, 1693
Adapt. by Felix Mendelssohn-Bartholdy, 1809–1847

599 The Hands That First Held Mary's Child

RESIGNATION CMD

1. The hands that first held Ma - ry's— child
2. When Jo - seph mar - veled at the— size
3. "This child shall be Em - man - u - el,
4. The tools which Jo - seph laid a - side

FAMILY

1. Were hard from work - ing wood,_____
2. Of___ that small breath - ing frame,_____
3. Not___ God up - on the throne,_____
4. A___ mob would lat - er lift_____

1. From boards they sawed and planed and filed
2. And___ gazed up - on those bright new eyes
3. But___ God with us, Em - man - u - el,
4. And___ use with an - ger, fear, and pride

1. And___ splin - ters they with - stood._____
2. And___ spoke the in - fant's name,_____
3. As___ close as blood and bone."_____
4. To___ cru - ci - fy God's gift._____

1. This day they_ gripped no tool of___ steel,
2. The an - gel's_ words he once had_ dreamed
3. The ti - ny___ form in Jo - seph's palms
4. Let us, O___ Lord, not on - ly___ hold

1. They drove no___ i - ron nail,_____
2. Poured down from heav - en's height,_____
3. Con - firmed what he had heard,_____
4. The_ Child who's born to - day,_____

1. But_ cra - dled from the head to___ heel
2. And like the___ host of stars that beamed
3. And from his___ heart rose hymns and psalms
4. But_ charged with_ faith may we be___ bold

1. Our___ Lord, new - born and frail._____
2. Blessed earth with wel - come light._____
3. For___ heav - en's hu - man word._____
4. To___ fol - low in his way._____

Thomas H. Troeger
Text © 1985, Oxford University Press

William Walker's *Southern Harmony*, 1835

600 Come, Sing a Home and Family

MOZART CMD

1. Come, sing a home and fam - i - ly in
2. At Ma - ry's ta - ble, Je - sus learned to
3. By Jo - seph's side young Je - sus learned to
4. What - ev - er form our fam - 'ly takes, the

1. Naz - a - reth of old, Whose hum - ble grace a
2. bless, give thanks, and eat, To wel - come all as
3. work and read and pray, The law and love of
4. gos - pel way we seek: To feed the hun - gry,

1. no - ble place in Chris - tian life now holds:
2. hon - ored guests by wash - ing wea - ry feet.
3. God a - bove placed in his heart to stay.
4. heal the sick, lift up the poor and weak.

1. A maid - en's ho - ly, vi - brant faith which
2. Her sweep - ing floors and light - ing lamps, her
3. While cra - dled by the car - pen - ter, the
4. In dai - ly life and sim - ple tasks our

1. said, "Let it be done," A dream - er who risked
2. knead - ing bread with leav'n, Her jour - neys to the
3. boy came to dis - cern That prod - i - gal, for -
4. song must nev - er cease Of dream - ing work - er,

1. life and limb pro - tec - ting God's own Son.
2. well fore - told to Christ the reign of heav'n.
3. giv - ing arms a - wait a child's re - turn.
4. maid - en bold, and child of last - ing peace.

Alan J. Hommerding
Text © 1994, WLP

Wolfgang A. Mozart, 1756–1791

Hail, Maiden Mary / Ave, Maria **601**

AVE, MARIA Irregular

Hail, maid - en Ma - ry, la - den with grac - es,
A - ve, Ma - rí - a, grá - ti - a ple - na,

God dwells with - in you; blest in - deed are you,
Dó - mi - nus te - cum, be - ne - dí - cta tu

most fair of____ all wo - men, and blest is he, the
in____ mu - li - é - ri - bus, et be - ne - dí - ctus

won - drous fruit of your womb, Je - sus.____
fru - ctus ven - tris tu - i,____ Je - sus.____

O ho - ly Ma - ry, God's true Moth - er,
San - cta Ma - rí - a, Ma - ter De - i,

pray for us sin - ners, weak through E - den's fall;
o - ra pro no - bis pec - ca - tó - ri - bus,

pray for us____ now____ and in our last____ hour. A - men.
nunc et in____ ho - ra mor - tis no - strae. A - men.

Tr. by Omer Westendorf
Tr. © 1964, WLP

Chant, Mode I

602 Hail, Holy Queen Enthroned Above

SALVE, REGINA CAELITUM   84 84 7779

1. Hail, ho-ly Queen en-throned a-bove,
2. The cause of joy to us be-low,
3. O_ gen-tle, lov-ing, ho-ly one,

O Ma-ri-a.

1. Hail, Queen of mer-cy and of love,
2. The spring through which all gra-ces flow,
3. The God of light be-came your Son,

O Ma-ri-a.

1. Tri-umph, all ye_ cher-u-bim;   Sing with us, ye_
2. An-gels, all your prais-es bring;   Earth and heav-en,_
3. Tri-umph, all ye_ cher-u-bim;   Sing with us, ye_

1. ser-a-phim.   Heav'n and earth re-sound the hymn:
2. with us sing;   All cre-a-tion e-cho-ing:
3. ser-a-phim.   Heav'n and earth re-sound the hymn:

Sal-ve, sal-ve, sal-ve, Re-gi-na!

Ascr. to Hermanus Contractus, 1013–1054
Tr. by Anon., 1842

German melody, Hildesheim, 1736

603 Star upon the Ocean

MARIA   99 69

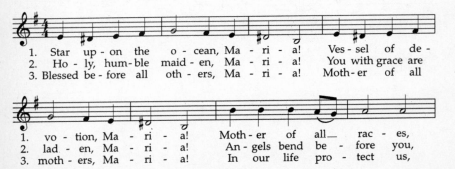

1. Star up-on the o-cean, Ma-ri-a!   Ves-sel of de-
2. Ho-ly, hum-ble maid-en, Ma-ri-a!   You with grace are
3. Blessed be-fore all oth-ers, Ma-ri-a!   Moth-er of all

1. vo-tion, Ma-ri-a!   Moth-er of all_ rac-es,
2. lad-en, Ma-ri-a!   An-gels bend be-fore you,
3. moth-ers, Ma-ri-a!   In our life pro-tect us,

1. Queen of heav - en's_ grac - es, Ma - ri - a!
2. All on earth im - plore you, Ma - ri - a!
3. In our death di - rect us, Ma - ri - a!

Michael Gannon
Text © 1955, WLP

Choral-Buch für katholische Kirchen, 1840

You Are the Honor 604

REFRAIN

Cantor/All

You are the hon - or, you are the glo - ry of our

peo - ple, Ho - ly Vir - gin Ma - ry.

VERSES

Cantor

1. You are the glo - ry of Je - ru - sa - lem,
2. You are the great - est joy of Is - ra - el,
3. You are the high - est hon - or of our race,

All

Ho - ly Vir - gin Ma - ry.

Cantor

4. May you be blessed by the Lord most high,
5. Now, and for all a - ges with - out end,
6. Give praise to God in the Church, and Christ,

All

Last time to Refrain

Ho - ly Vir - gin Ma - ry.

Lucien Deiss
Text and music © 1965, 1966, 1968, 1973, WLP

605 Our Lady's Song of Praise

MAGNIFICAT   Irregular with Refrain

REFRAIN

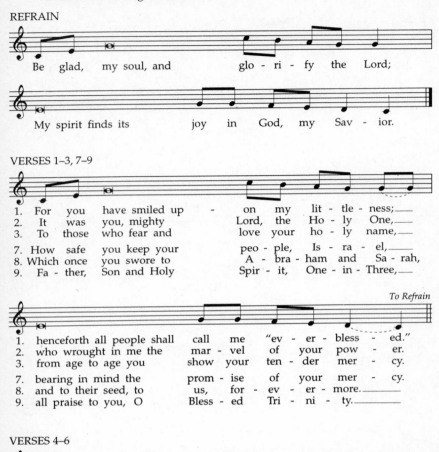

Be glad, my soul, and glo - ri - fy the Lord;

My spirit finds its joy in God, my Sav - ior.

VERSES 1–3, 7–9

1. For you have smiled up - on my lit - tle - ness;___
2. It was you, mighty Lord, the Ho - ly One,___
3. To those who fear and love your ho - ly name,___
7. How safe you keep your peo - ple, Is - ra - el,___
8. Which once you swore to A - bra - ham and Sa - rah,
9. Fa - ther, Son and Holy Spir - it, One - in - Three,___

To Refrain

1. henceforth all people shall call me "ev - er - bless - ed."
2. who wrought in me the mar - vel of your pow - er.
3. from age to age you show your ten - der mer - cy.
7. bearing in mind the prom - ise of your mer - cy.
8. and to their seed, to us, for - ev - er - more.___
9. all praise to you, O Bless - ed Tri - ni - ty.___

VERSES 4–6

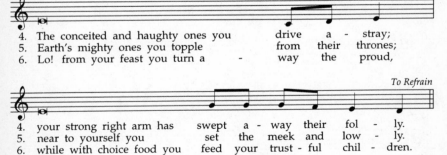

4. The conceited and haughty ones you drive a - stray;
5. Earth's mighty ones you topple from their thrones;
6. Lo! from your feast you turn a - way the proud,

To Refrain

4. your strong right arm has swept a - way their fol - ly.
5. near to yourself you set the meek and low - ly.
6. while with choice food you feed your trust - ful chil - dren.

Lk 1:46–55

Richard Arnandez
Adapt. by Charles G. Frischmann
Text and music © 1969, 1976, WLP

She Will Show Us the Promised One 606

PROMISED LAND   CM with Refrain

1. At__ Naz - a - reth__ she heard the voice Of
2. At__ Beth - le - hem__ she bore her son__ And
3. At__ Ca - na when the wine ran out,__ He
4. At__ Gol - go - tha__ she felt the pain, And
5. At__ Eas - ter when she heard the news, Her
6. In__ heav - en where she reigns as queen, She

1. Ga - bri - el__ to say: "O__ Ma - ry,__ you are
2. gave the world a king, Yet__ poor and__ hum - ble
3. saw her trou - bled face, And Je - sus__ did a
4. cross she saw__ him bear, They took his__ bro - ken
5. heart filled up__ with joy, With mem - o - ries of
6. keeps a moth - er's heart; She__ sides with all who

1. full of grace, The__ Lord's with you to - day."
2. was that place Where an - gel__ hosts did sing.
3. won - drous thing, His__ kind - ness filled that place.
4. bod - y down; Her__ arms re - ceived him there.
5. ear - ly years When Je - sus__ was a boy.
6. strug - gle here, And takes the__ sin - ner's part.

She will show us the Prom - ised One,_____ She will

show us the Prom - ised One; O__ Moth - er of Je - sus,

be so kind As to show us the Prom - ised One.

Willard F. Jabusch
Text © 1975, 1977, WLP

William Walker's *Southern Harmony*, 1835
Adapt. by Rigdon M. McIntosh, 1836–1899

607 Sing of Mary

PLEADING SAVIOR 87 87 D

1. Sing of Ma-ry, pure and low-ly, Vir-gin Moth-er
2. Sing of Je-sus, son of Ma-ry, In the home at
3. Joy-ful Moth-er, full of glad-ness, In your arms your
4. Glo-ry be to God the Fa-ther; Glo-ry be to

1. un-de-filed. Sing of God's own Son most ho-ly,
2. Naz-a-reth. Toil and la-bor can-not wea-ry
3. Lord was borne. Mourn-ful Moth-er, full of sad-ness,
4. God the Son; Glo-ry be to God the Spir-it;

1. Who be-came her lit-tle child. Fair-est Child of
2. Love en-dur-ing un-to death. Con-stant was the
3. All your heart with pain was torn. Glo-rious Moth-er,
4. Glo-ry to the Three-in-One. From the heart of

1. fair-est Moth-er, God the Lord who came to earth,
2. love he gave her, Though he went forth from her side,
3. now re-ward-ed With a crown at Je-sus' hand,
4. bless-ed Ma-ry, From all saints the song as-cends,

1. Word-made-flesh, our ver-y broth-er,
2. Forth to preach and heal and suf-fer,
3. Age to age your name re-cord-ed
4. And the Church the strain re-ech-oes

1. Takes our na-ture by his birth.
2. Till on Cal-va-ry he died.
3. Shall be blest in ev-ery land.
4. Un-to earth's re-mot-est ends.

Roland F. Palmer, 1891–1985, alt.
Text © Estate of Roland F. Palmer

Joshua Leavitt's *Christian Lyre*, 1830

Daily, Daily Sing to Mary 608

ALLE TAGE SING UND SAGE   87 87 D

1. Dai - ly, dai - ly sing to Ma - ry; Sing, my soul, her
2. She is might - y to de - liv - er; Call her, trust her
3. Sing, my tongue, the Vir - gin's hon - ors, Who for us__ her
4. All my sens - es, heart, af - fec - tions, Strive to sound her
5. All our joys do flow from Ma - ry; All then join__ her

1. prais - es due. All her glo - ri_ous ac - tions cher - ish,
2. lov - ing - ly. When the tem - pest rag - es 'round you,
3. Mak - er bore, For the curse of old in - flict - ed,
4. glo - ry forth. Spread a - broad the sweet me - mo - ri_als
5. praise to sing. Trem-bling, sing the Vir - gin Mo - ther,

1. With the heart's de - vo - tion true. Lost in
2. She will calm_ the trou - bled sea. Gifts of
3. Peace and bless - ings to re - store. Sing in
4. Of the Vir - gin's price - less worth. Where the
5. Mo - ther of__ our Lord and King. While we

1. wond - 'ring con - tem - pla - tion, Be her maj - es -
2. heav - en she has__ giv - en, No - ble La - dy,
3. songs of praise un - end - ing, Sing the world's ma -
4. voice of mu - sic__ thrill - ing, Where the tongues of
5. sing her awe - some glo - ry, Far a - bove our

1. ty con - fessed! Call her Moth - er, call her
2. to our race; She, the Queen, who clothes her
3. jes - tic Queen; Wea - ry not nor faint in
4. el - o - quence, That can ut - ter hymns be -
5. fan - cy's reach, Let our hearts be quick to

1. Vir - gin, Hap - py Moth - er,__ Vir - gin blest!
2. sub - jects With the light__ of__ God's own grace.
3. tell - ing All the gifts__ that__ earth has seen.
4. fit - ting All her match - less__ ex - cel - lence?
5. of - fer Love the heart a - lone can teach.

Bernard of Cluny (Morlaix), c. 1140
Tr. by Henry Bittleston, 1818–1886, alt.

Traditional German melody
Alte Katholische Geistliche Kirchengesäng, 1695

609 Stainless the Maiden

SERDECZNA MATKO 11 11 D

1. Stain - less the Maid - en Whom he chose for moth - er;
2. Lan - tern in dark - ness, When the sick are sigh - ing,
3. Je - sus has con - quered; To his side he raised her;
4. Come, sons and daugh - ters, Through the a - ges sing - ing,

1. Nine months she wait - ed, Bear - ing Christ, our broth - er;
2. Thresh - old of bright - ness, Com - fort for the dy - ing,
3. Queen of the an - gels, Ev - 'ry saint has praised her.
4. Prais - ing the Vir - gin, Joys and sor - rows bring - ing.

1. Think of her glad - ness When at last she saw him:
2. High she is hold - ing For a world a - dor - ing,
3. Yet, in her splen - dor, Ma - ry goes on draw - ing
4. Clothed with the sun - shine, Zi - on's fair - est flow - er,

1. God in a man - ger, Beth - le - hem a heav - en!
2. Hope of the na - tions, Je - sus Christ, our broth - er.
3. Sin - ners and ex - iles To their prom - ised glo - ry.
4. Spouse of the Spir - it, Be to us a moth - er.

Willard F. Jabusch
Text © 1976, 1977, Willard F. Jabusch

Traditional Polish hymn tune

610 Immaculate Mary

LOURDES 11 11 with Refrain

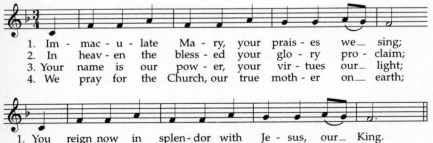

1. Im - mac - u - late Ma - ry, your prais - es we__ sing;
2. In heav - en the bless - ed your glo - ry pro - claim;
3. Your name is our pow - er, your vir - tues our__ light;
4. We pray for the Church, our true moth - er on__ earth;

1. You reign now in splen - dor with Je - sus, our__ King.
2. On earth we, your chil - dren, in - voke your sweet name.
3. Your love is our com - fort, your pray - ers our__ might.
4. And beg you to watch o'er the land of our__ birth.

A - ve, a - ve, a - ve, Ma - ri - a!

A - ve, a - ve, Ma - ri - a!

Vs. 1: Jeremiah Cummings, 1814–1866, alt.
Vss. 2–4: Anon.

Traditional Pyrenean melody

On This Day, O Beautiful Mother 611
BEAUTIFUL MOTHER   77 77 with Refrain

On__ this day, O beau - ti - ful Moth - er, On__ this

day we give thee our love. Near thee, Ma - don - na,

fond-ly we hov - er, Trust-ing thy gen - tle care__ to prove.

1. On this day we ask to share, Dear - est
2. Queen of an - gels, deign to hear Thy dear

1. Moth - er, thy sweet care; Aid us ere our
2. chil - dren's hum - ble prayer; Young hearts gain, O

D.C.

1. feet__ a - stray__ Wan - der from thy guid - ing way.
2. Vir - gin pure,__ Je - sus' love for them as - sure.

Anon.

Louis Lambillotte, 1796–1855

612 O Most Holy One/O Sanctissima   MARIAN

SICILIAN MARINERS   557 557

1. O most ho - ly one,— O most low - ly one,—
2. Vir - gin ev - er fair.— Moth - er, hear our prayer,

1. *O sanc - tís - si - ma,—* *O pi - ís - si - ma,—*
2. *Vir - go, rés - pi - ce;—* *Ma - ter, ád - spi - ce.—*

1. Lov - ing Vir - gin, Ma - ri - a! Moth - er, Maid of fair - est love,
2. Look up - on us, Ma - ri - a! Bring to us your treas - ure,

1. *Dul - cis Vir - go Ma - ri - a!* *Ma - ter a - má - ta*
2. *Au - di nos, O Ma - ri - a!* *Tu— me - di - cí - am*

1. La - dy, Queen of all a - bove, O - ra,— o - ra pro no - bis!
2. Grace be - yond all meas - ure; O - ra,— o - ra pro no - bis!

1. *in - te - me - rá - ta.* *O - ra,— o - ra pro no - bis!*
2. *por - tas di - ví - nam.* *O - ra,— o - ra pro no - bis!*

Latin hymn, 18th cent.
Tr. by Charles W. Leland

Traditional Sicilian melody, 18th cent.
James Merrick and William D. Tattersall's *Improved Psalmody*, 1794

---

613 Virgin Full of Grace

SICILIAN MARINERS   557 557

1. Virgin full of grace, purest of our race, Hear your children, O Mary!
   Maiden of gladness, banish our sadness: Pray for us, O pray for us, O Mary!

2. Mary, plead for us, intercede for us, Hope of sinners, O Mary!
   You are the portal to life immortal: Pray for us, O pray for us, O Mary!

3. Queen of saints above, wondrous in your love, Rise to shield us, O Mary!
   Show us, O Mother, Jesus, our Brother: Pray for us, O pray for us, O Mary!

4. Star of ocean bright, splendor in the night, Guide us homeward, O Mary!
   Help, we implore you, all here before you: Pray for us, O pray for us, O Mary!

Melvin L. Farrell, 1930–1986
Text © 1955, 1961, 1970, WLP

Memorare 614

MATHER 76 86

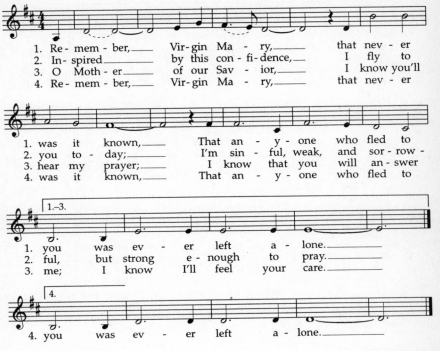

1. Re - mem - ber,___ Vir-gin Ma - ry,___ that nev - er
2. In- spired___ by this con - fi- dence,__ I fly to
3. O Moth - er___ of our Sav - ior,___ I know you'll
4. Re - mem - ber,___ Vir-gin Ma - ry,___ that nev - er

1. was it known,___ That an - y - one who fled to
2. you to - day;___ I'm sin - ful, weak, and sor - row -
3. hear my prayer;___ I know that you will an - swer
4. was it known,___ That an - y - one who fled to

1.–3.

1. you was ev - er left a - lone.___
2. ful, but strong e - nough to pray.___
3. me; I know I'll feel your care.___

4.

4. you was ev - er left a - lone.___

Adapt. from the *Raccolta*

Lauretta Mather, 1932–1980
Text and music © 1979, WLP

615 Mary's Song

NEW BRITAIN CM

1. My soul pro-claims the Lord my God. My spir - it___
2. All na - tions now will share my joy; For gifts God
3. For those who fear the Ho - ly One, God's mer - cy___
4. God fills the_ hun - gry with good things, And sends the
5. Then let all_ na - tions praise our God, The Fa - ther

1. sings God's praise,_____ Who looks__ on_ me, and
2. has out - poured._____ This low - ly_ one has
3. will not die._____ Whose strong_ right arm puts
4. rich a - way;_____ The prom - ise_ made to
5. and the Son,_____ The Spir - it_ blest, who

1. lifts__ me_ up, That glad - ness fills my days.___
2. been_ made great. I mag - ni - fy the Lord.___
3. down_ the_ proud, And lifts the_ low - ly high.___
4. A - bra - ham Is filled to_ end - less day.___
5. lives_ in_ us, While end - less a - ges run.___

Lk 1:46–55, *Magnificat*
Anne Carter, 1944–1993
Text © 1988, Society of the Sacred Heart

James P. Carrell and David S. Clayton's *Virginia Harmony*, 1831

616 Heart of Christ

STUTTGART 87 87

1. Heart of Christ, we sing your prais - es, Well-spring of e -
2. Heart of Christ, how you em - bod - y All the won - der
3. Heart of Christ, who brings us heal - ing, Touch the low - ly

1. ter - nal life! Through the sor - rows of your pas - sion
2. of God's love! How you tell the ten - der mer - cies
3. and the weak! Let us know your lov - ing kind - ness;

1. We find ref - uge from our strife.
2. Show - ered from our God a - bove!
3. Show your - self to all who seek!

Melvin L. Farrell, 1930–1986
Text © 1955, 1961, WLP

Christian F. Witt's *Psalmodia Sacra*, 1715
Adapt. in *Hymns Ancient and Modern*, 1861

O Living Bread from Heaven 617

AURELIA 76 76 D

1. O liv - ing bread from heav - en, How you have fed your
2. My Lord, you here have led me With - in your ho - liest
3. You gave me all I want - ed, That food can death de -
4. Lord, grant me that, thus strength - ened With heav'n-ly food, while

1. guest! The gifts you now have giv - en Have
2. place, And here your - self have fed me With
3. stroy; And you have free - ly grant - ed The
4. here My course on earth is length - ened, To

1. filled my heart with rest. O won - drous food of
2. treas - ures of your grace; And you have free - ly
3. cup of end - less joy. Ah, Lord, I do not
4. serve you, Lord most dear. And when you call my

1. bless - ing, O cup that heals our woes, My
2. giv - en What earth could nev - er buy, The
3. mer - it The fa - vor you have shown, And
4. spir - it To leave this world be - low, I

1. heart, this gift pos - sess - ing, In thank-ful song o'er - flows!
2. bread of life from heav - en, That now I shall not die.
3. all my soul and spir - it Bow down be - fore your throne.
4. en - ter, through your mer - it, Where joys un - min-gled flow.

Johann Rist, 1607–1667
Tr. by Catherine Winkworth, 1827–1878, alt.

Samuel S. Wesley, 1810–1876

618 Beautiful Savior

ST. ELIZABETH   557 558

1. Beau - ti - ful Sav - ior, King of cre - a - tion,
2. Fair are the mead - ows, Fair are the wood - lands,
3. Fair is the sun - shine, Fair is the moon - light,
4. Beau - ti - ful Sav - ior, Lord of the na - tions,

1. Son of___ God and__ Son of Man!
2. Robed in___ flow'rs of__ bloom - ing spring;
3. Bright the__ spar - kling__ stars on high;
4. Son of___ God and__ Son of Man!

1. You will we cher - ish, You will we hon - or,
2. Je - sus is fair - er, Je - sus is pur - er,
3. Je - sus shines bright - er, Je - sus shines pur - er
4. Glo - ry and hon - or, Praise, ad - o - ra - tion,

1. Light of our souls, their joy and crown.
2. He makes our sor - rowing spir - it sing.
3. Than all the an - gels in the sky.
4. Now and for - ev - er - more be thine!

Anon. from *Münster Gesangbuch*, 1677
Schlesische Volkslieder, 1842, alt.
Tr. by Joseph A. Seiss, 1823–1904

Silesian folk melody
August Heinrich Hoffman von Fallersleben's *Schlesische Volkslieder*, Leipzig, 1842

619 Jesus, Our Living Bread/Panis Angelicus

SACRIS SOLEMNIIS   12 12 12 8

1. Je - sus, our liv - ing bread, Great gift from heav - en sent,
2. O bless - ed Trin - i - ty, We__ praise and wor - ship you;

1. *Pa - nis an - gé - li - cus fit__ pa - nis hó - mi - num;*
2. *Te, tri - na Dé - i - tas u - ná - que, pó - sci - mus,*

1. Ful - fill the signs of old, And be our nour - ish - ment.
2. Strength-en our u - ni - ty, Our faith and trust___ re - new.

1. *Dat pa - nis cáe - li - cus fi - gú - ris tér - mi - num.*
2. *Sic nos tu ví - si - ta, sic - ut te có - li - mus;*

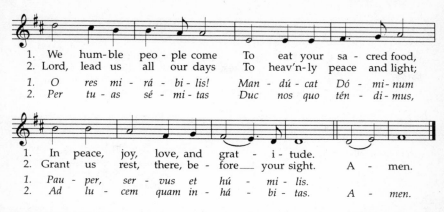

1. We hum-ble peo - ple come To eat your sa - cred food,
2. Lord, lead us all our days To heav'n-ly peace and light;
1. O res mi - rá - bi - lis! Man - dú - cat Dó - mi - num
2. Per tu - as sé - mi - tas Duc nos quo tén - di - mus,

1. In peace, joy, love, and grat - i - tude.
2. Grant us rest, there, be - fore___ your sight. A - men.
1. Pau - per, ser - vus et hú - mi - lis.
2. Ad lu - cem quam in - há - bi - tas. A - men.

Thomas Aquinas, 1227–1274
Tr. by Jerome Siwek
Tr. © 1986, Jerome Siwek

Louis Lambillotte, 1796–1855

Jesus, the Very Thought of You 620
ST. AGNES   CM

1. Je - sus, the ver - y thought of you
2. No voice can sing, no heart can frame,
3. O hope of ev - 'ry hum - ble soul,
4. O Je - sus, be our joy to - day;

1. Fills us with sweet de - light; But sweet - er far your
2. Nor can the mind re - call A sweet - er sound than
3. O joy of all the meek, How kind you are to
4. Help us to prize your love; Grant us at last to

1. face to view And rest with - in your light.
2. your blest name, O Sav - ior of us all!
3. those who fall, How good to those who seek!
4. hear you say: "Come, share my home a - bove."

Jesu, dulcis memoria, c. 12th cent.
Ascr. to Bernard of Clairvaux, 1091–1153
Tr. by Edward Caswall, 1814–1878, alt.

John B. Dykes, 1823–1876

621 O Lord, I Am Not Worthy

NON DIGNUS 76 76

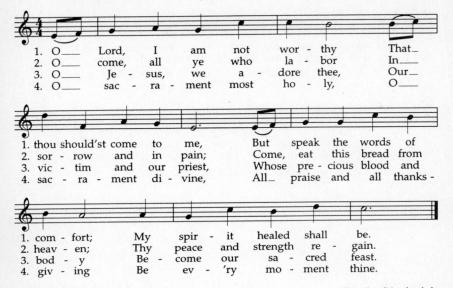

1. O— Lord, I am not wor - thy That— thou should'st come to me, But speak the words of com - fort; My spir - it healed shall be.
2. O— come, all ye who la - bor In— sor - row and in pain; Come, eat this bread from heav - en; Thy peace and strength re - gain.
3. O— Je - sus, we a - dore thee, Our— vic - tim and our priest, Whose pre - cious blood and bod - y Be - come our sa - cred feast.
4. O— sac - ra - ment most ho - ly, O— sac - ra - ment di - vine, All— praise and all thanks - giv - ing Be ev - 'ry mo - ment thine.

Mt 8:8; 11:28; Jn 6:50, 58

"Burns" traditional melody

Vs. 1: Anon.; Vss. 2–3: Irvin Udulutsch; Vs. 4: *Raccolta*
Text (vss. 2–3) © 1958, The Basilian Fathers

622 O Living Bread from Heaven

NON DIGNUS 76 76

1. O living bread from heaven, O saving cup divine,
   Your death and resurrection Make known in holy signs.

2. When Christ saw those who hungered, He called for loaves of bread;
   By taking, blessing, breaking, The multitude was fed.

3. We long to hear you tell us, "I am the living bread."
   Our lives in you are strengthened And all our hungers fed.

4. Now help us to remember Your words, "I am the vine,"
   To lives of service lead us, Poured out as living wine.

5. Then let our feast continue Through works of charity,
   That, as we feed the hungry, Your reign on earth we see.

Alan J. Hommerding
Text © 1994, WLP

Jesus, My Lord, My God, My All 623

SWEET SACRAMENT LM with Refrain

1. Je - sus, my Lord,— my God,— my All,—
2. Had I but Mar - y's sin - less heart—
3. Thy Bod - y, Soul,— and God - head, all,—

1. How can I love thee as I ought?
2. To love thee with, my dear - est King,
3. O mys - ter - y of love di - vine.

1. And how re - vere— this won - drous gift,—
2. Oh, with what bursts— of fer - vent praise—
3. I can - not com - pass all— I have,—

1. So far sur - pass - ing hope or thought?
2. Thy good - ness, Je - sus would I sing.
3. For all thou hast and art are mine.

Sweet Sac - ra - ment, we thee a - dore;

Oh, make us love thee more— and more.—

Oh, make us love thee more and more.

Frederick W. Faber, 1814–1863

Römisch-katholisches Gesangbüchlein, 1826

624 O Jesus, Joy of Loving Hearts

QUEBEC LM

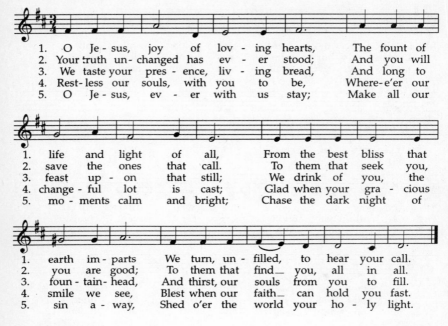

1. O Je - sus, joy of lov - ing hearts, The fount of
2. Your truth un - changed has ev - er stood; And you will
3. We taste your pres - ence, liv - ing bread, And long to
4. Rest - less our souls, with you to be, Where - e'er our
5. O Je - sus, ev - er with us stay; Make all our

1. life and light of all, From the best bliss that
2. save the ones that call. To them that seek you,
3. feast up - on that still; We drink of you, the
4. change - ful lot is cast; Glad when your gra - cious
5. mo - ments calm and bright; Chase the dark night of

1. earth im - parts We turn, un - filled, to hear your call.
2. you are good; To them that find you, all in all.
3. foun - tain - head, And thirst, our souls from you to fill.
4. smile we see, Blest when our faith can hold you fast.
5. sin a - way, Shed o'er the world your ho - ly light.

Jesu, dulcis memoria, cento
Ascr. to Bernard of Clairvaux, 1091–1153
Tr. by Ray Palmer, 1808–1887, alt.

Henry Baker, 1835–1910

625 O Sacrament Most Holy

FULDA MELODY 76 76 with Refrain

1. O Je - sus, we a - dore you, Who,
2. O Je - sus, we a - dore you, Our
3. O Je - sus, we a - dore you, Our
4. O Je - sus, we a - dore you; Come,
5. O come, all you who la - bor In

1. in your love di - vine, Con - ceal your might - y
2. vic - tim and our priest, Whose pre - cious blood and
3. Sav - ior and our King, And with the saints and
4. live in us, we pray, That all our thoughts and
5. sor - row and in pain; Come, eat this bread from

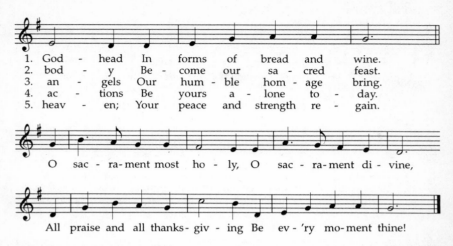

1. God - head In forms of bread and wine.
2. bod - y Be - come our sa - cred feast.
3. an - gels Our hum - ble hom - age bring.
4. ac - tions Be yours a - lone to - day.
5. heav - en; Your peace and strength re - gain.

O sac - ra-ment most ho - ly, O sac - ra-ment di - vine,

All praise and all thanks- giv - ing Be ev - 'ry mo-ment thine!

Irvin Udulutsch, © 1958, The Basilian Fathers
Refrain from the *Raccolta*

Gesangbuch, Fulda, 1891

O Christ, We Come to Meet You 626
FULDA MELODY 76 76 with Refrain

1. O Christ, we come to meet you,
Here present to adore,
As living God we greet you,
And bless you evermore. *Refrain*

REFRAIN
O Body of redemption,
O Blood which set us free,
To lives of goodness lead us,
Through prayer and charity.

2. O Christ our Paschal Victim,
Upon the cross upraised,
Now reigning for all ages,
To you we bring our praise. *Refrain*

3. O Christ who sat at table
With greatest and the least,
Make of our lives the image
Of heaven's wedding feast. *Refrain*

4. O Christ, delightful banquet
In gifts of wine and bread,
Our cup is overflowing,
A table you have spread. *Refrain*

5. O Christ, your call is constant,
To heal and clothe and feed,
To be your living presence
To all who are in need. *Refrain*

6. Your sacrifice recalling,
Your passion and your death,
Your rising in the Spirit,
Your Word, our hope, our breath. *Refrain*

Alan J. Hommerding
Text © 1994, WLP

627 Humbly Let Us Voice Our Homage/
Tantum Ergo Sacramentum

ST. THOMAS 87 87 87

1. Hum - bly let us voice our hom - age For so great a
2. Glo - ry, hon - or, ad - o - ra - tion Let us sing with

1. *Tan - tum er - go Sa - cra - mén - tum Ve - ne - ré - mur*
2. *Ge - ni - tó - ri, Ge - ni - tó - que Laus et ju - bi -*

1. sac - ra - ment; Let all form - er rites sur - ren - der
2. one ac - cord! Praised be God, al - might - y Fa - ther;

1. *cér - nu - i: Et an - tí - quum do - cu - mén - tum*
2. *lá - ti - o, Sa - lus, ho - nor, vir - tus quo - que*

1. To the Lord's New Tes - ta - ment; What our sens - es
2. Praised be Christ, his Son, our Lord; Praised be God the

1. *No - vo ce - dat rí - tu - i: Prae - stet fi - des*
2. *Sit et be - ne - díc - ti - o: Pro - ce - dén - ti*

1. fail to fath- om, Let us grasp through faith's con- sent!
2. Ho - ly Spir - it; Tri - une God - head be a - dored! A - men.

1. *sup - ple - mén - tum Sén - su - um de - féc - tu - i.*
2. *ab u - tró - que Com - par sit lau - dá - ti - o. A - men.*

Thomas Aquinas, 1227–1274
Tr. by Melvin L. Farrell, 1930–1986
Tr. © 1964, WLP

John F. Wade, 1711–1786

America 628
AMERICA 664 6664

1. My coun - try, 'tis of thee, Sweet land of
2. My na - tive coun - try, thee, Land of the
3. Let mu - sic swell the breeze, And ring from
4. Our fa - thers' God, to thee, Au - thor of

1. lib - er - ty, Of thee I sing; Land where my
2. no - ble free, Thy name I love; I love thy
3. all the trees Sweet free - dom's song: Let mor - tal
4. lib - er - ty, To thee we sing: Long may our

1. fa - thers died, Land of the pil - grims' pride,
2. rocks and rills, Thy woods and tem - pled hills;
3. tongues a - wake; Let all that breathe par - take;
4. land be bright With free - dom's ho - ly light;

1. From ev - 'ry— moun - tain - side Let— free - dom ring.
2. My heart with rap - ture thrills Like— that a - bove.
3. Let rocks their si - lence break, The— sound pro - long.
4. Pro - tect— us— by thy might, Great God, our King.

Samuel F. Smith, 1808–1895

Thesaurus Musicus, London, 1740

God Bless Our Native Land 629
AMERICA 664 6664

1. God bless our native land; Firm may she ever stand Through storm and night:
   When the wild tempests rave, Ruler of wind and wave,
   O God, our country save By your great might.

2. For her our prayer shall rise To God above the skies; On whom we wait;
   Lord, you are ever nigh, Guarding with watchful eye.
   To you aloud we cry, God save the state!

3. Not for this land alone, But be God's mercies shown From shore to shore;
   And may the nations see That all should neighbors be,
   And form one family The wide world o'er.

Vs. 1: Tr by Charles T. Brooks, 1812–1883, from the German of Siegfried August Mahlmann, 1771–1826
Vs. 2: Tr. by John S. Dwight, 1813–1893
Vs. 3: Tr. by William E. Hickson, 1803–1870

630 Lord of Nations, God Eternal

HYMN TO JOY   87 87 D

1. Lord of na-tions, God e-ter-nal Hear our songs of
2. Make our na-tion strong in jus-tice, That the peo-ple
3. Turn our eyes to things e-ter-nal; Let us learn the
4. Fill our hearts with hope and cour-age; Let us sing the

1. praise and plea For our na-tion strong and might-y;
2. still shall know Free-dom from all fear and dan-ger
3. truth a-new, That we nev-er find sal-va-tion
4. songs of peace, As in har-mo-ny we la-bor

1. May your bless-ings ev-er be On our land, a
2. From with-in, from out-ward foe. O, re-new us
3. By the things that we can do. Teach us that we
4. That true jus-tice may in-crease. Give us hearts that

1. land of beau-ty, Land of free-dom, land we love;
2. in true val-or, That like found-ers of this land,
3. are but pil-grims As our fore-bears were be-fore;
4. know com-pas-sion, Help-ing oth-ers on their way;

1. Fields and val-leys, plains and moun-tains,
2. We may stand for right and hon-or,
3. That we jour-ney here a sea-son,
4. Till the world shall live in free-dom,

1. Spread-ing 'neath blue skies a-bove.
2. Seek-ing guid-ance by your hand.
3. Trav-'ling to an un-known shore.
4. And ac-cept your sov-'reign sway.

H. Glen Lanier, 1924–1978
Text © 1975, The Hymn Society

Ludwig van Beethoven, 1770–1827
Adapt. by Edward Hodges, 1796–1867

America the Beautiful 631

MATERNA CMD

1. O beau-ti-ful for spac-ious skies, For am-ber waves of
2. O beau-ti-ful for pil-grim feet, Whose stern, im-pass-ioned
3. O beau-ti-ful for he-roes proved In lib-er-at-ing
4. O beau-ti-ful for pa-triot dream That sees be-yond the

1. grain, For pur-ple moun-tain maj-es-ties A-
2. stress A thor-ough-fare for free-dom beat A-
3. strife, Who more than self their coun-try loved, And
4. years Thine al-a-bas-ter cit-ies gleam, Un-

1. bove the fruit-ed plain! A-mer-i-ca! A-mer-i-ca! God
2. cross the wil-der-ness! A-mer-i-ca! A-mer-i-ca! God
3. mer-cy more than life! A-mer-i-ca! A-mer-i-ca! May
4. dimmed by hu-man tears! A-mer-i-ca! A-mer-i-ca! God

1. shed his grace on thee, And crown thy good with
2. mend thine ev-'ry flaw, Con-firm thy soul in
3. God thy gold re-fine, Till all suc-cess be
4. shed his grace on thee, And crown thy good with

1. broth-er-hood From sea to shin-ing sea.
2. self-con-trol, Thy lib-er-ty in law.
3. no-ble-ness, And ev-'ry gain di-vine.
4. broth-er-hood From sea to shin-ing sea.

Katherine Lee Bates, 1859–1929

Samuel A. Ward, 1848–1903

632 God of Our Fathers

NATIONAL HYMN   10 10 10 10

1. God of our fa - thers, whose al - might - y hand
2. Your love di - vine has led us in the past,
3. From war's a - larms, from dead - ly pes - ti - lence,
4. Re - fresh your peo - ple on their toil - some way,

1. Leads forth in beau - ty all the star - ry band
2. In this free land by you our lot is cast;
3. Make your strong arm our ev - er sure de - fense;
4. Lead us from night to nev - er - end - ing day;

1. Of shin - ing worlds in splen - dor through the skies,
2. You are our rul - er, guard - ian, guide and stay;
3. Your true re - li - gion in our hearts in - crease,
4. Fill all our lives with love and grace di - vine,

1. Our grate - ful songs be - fore your throne a - rise.
2. Your word our law, your paths our cho - sen way.
3. Your boun - teous good - ness nour - ish us in peace.
4. And glo - ry, laud and praise be ev - er thine.

Daniel C. Roberts, 1841–1907, alt.   George W. Warren, 1828–1902

This Is My Song 633

FINLANDIA 11 10 11 10 11 10

1. This is my song, O God of all the na - tions,_____
2. My coun-try's skies are blu - er than the o - cean,_____
3. This is my prayer, O Lord of all earth's king-doms,_____
4. This is my song, O God of all the na - tions,_____

1. A song of peace for lands a - far and mine._____
2. And sun-light beams on clo - ver - leaf and pine._____
3. Thy king-dom come; on earth thy will be done._____
4. A song of peace for those in ev - 'ry place;_____

1. This is my home, the coun-try where my heart is;_____
2. But oth - er lands have sun-light too, and clo - ver,_____
3. Let Christ be lift - ed up till all shall serve him,_____
4. And yet I pray for my be - lov - ed coun-try_____

1. Here are my hopes, my dreams, my ho - ly shrine;_____
2. And skies are ev - 'ry - where as blue as mine._____
3. And hearts u - nit - ed learn to live as one._____
4. The re - as - sur - ance of con - tin - ued grace._____

1. But oth - er hearts in oth - er lands are beat - ing_____
2. Oh, hear my song, Thou God of all the na - tions._____
3. Oh, hear my prayer, Thou God of all the na - tions._____
4. Lord, help us find our one-ness in the Sav - ior,_____

1. With hopes and dreams as true and high as mine._____
2. A song of peace for their land and for mine._____
3. My - self I give thee; let thy will be done._____
4. In spite of dif - f'ren-ces of age and race._____

Vss. 1–2: Lloyd Stone
Vs. 3: Georgia Harkness, 1891–1974
Vs. 4: Bryan J. Leech
Text (vss. 1–3) © 1934, 1962, 1964, Lorenz Corp.
Text (vs. 4) © 1976, Fred Bock Music Co.

Jean Sibelius, 1865–1957

634 Mine Eyes Have Seen the Glory

BATTLE HYMN OF THE REPUBLIC   15 15 15 6 with Refrain

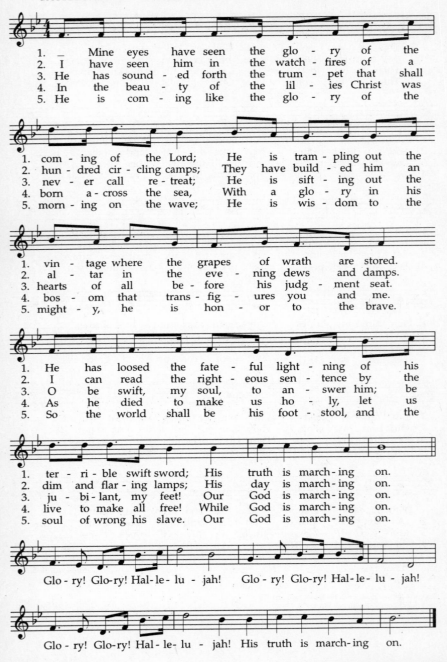

1. Mine eyes have seen the glo - ry of the
2. I have seen him in the watch - fires of a
3. He has sound - ed forth the trum - pet that shall
4. In the beau - ty of the lil - ies Christ was
5. He is com - ing like the glo - ry of the

1. com - ing of the Lord; He is tram - pling out the
2. hun - dred cir - cling camps; They have build - ed him an
3. nev - er call re - treat; He is sift - ing out the
4. born a - cross the sea, With a glo - ry in his
5. morn - ing on the wave; He is wis - dom to the

1. vin - tage where the grapes of wrath are stored.
2. al - tar in the eve - ning dews and damps.
3. hearts of all be - fore his judg - ment seat.
4. bos - om that trans - fig - ures you and me.
5. might - y, he is hon - or to the brave.

1. He has loosed the fate - ful light - ning of his
2. I can read the right - eous sen - tence by the
3. O be swift, my soul, to an - swer him; be
4. As he died to make us ho - ly, let us
5. So the world shall be his foot - stool, and the

1. ter - ri - ble swift sword; His truth is march - ing on.
2. dim and flar - ing lamps; His day is march - ing on.
3. ju - bi - lant, my feet! Our God is march - ing on.
4. live to make all free! While God is march - ing on.
5. soul of wrong his slave. Our God is march - ing on.

Glo - ry! Glo - ry! Hal - le - lu - jah!   Glo - ry! Glo - ry! Hal - le - lu - jah!

Glo - ry! Glo - ry! Hal - le - lu - jah! His truth is march - ing on.

Julia W. Howe, 1819–1910

American camp meeting tune, 1861
Attr. to John W. Steffe, c. 1820–1911

NATIONAL ANTHEM   Irregular

1. O— say, can you see, by the dawn's ear - ly light,
2. O— thus be it ev - er, when free - men shall stand

1. What so proud - ly we hailed at the twi-light's last gleam-ing,
2. Be - tween their loved homes and the war's des - o - la - tion!

1. Whose broad stripes and bright stars, through the per - il - ous fight,
2. Blest with vic - t'ry and peace, may the heav'n-res - cued land

1. O'er the ram - parts we watched, were so gal - lant - ly stream-ing?
2. Praise the Pow'r that has made and pre- served us a na - tion!

1. And the rock - ets' red glare, the bombs burst- ing in air,
2. Then— con - quer we must, when our cause it is just,

1. Gave proof through the night that our flag was still there.
2. And this be our mot - to, "In God is our trust."

1. O— say, does that star-span-gled ban - ner— yet— wave—
2. And the star-span - gled ban - ner in tri - umph shall wave—

1. O'er the land—— of the free and the home of the brave?
2. O'er the land—— of the free and the home of the brave!

Francis Scott Key, 1779–1843

Anon.
Ascr. to John S. Smith, 1750–1836

Titles and First Lines